CONTENTS

Part I

INDIVIDUAL AND SERIES OF AZEOTROPES

Chapter I

DEVELOPMENT OF RESEARCH ON AZEOTROPY

Chapter II

CLASSIFICATION OF SYSTEMS COMPOSED OF ONE LIQUID PHASE

Chapter III

HETEROAZEOTROPES AND HETEROZEOTROPES

Chapter IV
SERIES OF BINARY AZEOTROPES

Chapter V
THE INFLUENCE OF PRESSURE ON AZEOTROPIC RANGE CHANGES

Chapter VI
BINARY NEGATIVE AZEOTROPES

Chapter VII
TERNARY POSITIVE AZEOTROPES

Chapter VIII
THE EXAMINATION OF TERNARY POSITIVE AZEOTROPES

AZEOTROPY AND POLYAZEOTROPY

WOJCIECH ŚWIĘTOSŁAWSKI

Member of the Polish Academy of Sciences,
Professor of Physical Chemistry,
University of Warsaw

AZEOTROPY
AND
POLYAZEOTROPY

Edited by
K. RIDGWAY, Ph.D.
University College, London

A Pergamon Press Book

THE MACMILLAN COMPANY
NEW YORK

5 47.1362
S 976

THE MACMILLAN COMPANY
60 Fifth Avenue
New York 11, N.Y.

This book is distributed by
THE MACMILLAN COMPANY · NEW YORK
pursuant to a special arrangement with
PERGAMON PRESS LIMITED
Oxford, England

Copyright 1963
by
Państwowe Wydawnictwo Naukowe
(PWN—Polish Scientific Publishers)
Warszawa

The English edition has been published
by PWN jointly with PERGAMON PRESS

Printed in Poland (DNW)

Chapter IX

QUATERNARY POSITIVE AZEOTROPES

Chapter X

SADDLE TERNARY AZEOTROPES

Chapter XI

SERIES OF BINARY AND TERNARY HETEROAZEOTROPES

Chapter XII

AZEOTROPES AND THE CRITICAL STATE

Chapter XIII

SERIES OF POSITIVE TERNARY AZEOTROPES

Chapter XIV

INFLUENCE OF PRESSURE ON TERNARY AZEOTROPIC COMPOSITION

Part II

POLYAZEOTROPY

Chapter XV

PHYSICO-CHEMICAL CHARACTERISTICS OF ORGANIC RAW MATERIALS

Part III

POLYAZEOTROPIC SYSTEMS

Chapter XVI

THE ETHANOL DEHYDRATION PROCESS

PREFACE

THE extensive development of azeotropy may be attributed to the book published by M. Lecat in 1918. Since then a large number of azeotropes has been found, and numerical data have been published by M. Lecat in Europe, and by L. H. Horsley in the U.S.A. For a long time the main method of azeotrope examination was based on arbitrary choice of the components. The fractional distillation method was usually applied whether an expected binary or ternary azeotrope really existed; no one had tried to give an answer as to whether or not organic raw materials containing one, two or several series of homologues and their isomers should form, in the course of their fractional distillation, a very large number of known, or hitherto unknown, azeotropes.

Our group began work on azeotropy in 1928 and used ebulliometers for studying typical homo- and heteroazeotropes. In 1946 the author of this monograph returned to Poland from the United States of America and started work with his collaborators on problems constituting a relatively new branch of physico-chemical science now called "polyazeotropy". It was clear to us even then that, instead of individual azeotropes, series of them should be examined. Due to this, a relatively large variety of unknown, especially quaternary positive homo- and heteroazeotropes as well as quaternary saddle homoazeotropes have been examined and the existence of two binegative-positive saddle azeotropes has been demonstrated.

The combined distillation and ebulliometric method was found to be the best for determining the compositions and the normal boiling temperatures of azeotropes.

This book is not a simple translation of the Polish monograph published in 1957. Most of the chapters have been supplemented and the material rearranged and considerably enlarged owing to the results collected by our group in the course of examination of new azeotropes. Part IV, containing some thermochemical measurements, has also been added.

It is the author's hope that this book will be useful to chemists working on theoretical as well as experimental problems associated with azeotropy and with physical chemistry of organic raw materials which are mixtures of several series of homologues.

On the basis of the research carried out by our group, the author published in 1956 the monograph "Physical-Chemistry of Coal Tar". The examination of the processes taking place in the course of fractional distillation of the coal tar oils proved to be useful for a number of industrial purposes. This is the reason why, in this book, more attention is given to the methods used for the examination of polyazeotropic mixtures.

Finally, a new terminology and new symbols are used to designate different kinds of known, and so far unknown, azeotropes.

W. Świętosławski

Part I

INDIVIDUAL
AND SERIES OF AZEOTROPES

Chapter I

DEVELOPMENT OF RESEARCH ON AZEOTROPY

§ **1. Minimum and Maximum Vapour Pressure in Binary Mixtures.** The first observations of the appearance of minimum vapour pressure in binary mixtures were made by DALTON [1], who noticed that at the end of the distillation of aqueous solutions of hydrochloric and nitric acids both the boiling temperature and the composition of the distillates remained constant. However, the boiling temperature was always higher than that of the higher boiling component. Thus there must have been a minimum in the curve of vapour pressure against composition.

The interpretation given by ROSCOE [2] in 1859 was not correct: he supposed that the formation of chemical compounds produced the vapour pressure decreases.

It should be pointed out that in the past the appearance of a maximum or a minimum on curves obtained by plotting the values of the physicochemical properties of a binary mixture against concentration was very often ascribed to the formation of a chemical compound. We now know that the appearance of an extremum on curves cannot be considered to be a proof that a chemical compound is formed. On the contrary, very often other circumstances are responsible for the appearance of an extremum on the curve. In the last two decades of the 19th century the appearance of an extremum vapour pressure and boiling temperature of binary mixtures was believed to be a rare exception. For this reason Wilhelm OSTWALD [8] used the term "ausgezeichnete Lösungen", emphasizing that the phenomenon is not often encountered.

Between 1881 and 1884 the Russian physical chemist KONOVALOV [3] explained the conditions under which minima and maxima of vapour pressures and maxima and minima of boiling temperatures occur in mixtures of two liquid substances. The same author proved that at the extremum point both the liquid and the gaseous phases had the same composition. In Konovalov's classification the absence of any extremal point constitutes a third case. At the present time a large number of cases are known where extrema occur on the curves representing the variation of physico-chemical properties with composition, but chemical compound formation does not take place.

KONOVALOV has formulated a rule, confirmed by his own experiments and expressed in the following way: *the vapour phase of a binary mixture A + B is enriched in that component, the addition of which produces an increase of the total vapour pressure.* He has also proved that a maximum vapour pressure is associated

13

with a minimum boiling temperature and a minimum vapour pressure with a maximum boiling temperature. Konovalov's rules have been recently discussed for multicomponent systems by STORONKIN [118, 119]. The general theory of constant boiling mixtures has been developed by DUHEM [5], MARGULES [6], LEHFELD [7] and many others.

Classical experimental and thermodynamic investigations were carried out by J. ZAWIDZKI [9] in 1900, and he examined in detail the total and partial vapour pressures of a number of binary mixtures including some which gave a maximum, some which gave a minimum, and some which had no extremum at all.

ZAWIDZKI'S work still remains a valuable contribution to this branch of physical chemistry. The same author has introduced a classification of vapour pressure curves; they are either symmetrical or asymmetrical. He proved that MARGULES' [6] equations make it possible to foresee theoretically what type of vapour pressure curve will be observed for a mixture of two liquids.

It should be pointed out that seven years before ZAWIDZKI'S investigations S. YOUNG [10] discovered a series of azeotropes, including some ternary ones, which have found important practical applications.

§ 2. **Ternary Systems with Maximum Vapour Pressure.** The name of YOUNG has been mentioned in § 1 in connection with his extensive investigations on pure liquids and their mixtures. His experiments differ in principle from those carried out by ZAWIDZKI. YOUNG studied the vapour pressures of a large number of organic liquids over large temperature ranges up to and including the critical state. For these experiments, the liquids were purified by careful fractional distillation. It seems probable that, at that time, YOUNG had already started to carry out the distillation of mixtures containing two and three organic liquid compounds. In such experiments boiling temperature decreases often occur due to the formation of a number of vapour pressure maxima of binary as well as of ternary systems. The contamination of the mixture with moisture causes a further lowering of the boiling temperature of many binary mixtures. If more water is present in such mixtures, two liquid phases will be formed. YOUNG observed these phenomena in a large number of cases and also showed how a liquid phase containing water could be easily removed from the distilling flask. He discovered that the azeotrope ethanol-water could be dehydrated by adding benzene or other organic liquid before distilling, and he noticed also that, in the course of the dehydration of ethanol or other organic liquids, the distillation could be carried out each time at constant temperature. He found that the ternary mixture of ethanol, benzene and water underwent distillation at 64.85°C, and the constant boiling fraction consisting of two liquid phases contained 7 per cent of water, 18 per cent of ethanol and 75 per cent of benzene. These results of fractionation could be compared with the known fact that the constant boiling temperature of a mixture containing 5 per cent of water and 95 per cent of ethanol was 78.15°C, i.e. more than 13.3°C higher than that which was found by YOUNG for the constant boiling temperature of a mixture of benzene, ethanol and water. If one takes into consideration that the ratio of ethanol and water content in the ternary mixture is 18:7 and in the constant boiling ethanol-water mixture (rectificate) is considerably higher, namely 95:5, it is easy to see why YOUNG concluded that the addition of benzene to the rectificate would be a useful industrial method of producing anhydrous ethanol.

§ 3. **Young's Method of Ethanol Dehydration.** As far as the author knows, the German firm KAHLBAUM bought the licence of Young's patent for ethanol dehydration by using benzene (or other liquids) as a water entrainer. It is not known why in spite of this, the method has never been employed by KAHLBAUM. It might be that at that time the theory of the method was not properly understood; it is more likely, however, that before World War I the demand for dehydrated ethanol for industrial purposes was not large enough to stimulate the Germans to increase considerably the yearly output of dehydrated ethanol, or to build any distillery using a new technical process.

At the time of YOUNG's discovery it was difficult to understand why water — the highest boiling component—could be removed by adding benzene (boiling point 80.1°C) to the rectificate with a boiling point of 78.15°C.

In spite of the fact that a simple and efficient method of ethanol dehydration had been found, there were some technological difficulties in carrying out the process on a large scale, notably the separation of the two phases.

After the World War I in many countries there was a large demand for dehydrated ethanol due to the high price of motor gasoline. Ethanol had to be mixed with gasoline without forming two liquid phases. Many years after the end of hostilities GUINOT [51] discovered that the separation of the two liquid phases found in the distillate proceeds more smoothly if, instead of pure benzene, a certain amount of gasoline collected within a narrow temperature range from 101°C to 102°C is added. Basic research was not carried out at that time and no theoretical explanation was given of why the gasoline fraction boiling in the range 101–102°C was claimed in GUINOT's patent. Further remarks on this question are made in §§ 60 and 64.

§ 4. **Azeotropy.** In 1911 WADE and MERRIMAN [11] introduced the term "azeotrope" to designate all binary and ternary mixtures characterized by minimum or maximum vapour pressure. Since then the term *azeotropy* has been used for that branch of physico-chemical science which deals with systems forming one or several extremum points on the boiling temperature isobar at atmospheric or any other pressure.

The term azeotrope is taken from the Greek language. It indicates that the components cannot be separated from one another. In 1931 the author of this monograph proposed the term *zeotrope* for any mixture of two or several constituents which can be separated from one another by distillation. The term zeotrope applies in three cases: (1) if the mixture obeys RAOULT's law; (2) if the deviations from RAOULT's law are positive; (3) if these deviations are negative.

In the USA the term *non-azeotropic* is used to designate the three kinds of liquid mixtures mentioned above. Some objections, however, may be put forward against the use of this term. In Greek "a" means "non", therefore non-azeotrope may be replaced by non-non-zeotrope. It is obvious that, instead of the use of two negations, it is reasonable to use the simple term zeotrope.

Neither azeotrope nor zeotrope gives any indication whether the vapour phase coexists with one or with two liquid phases. To make this clear, the terms homo- and heteroazeotrope and homo- and heterozeotrope are used in this monograph, following the proposal made by the author [12]. More details of the terminology and symbols designating different kinds of azeotropes and zeotropes are given in §§ 29–32.

§ 5. Change in Azeotropic Composition with Change in Pressure.

The composition of an azeotrope may be expressed either in molar or weight per cent. On the graph, the azeotropic point of binary and ternary azeotropes—at a given pressure—corresponds exactly to the extremum on the vapour pressure curve or three-dimensional surface. In 1910 the Russian scientist VREVSKI [13] formulated a general rule for changes in the composition of a binary azeotrope with change of pressure. According to VREVSKI's rule, in the *case of a maximum vapour pressure the concentration of that component which has a higher evaporation enthalpy is increased with pressure.* On the other hand, if a minimum vapour pressure is found under isothermal conditions, the change in pressure produces a decrease in the concentration of the component having a higher evaporation enthalpy.

Thermodynamic considerations have lead STORONKIN [119] to a more precise formulation of VREVSKI's rule.

§ 6. Lecat's Monograph on Azeotropy.

In 1918 LECAT [14] published in French *L'azéotropisme,* the first monograph devoted to the thermodynamics of azeotropes. In addition, LECAT collected all "azeotropic" and "zeotropic" data then known. LECAT's monograph has had a decisive influence on the further development of this branch of physical chemistry. It should be pointed out that this turning point in the history of azeotropy was reached by a mathematician and philosopher. He started work in the field of azeotropy during the first occupation of Belgium by the Germans in the period 1914 to 1918. LECAT carried out his experiments alone, under very difficult conditions, without any technical aid. At that time, he collected all data before his book appeared and supplemented them by his own experiments.

After the World War I he critically reviewed his own numerical data and by 1928 had repeated most of his investigations under much more favourable conditions, taking care to use well purified substances.

In 1949 he published the first volume of azeotropic data entitled: *Tables Azéo-tropiques* [15]. He died several years later. It is believed that the next volume will be published by his son.

In spite of the fact that the first impression of *Azeotropy* published in 1918 was very limited (of the order of 300 to 500 copies) this monograph showed that the appearance of maximum or minimum vapour pressures of binary and ternary mixtures should not be regarded as a rare phenomenon. On the contrary, the number of azeotropes known in 1918 was amazingly large. From then on many physical chemists and technologists began to take an interest in the theoretical and practical applications of azeotropy.

In the first volume published by LECAT in 1949 the data for 13,290 binary systems were given. The number of azeotropes reached 6287 against 7003 of zeotropes, or—47% of the systems examined. It is true that the high percentage of binary azeotropes indicates that a selection has been made of the examined systems in favour of those forming azeotropes. The opinion, however, that azeotropy presents a rarely encountered phenomenon has to be abandoned, and the term "aus-gezeichnete Lösungen" suggested by OSTWALD should not be used.

The collection of numerous azeotropic data stimulated LECAT to find empirical equations relating the compositions of a series of similar azeotropes to their normal boiling temperatures.

In each of the papers published by LECAT a small number of graphical presentations are found. In many cases striking analogies are not underlined. In his first book (published in 1918) the heteroazeotropes are called pseudoazeotropes. When the classification of azeotropes was published in 1930 [40] by the present author, he received a letter from LECAT informing him that he perfectly agreed with the new terms including homoazeotropes and heteroazeotropes. In fact, the analogy betwcen the homo- and heteroazeotropes is obvious, if one takes into consideration the fact that with change of pressure the transition from heteroaze-otropes to homoazeotropes is a very frequently encountered phenomenon.

§ 7. Horsley's Azeotropic Data. In 1947 and 1948 in the American journal *Analytical Chemistry* two comprehensive articles appeared in which HORSLEY [16] collected all experimental data on binary and ternary azeotropes and zeotropes (for the latter the term "non-azeotrope" was used). Shortly afterwards two articles, in the form of a monograph—edited by the American Chemical Society—were published by HORSLEY under the title *Azeotropic Data*. In 1953 the same author presented supplements to his monograph.

LECAT expressed his disappointment that in HORSLEY's tables no selection had been made between his own data published in 1918 and those obtained by him in experiments, with purer substances under much improved conditions.

§ 8. Positive and Negative Azeotropes. For many years azeotropes were classified into two broad groups, according to whether they had a maximum or a minimum boiling temperature, and the groups were called negative and positive azeotropes respectively. More recently, however, some ternary azeotropes have been discovered which do not fall into this broad classification. In these, two constituents A and B form a binary negative azeotrope. The third component C may form a positive azeotrope with each of the other components. Due to the "saddle" shape of the threedimensional surface, the ternary azeotropes which may be formed in such systems are often called saddle ternary azeotropes. Sometimes two binary azeotropes (or one) are replaced by zeotropic mixtures of A with C and B with C. Due to the fact that recently the existence of other kinds of saddle azeotropes has been discovered, the terminology and symbols for both groups of saddle azeotropes had to be revised.

This is explained more fully in §§ 69–87.

§ 9. **Deviations from Raoult's Law.** The existence of small and large deviations from RAOULT's law has been known for a long time. The appearance of minima and maxima in the vapour pressures is the extreme case of such deviations. It has been stated that the deviations from RAOULT's law are caused by the association of the liquid components taken separately or in their mixtures. Most of the authors explain that the cause of the deviations lies in the differences between the VAN DER WAALS forces. If symbols a_{AA}, a_{BB} and a_{AB} are used to designate the van der Waals forces acting between two identical and two different molecules, two alternatives, broadly speaking are possible:

$$a_{AA} > a_{AB} < a_{BB}$$

or

$$a_{AA} < a_{AB} > a_{BB}$$

In the first case one may expect the existence of positive, in the second of negative deviations from RAOULT's law. Consequently, positive and negative zeotropes and azeotropes are formed.

The explanation mentioned above is only a qualitative one and cannot be regarded as the unique factor governing the appearance of minima or maxima on the respective boiling temperature isobars [17].

§ 10. **Azeotropy and the Critical State of Mixtures.** VAN DER WAALS was the first [17] scientist who discussed the causes of the existence or disappearance of minima and maxima at the critical state of mixtures. PAWLEWSKI [18] has carried out many experiments and has given a rule—bearing his name—predicting the behaviour of binary liquid mixtures at their critical state. He has found that in the simplest case a linear proportionality exists between the increase of the critical temperature and the increase in concentration of the component having the higher critical temperature. PAWLEWSKI's rule is based on experiments carried out in sealed capillary tubes (practically at $v =$ const.).

Numerous cases have been found since, showing large deviations from this rule. As regards azeotropes, VAN DER WAALS expressed the opinion that two kinds of phenomena may be observed: first, the azeotrope may persist, although its composition may change, right up to the critical point; alternatively, the azeotrope disappears before the critical point is reached.

In principle the VAN DER WAALS point of view has been found correct in many cases. However, the number of systems thus far examined is relatively small and more experimental observations are needed.

Before World War II the author of this monograph in collaboration with PIESZCZEK [19] found that mixtures of acetone with carbon disulphide gave a concave curve with a distinct minimum. This indicates that, independently of concentration changes, large positive deviations from RAOULT'S law characterize each mixture of acetone with carbon disulphide with the formation of maximum vapour pressure at the azeotropic point. The same experiments were also made in sealed tubes under practically isochoric conditions.

In 1953 KRĘGLEWSKI [77] started systematic investigations on critical phenomena taking place in some binary and ternary systems. He was able to prove that under isochoric conditions at the critical temperature binary negative and positive azeotropes exist, and in one particular case he proved the formation of a ternary positive azeotrope (under constant volume conditions).

As has been pointed out most of the binary and ternary systems were examined in sealed capillary tubes. For this reason, the minima and maxima were observed under conditions of varying pressure and temperature. It would be useful to repeat the measurements at constant pressure and at constant temperature. In spite of the fact that these conditions were not observed, KRĘGLEWSKI'S experiments represent a valuable contribution in the field of critical states of binary and ternary mixtures.

§ **11. The Collection of Azeotropic Data.** Since 1918, when LECAT'S first monograph appeared, extensive experimental research work has been carried out.

However, investigations having in view the collection of material leading to some broader generalization were lacking. This may be explained by the fact that azeotropy was still looked upon as a rare phenomenon, which might find technical application in some specific cases, but could not be regarded as an important topic of scientific or industrial significance. Nor have extensive investigations been made for the systematical study of ternary positive or of binary negative azeotropes. Even after VREVSKI'S rule had been formulated in 1912 no extensive programme for the examination of binary and ternary azeotropes under high pressure was carried out. The close analogy existing between homo- and heteroazeotropes did not stimulate experimenters to carry out detailed examination of these systems, where the direct transformation of heteroazeotropes into homoazeotrope might have been observed.

The application of azeotropic agents in ethanol dehydration, was introduced by YOUNG in 1901. It was improved in 1924 by GUINOT and applied by 45 ethanol distilleries, but until 1951 no basic research had been carried out to account for the phenomena taking place during dehydration of ethyl alcohol by a mixture of benzene and a close boiling gasoline fraction collected, as claimed by the patent, in the range 101–102°C. No reason had been given why such a fraction had to be used, as no paraffins and no naphthene had ever been found in the range 101–102°C.

More details can be found as concerns some series of binary azeotropes formed by component A with a series (H) of homologues. In spite of this fact up to 1930 no series (H) of homologues and their isomers could be found, characterized by the formation of a binary azeotrope with one azeotropic agent A. The opinion that ternary azeotropes could be found more or less accidentally by investigation of three suitable components, was also generally accepted. Investigations on the influence of pressure on the composition change of ternary azeotropes were carried out only in a few exceptional cases.

§ 12. The Bancroft Rule.

Owing to the facts mentioned above, the BANCROFT rule [20] was received with satisfaction. According to this rule, binary azeotropes are formed in those cases in which the vapour pressure curves of the two liquid compounds cross each other within temperature ranges, which were not strictly formulated, but in general were in the region of the normal boiling points of the two pure compounds. Exceptions to this rule are found even among substances having a similar structure and similar physico-chemical properties. Usually, their mixtures obey RAOULT's law or show small deviation from it.

The BANCROFT rule has exerted a positive influence on the development of azeotropy, at the same time, however, more attention was paid to finding individual compounds obeying this rule because other phenomena which might have stimulated wider ideas remained unknown. At that time nobody had ever tried to find either natural or industrially obtained organic raw materials containing substances, or series of them which could form various and numerous azeotropes in the course of their fractional distillation.

At the present stage of knowledge on azeotropy the BANCROFT rule no longer plays an important role.

§ 13. Classification of Liquid Mixtures and Thermodynamic Relations.

As mentioned in the preface, this monograph does not deal with the thermodynamics of azeotropes and zeotropes. The classification of liquid systems is given below with the intention of presenting a general idea of all kinds of azeotropes and zeotropes encountered or purposely prepared by mixing different organic compounds as well as mixtures of homologous series. It should be pointed out that the theoretical and experimental background was built up in chronological order by

KONOVALOV, VREVSKI, YOUNG and ZAWIDZKI. LECAT showed that azeotropy was not a rare phenomenon, and this is why his monograph and his own experiments created a new era in this branch of physical chemistry. Up to 1951 inadequate attention was paid to the fact that azeotropy was a phenomenon which should be taken into account by chemists and chemical engineers engaged in plants dealing with organic raw materials.

At the present time much has been accomplished in the way of theory; in particular one ought to mention the creation by PRIGOGINE, HAASE, MALESIŃSKI, STECKI, ZIĘBORAK, STORONKIN, BUSHMAKIN and many other scientists of a thermodynamic background explaining and generalizing the phenomena of azeotropy and zeotropy. Extensive investigations having in view the study of vapour-liquid equilibria should be regarded as an important step favouring the further development of azeotropy and polyazeotropy. A large number of scientists are working in this field, extending our basic knowledge and facilitating the industrial application of the theoretical background.

Chapter II

CLASSIFICATION OF SYSTEMS COMPOSED OF ONE LIQUID PHASE

§ 14. The Contribution of Polish Scientists. Below is given a short summary of the investigations carried out on azeotropy, especially in the period 1930–1939. Most of the papers published by Polish chemists have been written in their own language and for this reason they very often remained unknown to many scientists working in the same field. Most of the experimental investigations have been carried out by making comparative measurements using carefully chosen standard substances [21]. In this way a large number of thermometric and other corrections could be eliminated. Much attention has been paid to the classification of the systems examined. In connection with this, besides a large group of the author's collaborators, the following Polish scientists have published papers on azeotropy: KAMIEŃSKI [22], RABCEWICZ-ZUBKOWSKI [23], SOSNOWSKI and TRESZCZANOWICZ [24] and TRESZCZA-NOWICZ and BĄKOWSKI [25]. The latter authors dealt with the problem of ethanol dehydration.

It should be emphasized that two different factors have stimulated our group to make experimental investigations on azeotropes in the period 1925–1939. Since 1925 a relatively large group of the author's collaborators has carried out extensive investigations in which a number of differential ebulliometers were used. They were found to be extremely accurate when used for the simultaneous measurement of boiling and condensation temperatures of liquid compounds and their mixtures. If instead of two-stage, multistage ebulliometers were used, it was possible to determine the boiling and several condensation temperatures along the upper part of the ebulliometer, where on several levels thermometer wells were located. In this way the new possibility of precise examination of different kinds of azeotropes has been exploited. All experiments carried out by Polish scientists have been described [26] in one Polish edition (1935) and two English (1936, 1938) editions of *Ebulliometry*. The last English edition, entitled *Ebulliometric Measurements* [31] and supplemented by new observations, appeared in 1945.

The second factor responsible for the increased interest in azeotropy was associated with the examination of motor fuels. The observations made on this topic in 1930 stimulated the present author to give a graphical explanation of the phenomena associated with the series of binary azeotropes formed by a given agent A with a series (H) of homologues and isomers (see Fig. IV 3, § 35).

After World War II new methods, and kinds of ebulliometers for precise determination of both the boiling and condensation temperatures of azeotropes at various pressures, and of the composition of the azeotrope under examination, came into use. Moreover, any desired boiling temperature isobars of two individual liquid compounds or two more complicated mixtures could also be determined with high precision by the use of the appropriate type of ebulliometer (§§ 55–59, and §§ 69–87).

The extension of investigations of one and two liquid phase systems has proved how important is an adequate classification of liquid systems. It should be emphasized that further efforts are necessary in order to obtain the maximum benefit which could arise from the possession of a more precise classification of both zeotropic and azeotropic phenomena.

§ 15. General Remarks Concerning the Classification of Liquid Systems. The gradual development of our knowledge on azeotropy and polyazeotropy (Part II, Chapts. XIV–XVII) was associated with the necessity of using a new terminology and new classification of various known and new kinds of azeotropes. The changes thus far introduced have favoured a better understanding of the complicated phenomena which occur in the course of the fractional distillation of a large number of organic raw materials. However, the author of this monograph was obliged to introduce new terms in addition to those previously used. This terminology, including symbols for designating all the types of azeotropes known thus far, was introduced a few years after LECAT's second book on azeotropy and HORSLEY's monograph "Azeotropic Data" had been published [40].

§ 16. Raoult's Law and its Application to Liquid Mixtures. Let us recall the general expression of RAOULT's law:

$$P = \sum p = \sum \frac{n_i}{\sum n} p_i,$$ (1)

P being the total vapour pressure at a given temperature, and $\sum \frac{n_i}{\sum n} p_i$, the sum

of expressions $\frac{n_i}{\sum n} p_i$, in which p_i is the partial pressure of component n_i of a series, $a, b, \ldots n_i \ldots n$. Consequently, we have:

$$\frac{n_a}{\sum n} p_a, \frac{n_b}{\sum n} p_b, \ldots \frac{n_i}{\sum n} p_i.$$

RAOULT's law represents one of the examples of a more general additivity law applicable in the case of what are usually called "ideal" systems. The latter are encountered in mixtures formed by chemically closely related substances. For instance, mixtures such as fluoro-, bromo-, and chlorobenzene, benzene-toluene or n-hexane-n-heptane. The heat of mixing of such components is approximately zero, and if two such components are mixed together, their total volume before and after mixing is the same. From the physico-chemical point of view, we assume that the VAN DER WAALS forces of chemically related substances do not differ or differ only slightly from one another.

It has to be emphasized that most mixtures of organic compounds form non-ideal systems, which show more or less large deviations from RAOULT's law. The presence of some specific groups, and particularly of polar groups, increases these deviations, which very often become so large that minima or maxima of vapour pressure appear under isothermal conditions, or boiling temperature extrema at constant pressure. Owing to these extremal points on the respective curves, the formation of different kinds of azeotropes is observed.

§ 17. Positive and Negative Deviations from Raoult's Law. In Figure II. 1 *a*, *b*, *c*, *d*, *e*, *f*, *h*, and *i*, typical examples of deviations from Raoult's law are given. Depending on the shape of the isothermal curves we call the deviations positive (+),

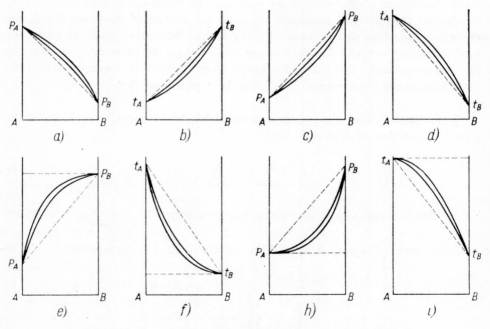

FIG. II. 1 *a*, *b*, *c*, *d*, *e*, *f*, *h* and *i*. Four typical cases of zeotropes are presented: *a*, *b*, *c* and *d* are the respective isotherms and isobars showing positive and negative deviations without forming any extremum points. In diagrams, *e*, *f*, *h* and *i* the respective isotherms and isobars are also shown; they differ, however, from those mentioned above by the shapes of the curves at points being almost tangent to the horizontal line drawn through the points P_B, P_A (*e* and *h*) and t_B, t_A (*f* and *i*).

if the total vapour pressures are larger than those predicted by RAOULT's law (schemes *a* and *e*): or negative (−), if the total vapour pressures are less than that corresponding to the straight line representing the RAOULT's law (schemes *c* and *h*). If, instead of vapour pressures, the boiling temperature isobars are examined, they will be found to vary in the opposite sense to the isotherms. To illustrate this, Figure II, 2 is given in which the isotherms are shown in the upper part of the diagram and the isobars below the horizontal axis *AB* (§ 18).

In Figure II. 1 *e*, *f*, *h* and *i* examples are shown in which both the isotherms and the isobars are *almost tangent* to the horizontal line drawn through the respective points P_A and t_A. We will call such systems almost tangent *zeotropic systems*. They play a very important role in polyazeotropic mixtures since they are the last zeotropes formed in the course of the fractional distillation of complicated systems containing mixtures of two or several series of homologues and their isomers. In the next stage of the distillation, tangent and almost tangent azeotropes are collected in the receiver. For this reason, the almost tangent zeotropes play the role of limiting points in these systems. More details on this matter are given in §§ 35, 108.

It must be emphasized that all the systems mentioned above are characterized by the presence of only one liquid phase. Because of this they may be called homozeotropes. The symbols $(A, B)_z$, $(A, B, C)_z$, $(A, B, C, D)_z$ may be applied to them. The characteristic property of all homozeotropes is the condition:

$$\frac{\mathrm{d}t}{\mathrm{d}n} \neq 0, \tag{1}$$

and this does not depend on whether the system obeys RAOULT's law or not.

§ 18. Separation of Components of Homozeotropic Mixtures by Fractional Distillation.

Figure II. 2 represents a common property expressed by inequality (1) (§ 17), namely the inequality of the composition of the liquid and vapour phases for any zeotrope. For this reason, we assume that on any plate of a distillation column a "mobile" quasiequilibrium is established between the two phases. This equilibrium differs to some extent from the thermodynamic (static) equilibrium. At the same time a certain temperature is established on each plate. The temperature decreases with the transition of the vapours from the lower to the upper plate. The condensation temperature of the vapour thus above a plate steadily decreases with the increase of the height of the given plate from the base of the column. Thus, the distillation of zeotropic mixtures makes it possible to separate the compounds found in mixtures submitted to fractional distillation. The effectiveness of this separation depends upon the difference of the concentrations of the liquid and the vapour phase on each plate.

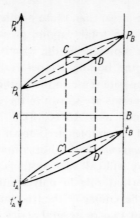

FIG. II. 2. Isotherm and isobar presented on a common diagram. Points C and C', show the compositions of the liquid phase, D and D' the composition of the gaseous phase being in equilibrium with the liquid phase.

§ 19. Homozeotropy of Ternary Systems.

Ternary homozeotropic systems are characterized by the same conditions as the binary ones. Let us suppose that A, B and H form a zeotropic system. This means that two of these values

$$\frac{dt}{dn_A}, \frac{dt}{dn_B} \text{ and } \frac{dt}{dn_H} \text{ differ from zero.}$$

These conditions are fulfilled, if the components A B and H form neither binary nor ternary mixtures having extremum boiling temperatures.

Ternary systems can be represented graphically on a GIBBS concentration triangle. In Figure II. 3 such a triangle is shown.

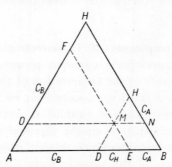

FIG. II. 3. The composition of a mixture represented by point M may be graphically obtained by drawing through the point M three lines parallel to the sides of the triangle.

The composition of a mixture represented by point M may be graphically obtained by drawing through M three lines DH, EF and NO parallel to the sides of the triangle. Sections C_A, C_B and C_H are proportional to the concentrations of components

A, B and H of mixture M. Since $C_A + C_B + C_H$ must total 100%, it can be seen that concentrations may be expressed as weight % and molar %. In the latter case each of the points A, B and H will represent one mole of the component.

If the boiling temperatures of the pure substances and of the binary and ternary mixtures are to be graphically represented, a tridimensional model is used and the temperatures are plotted against compositions perpendicularly to the plane ABH. If the mixtures of the components A, B and H obeyed RAOULT's law, their boiling temperature points would lie on the plane t_A, t_B, t_H. In the case of positive deviations a concave surface passing through the three points t_A, t_B and t_H is formed. On the contrary, if there were negative deviations from Raoult's law, a convex tridimensional surface would occur. No minima or maxima will be observed if A, B and H form zeotropic mixtures. In other words, no point X on the tridimensional surface can be found possessing a horizontal plane tangent.

In addition to the surface on which the vapour pressure of all the mixtures of A, B and H lie, there is another surface, on which the compositions of the vapour in equilibrium with the respective coexisting liquid phase can be drawn. No point representing either a maximum or minimum vapour pressure would exist. These two surfaces form a closed lens with a varying degree of convexity or concavity. Nowhere do these two surfaces touch, since the bubble and dew points are not equal to one another. If mixtures of components A, B and H were submitted to fractional distillation, it would be found that the temperature established in the column decreased steadily starting with the highest temperature at the bottom and the lowest at the head of the column. The separation of the components by rectification is possible, and depends both upon the differences between t_A, t_B and t_H and upon the efficiency of the column.

§ 20. Positive Binary Homoazeotropes.

Positive binary homoazeotropes are mixtures of two components A and B which have, at $p = $ const., a minimum boiling temperature. Frequently the experiments are carried out with the use of a distillation column before the boiling temperature isobars are examined. Figure II. 4 shows the shape of a boiling temperature isobar formed by two components A and B.

It is easy to see that the isobar is composed of two parts divided by the vertical line drawn through t_{Az}. A binary positive azeotrope is a mixture of two components A and B having an equal composition in the liquid and the vapour phases. For this we will use the symbol (A, B).

Points C and D or E and F show the composition of the coexisting liquid (C and E) and gaseous (D and F) phases. At t_{Az}

$$\frac{\mathrm{d}t}{\mathrm{d}n_A} = \frac{\mathrm{d}t}{\mathrm{d}n_B} = 0.$$

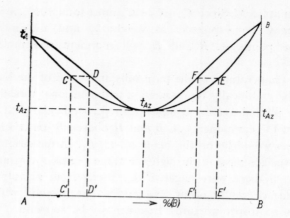

FIG. II. 4. Boiling temperature isobar with minimum t_{Az} formed by the compositions of the liquid and gaseous phases.

This relation is encountered in other systems composed of a larger number of constituents, e.g. in a ternary system

$$\frac{dt}{dn_A} = \frac{dt}{dn_B} = \frac{dt}{dn_C} = 0.$$

§ 21. Distillation Method of Binary Azeotrope Preparation. For many years the fractional distillation method has been used for the preparation of all kinds of positive binary azeotropes. In numerous cases this method was used with success. Some doubts, however, exist [28], whether this method may be used without any restrictions associated with specific shapes of the boiling temperature isobars. Three different shapes of the latter are shown in Figure II. 5 a, b, c. In the first case (a) the boiling temperature isobar is tangent to the horizontal line drawn through the point t_A representing the normal boiling temperature of the lower boiling component A. The azeotrope formed by component B with A is called a tangent one. It is often encountered in the course of fractional distillation of polyazeotropic mixtures, which is discussed in the second part of this monograph (§ 106–112). The mixture of naphthalene with para- and metacresol [89] is a typical example. In fact, if a large number of representatives of a series (H) of homologues and their isomers forming positive azeotropes with agent A are present in the mixture, beside almost tangent azeotropes (A, H_{e-2}) (A, H_{e-1}), tangent (A, H_e) and almost tangent (A, H_{e+1}) and (A, H_{e+2}) zeotropes etc. are collected in the receiver within a narrow temperature range.

In the case presented in Fig. II. 5 a, fractions are collected containing substance A still contaminated with a small amount of B.

In Figure II. 5 b, a case is shown in which the two branches of the boiling temperature isobar are symmetrical. If their curvature is large enough, one may expect to collect the main fraction having the composition of a binary azeotrope (A, B). In some cases a very small excess of either A or B might be found in the receiver.

In Figure II. 5 c an asymmetry of two sections of the boiling temperature isobar occurs. The fractional distillation may lead to the collection of the main fraction containing a slight excess of A as compared with the real composition of the azeotrope (A, B). This is due to the shape of section I of the isobars which resembles the shape of the isobar shown in Figure II. 5 a.

Different shapes of the boiling temperature isobars result in an exact determination of the composition of azeotropes by the distillation method being associated with some difficulties. In addition, this method requires relatively large quantities of the plates, if an effective distillation column is used.

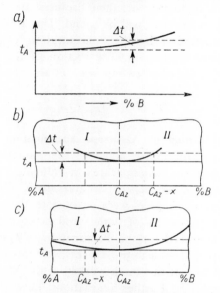

Fig. II. 5 a, b, c.: (a) Tangent azeotrope; (b) Symmetric boiling temperature isobar; (c) Asymmetrical boiling temperature isobars, I being characterized by considerably smaller curvature compared with II.

There is also another advantage, which should be stressed. In practice even components purified with the greatest care still contain small quantities of impurities. It often happens that some of these contaminants are distilled off before the main fraction is collected, or they are found in the bottom product, and so the main fraction usually contains less contaminants than the mixture of the purified components. This cannot be overlooked in azeotrope preparation.

As the distillation mentioned above proceeds higher boiling positive binary azeotropes (A, H_i) are distilled off—i being larger than e and smaller than k:

$$e < i < k \tag{1}$$

In this inequality e and k represent the lowest and highest boiling compound forming with A the upper or lowest tangent or almost tangent boiling temperature isobar.

At the end of the fractional distillation two different phenomena may be observed. They depend on the concentration of the last representative H_k terminating the "azeotropic" distillation of azeotropes (A, H_i). If we use the series of homologues and their isomers (H) containing equal molar quantities of all representatives of that series, the final stage of that distillation will be similar to the first stage. This means that a mixture of H_{k-2}, H_{k-1}, H_{k+1} and H_{k+2} will be collected beside H_k. The concentration of H_k will be the highest; then smaller amounts of H_{k-1}, and H_{k+1} will be found; the content of H_{k-2} and H_{k+2} will be the smallest one.

On the other hand if the concentration of H_k is considerably larger than that of the neighbouring homologues or their isomers on the distillation curve, a horizontal section on the level t_A will be found. This will mean that the tangent azeotrope (A, H_k) characterized by the concentration C_{Hk} practically equal or close to zero will undergo distillation. The section of the horizontal line drawn through the point t_A is called the "ceiling line" of the azeotropic range:

$$Z_A(H) = t_{H_k} - t_{H_e}.$$

§ **22. Ebulliometric Method of Azeotrope Examination.** In 1935 the author of this book published in the Polish language the monograph *Ebulliometry* [26]. Since then two English editions have appeared in 1936 and 1939, and in 1945 a supplemented English book *Ebulliometric Measurements* [31] was published. In each of these books several chapters were devoted to the ebulliometric technique of examination of the composition of homo- and heteroazeotropes. Several types of ebulliometers were described for the examination of systems consisting of one and two liquid phase systems. Some improvements were introduced during the period 1940–1946, when the author of this book worked at the Mellon Institute of Industrial Research, Pittsburgh, Pa. Further adaptations, closely associated with investigations of new kinds of azeotropes, have been made in the period 1946–1958. In addition, due to the initiative of ZIĘBORAK, modified ebulliometers have been employed for examining the liquid-vapour equilibria of different systems; some of these ebulliometers make it possible to get a definite answer, whether or not the components form azeotropes.

In the following paragraph the use of the ebulliometric method for the investigation of binary positive systems is described.

§ **23. Methods of Determining the Composition of Binary Positive Azeotropes.** For determining the composition of binary positive azeotropes two- or three-stage ebulliometers are usually employed. In Figure II. 6a five standard parts are represented by means of which it is possible to build any type of ebulliometer which may be required. Ground joints are used to give the necessary degree of interchangeability. Experience has shown, however, that it is better to seal the different parts together, as some leakage through the ground joints is unavoidable.

Examples are given below of the kinds of ebulliometer which can be constructed with the standard parts shown in Figure II. 6 a.

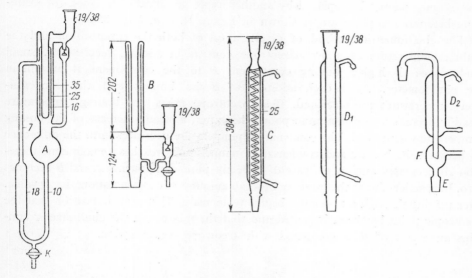

FIG. II. 6 a, Ebulliometer parts for the construction of any type of ebulliometer. All dimensions are in millimeters.

1. $A+D_1$ — a one-stage ebulliometer for measuring the boiling temperature of any one-phase liquid system. This apparatus is used for measuring changes in barometric pressure by determining the boiling temperature of a standard liquid, usually water, to within $\pm0.002°C$; it is then known as a barometric ebulliometer, or hypsometer. Other liquids, even azeotropes, may be used as the standard liquid, provided that the coefficient $\dfrac{dt}{dp}$ is known.

Experiments carried out with a platinum resistance thermometer have proved that the boiling temperature established in the thermometer well (Fig. II 6 a) may be measured to within $\pm0.0005°C$, so that atmospheric pressure changes may be measured with considerable accuracy.

2. $A+B+D_1$ — a differential ebulliometer for simultaneous measurements of the boiling and condensation temperatures of any liquid mixture. This ebulliometer is usually employed for molecular weight determination. In the monograph "Ebulliometric Measurements" [31] it is shown that it is possible to eliminate the correction for the dead space of the apparatus.

3. $A+C+B+D_1+D_2$ — an ebulliometer for the determination of the degree of purity of individual chemical compounds.

This apparatus is usually used for determining both the composition and the boiling temperature of any homoazeotrope. In some cases correct results are obtained with heteroazeotropes, provided that the liquid phases are partly soluble in one another. If two practically insoluble liquids are examined, then this ebulliometer should be replaced by another type, specifically designed for examining heteroazeotrope; example shown in Figure II. 8 *a, b* (p. 35).

The ebulliometric method of determiation of both the composition and the boiling temperature of a homoazeotrope consists in adding, successively, small amounts of th higher boiling component *B* to the component *A* present in the ebulliometer. After each addition of *B* the boiling and the condensation temperatures are measured. If an azeotrope exists, the boiling temperature steadily decreases to a minimum point; thereafter, a steady increase of the boiling temperature is noticed. The condenation temperature decreases until the difference Δt between the boiling and condensation temperatures reaches a maximum; thereafter Δt decreases and in the case of perfectly pure components *A* and *B* becomes zero. In practice, due to the presence of small amounts of contamination, the Δt value, after passing through a minimum begins to increase. This is an indication that the azeotropic point has been bypassed and that the mixture in the ebulliometer contains an excess of *B* as compared with azeotrope concentration.

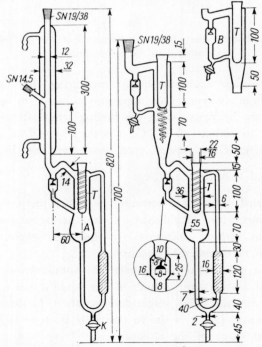

Fig. II. 6 *b*. Ebulliometers having small structure changes, suitable for examining homo- and in some cases heteroazeotropes.

It often happens that water is the main contaminating substance. For this reason care should be taken to prevent the ingress of water, and methods are given in the literature [32, 33] for the avoidance or the removal of moisture in the course of ebulliometric measurements.

4. $A+C+B+C+B+D_1+D_2$ — the simplest multi-stage ebulliometer. It is often used for determining the azeotrope composition of a system which intensively absorbs moisture.

The condenser D_2 joined to D_1 is used for removing traces of water. In this case the water jacket of condenser D_1 remains empty. If a high-boiling liquid is being examined it is necessary to heat the condenser D_1 electrically, and for this purpose, a wire spiral should be wound around the external surface of D_1.

In Figure II. 6b two ebulliometers are shown which have slight structural alterations, rendering them more suitable for examining azeotropes.

It sometimes happens that one or even several drops of water still remain in the bent tube (Fig. II. 7) below the drop-counter F. If a low-boiling liquid is being examined and water drops are found in the bending F_2 or F_3, the dehydration of the apparatus is rendered impossible. In this event both bent tubes F_2 and F_3 should be heated by a microburner or by an electric heater so as to expel the water from this part of the ebulliometer. In most cases it is easy to find out whether water circulates in this part of the ebulliometer, because if a small amount of water is present, a fog appears in the lower part of condenser D_2 (Fig. II. 7), and the $\Delta t = t_2 - t_1$ value of the condensation temperature difference is unusually large. It may happen that the amount of water found at F_2 and F_3 is too small for water drops to be noticeable; in this case a fog formed in the lower part of condenser D may be visible.

If necessary, the two bent tubes F_2 and F_3 are provided with small stopcocks. They are used not only for removing water drops but also for collecting some of the mixture for analysis.

It has been mentioned above that modifications of the ebulliometers shown in Figure II. 6 a, b and II. 7 may be used with success for boiling temperature measurements of a relatively large number of heteroazeotropes. However, a condition which should be fulfilled is that the quantity of the lower phase—which in most cases is the saturated solution of other components in water—be considerably smaller than the quantity of the upper one. There exist, however, heteroazeotropes consisting of two practically insoluble components. The examination of these systems cannot be carried out in any simple modification of the ebulliometers previously described.

In the editions of *Ebulliometry* [21] including that entitled "Ebulliometric Measurements" published in 1945 [31] two pieces of apparatus adapted for examining two liquid phase systems were described. Recently we have found, however, that even in these appliances difficulties are encountered if the mutual solubility of the two liquids is practically zero. For this reason OLSZEWSKI [172] has improved the two

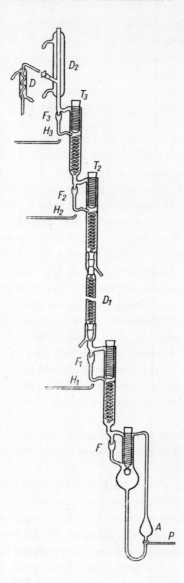

FIG. II. 7. Ebulliometer for testing the purity of a liquid substance or an azeotrope.

liquid phase ebulliometers so that the boiling temperature determinations could be made for any pair of immiscible liquids. The essential change was to use two electric heaters instead of one so as to be able to heat both liquid phases. It is necessary, however, to have the phase with the largest evaporation enthalpy in the lower container, where it may be heated more intensively; this means that two slightly different ebulliometers are needed in order to deal with all possible binary heterogeneous, liquid systems.

In Figure II. 8 *a* and *b* the two-liquid phase ebulliometers are shown in detail. The liquid having the higher evaporation enthalpy L_{II} flows into the lower portion of the apparatus and is brought to the boil in the large tube *B*. The inner surface (at *a* and *b*) of the latter should be activated in the manner previously described [31].

Liquid phase L_I flows into the upper space *b* of tube *B*. Two independent electrical heaters E_I and E_{II} are used for heating the upper and lower portions of *B*. At the constriction *Z* liquid *I* is entrained by boiling liquid *II*.

The experimenter must adjust the current flowing in both heaters in order to get a constant temperature as measured by a thermometer located in the thermometer well *W*.

If both the evaporation enthalpy and the density of liquid *II* are higher than those of liquid *I*, the middle portion of the two liquid phase ebulliometer should be replaced by another of the type shown in Figure II, 8 *b*. At *Z*, liquid *I* is entrained by liquid *II*.

Experiments have shown that proper heating conditions may be established for any pair of immiscible liquids, but closer control is required than with ebulliometers such as those shown in Figure II, 6 and II, 7.

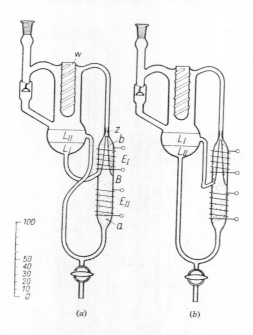

FIG. II. 8 *a*, *b*. Ebulliometers for examination of systems composed of two liquid phases: (a) the denser phase is characterized by lower evaporation enthalpy; (b) the denser phase has a higher evaporation enthalpy.

A different type of apparatus suitable for the examination liquid-vapour equilibria may also be employed for proving whether or not compounds form a binary azeotrope. A very large number of devices for this purpose have been described [128–137]. Most of them work well and have been used by numerous investigators for determining the compositions of the liquid and vapour phases at equilibrium. ZIĘBORAK constructed a modified one stage ebulliometer [138] for liquid-vapour equilibrium investigations. This device makes it possible to determine the boiling temperature of the liquid mixture examined and to eliminate the error due to the dead space of the apparatus. In Figure II. 9 a somewhat improved form of this apparatus is shown.

The examined liquid is boiled in the vertical tube A which has the usual activated inner surface. The vapour raises the boiling liquid and throws it on to the surface of the thermometer well T, where the boiling temperature is measured. The liquid drips down and fills the funnel V_2 which is connected by a small tube a with the stopcock K_3. The condensate flows down through drop-counter F into the trap V_1 and, after filling it, reaches tube B where it mixes with the liquid flowing down along the interior surface of the walls.

In order to reach an equilibrium in the whole system, the tube a is heated from time to time in order to evaporate the liquid present in the funnel V_2. It thus becomes possible to remove the first condensate in the funnel and after several evaporations

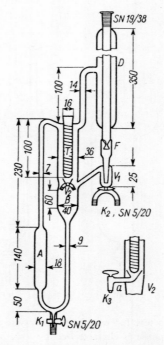

FIG. II. 9. Ebulliometer adapted for determining the vapour-liquid phase equilibria.

of this liquid to establish the desired equilibrium in the system. To avoid the influence of the dead space of the apparatus, the heating should be stopped for a while and the liquid removed from A by opening the stopcock K_1 and a new portion of the starting liquid introduced into the apparatus through the same stopcock. If this procedure is repeated several times the influence of the dead space may be completely eliminated (see § 9 of *Ebulliometric Measurements*) [31].

If the composition of the vapour is equal to that of the liquid, this indicates that the composition of the azeotrope has been reached. Its boiling temperature under atmospheric or any other pressure is recorded by a thermometer in well T.

The method mentioned above requires the use of very carefully purified compounds. Care should be taken to avoid absorption of humidity, especially if hygroscopic mixtures are being examined.

§ 24. Determination of the Composition and Boiling Temperature of Binary Azeotropes.

The precise determination of the composition and of the normal boiling point (at any desired pressure) is a lengthy procedure. The first step is to prepare by fractional distillation a main fraction collected within a narrow temperature range. This operation enables most of the impurities to be removed in the foreruns and in the bottom product of the column. The fractional distillation should be associated with the determination of changes in the condensation temperatures due to changes of the atmospheric pressure. For this reason, a "barometric" one-stage ebulliometer [31] should be located next to the distillation column, and the changes in temperature corrected for pressure variation.

It is desirable for the main fraction to lie within a range of $\pm 0.01°$C. Sometimes the nature of the components makes it necessary to accept a range of 0.04–0.07°C.

Before starting the distillation a well dried two- or three-stage ebulliometer should be prepared by collecting 20 ml. of the main fraction, which is then brought to boiling point in order to remove from the ebulliometer walls all impurities adsorbed on them. During this operation the distillation column should be kept running at total reflux. Subsequently, the small amount of the main fraction used for washing the ebulliometer should be discarded and a new portion ($\sim$50 ml.) should be distilled into the ebulliometer. It is useful to determine a reasonable boil-up rate for the ebulliometer by noting the number of drops per minute in the drop counter at the head of the ebulliometer during the boiling of the initial 20 ml. of the main fraction. The next step is to determine the "ebulliometric degree of purity" of the azeotrope obtained by fractional distillation [31].

Let us recall that the ebulliometric degree of purity is found by measuring four successive differences Δt, Δt_1, Δt_2 and Δt_3 between the boiling t, t_1, t_2 and t_3 and the condensation $(t', t'_1, t'_2$ and $t'_3)$ temperatures. Δt refers to the main fraction collected and subscripts 1, 2 and 3 to the Δt value after the successive removal by distillation from the ebulliometer of $2+2+2 = 6$ ml. of the sample. Small values of the differences Δt, Δt_1, Δt_2 and Δt_3 indicate that the main fraction of the azeotrope contains a very small amount of impurities. If Δt is larger than Δt_1 and Δt_1 differs slightly from Δt_2 and Δt_3, it is a proof that some volatile contaminants, mostly small amounts of water, could have been removed. If an inequality $\Delta t_1 < \Delta t_2 < \Delta t_3$ is observed, the main fraction of the azeotrope still contains some impurities which are not easy to remove. In the latter case other methods should be applied for more effective purification of the components, before the fractional distillation of the azeotrope formed by them is undertaken.

Let us return to the case in which the main fraction seems to be well purified. This does not mean that it represents a mixture having the true azeotrope composition. It may happen, due to the shape of the boiling temperature isobar (see § 21, Fig. II. 5), that the concentrations of the components differ from those in the azeotrope. For this reason two successive ebulliometric measurements have to be carried out. First, the main fraction previously obtained by fractional distillation of the mixture of the two binary azeotrope components is taken, and several small amounts of one of the components are successively added. The boiling and the condensation temperatures should be determined after each addition. In this way, a relatively small section of the boiling temperature isobar characterized by an excess of the component added is determined. Thereafter, small amounts of the second component are added so as to by-pass the composition of the main fraction and to obtain a point on the boiling temperature isobar lying this time on the other side of the azeotropic composition.

If both sections of the curves obtained are tangent to the horizontal line drawn through the point representing the composition of the main fraction obtained by fractional distillation of the mixture of both components, it should be considered as proof that the main fraction has the composition of the azeotrope. If, however, one of the sections of the boiling temperature isobars has a minimum lying outside the point representing the composition of the main fraction, this proves that the main fraction does not correspond to the real concentration of the azeotrope under examination; it rather indicates that the azeotrope cannot be obtained by fractional distillation of a mixture of the two components.

The composition and the boiling point of the azeotrope are given by the coordinates of the minimum found by the foregoing method, although it is perhaps more satisfactory to make a chemical analysis for the final determination of the azeotrope composition. ORSZAGH [35] used a modified V. MEYER method for precise measurement of the vapour density of the azeotrope. The modification of V. MEYER'S apparatus consists of replacing the enlarged lower portion of the tube by a labyrinth which prevents any of the vapour from reaching the upper part of the apparatus, where only air should be present.

It may happen that the amounts of components A and B available are too small for a fractional distillation to be performed in a multi-plate column. In this case exclusively ebulliometric measurements have to be made. For this purpose two-

or three-stage ebulliometers (Fig. II 6) should be employed. They should be carefully dried, then filled with the lower boiling component (say A). The boiling and
condensation temperature isobars are determined by the successive addition of
component B, until an end point is reached lying somewhere on the other side of
the extremum.

It is easy to conclude that the minimum boiling point corresponds to a minimum difference $\Delta t = t - t_1$ between, the boiling (t) and condensation (t_1) temperatures. If there are no contaminants the equality $t = t_1$ would characterize the real
composition of the azeotrope. In fact, such high purity of both components is very
rarely encountered.

If the positive azeotrope (A, B) forms a ternary one (A, B, W) with water (W)
a relatively large difference $\Delta t = t - t_1$ is usually observed. If $t_{A,B}$ is higher than
the normal boiling temperature of water, very small percentages of water produce
large temperature depressions. In this case, it may happen that the ternary azeotrope (A, B, W) accumulates entirely in the upper portion of the three-stage ebulliometer (Fig. II. 6) so that t is equal to the real boiling temperature of the binary
azeotrope (A, B) and $t - t_1 = \Delta t$ is due to the presence of the ternary azeotrope
(A, B, W). If Δt is not greater than 0.005–0.010°C, it may be concluded that the
azeotrope contains only very small amounts of impurities.

Sometimes the experimenter wants to know whether or not the boiling temperature isobar has two symmetrical sections merging together at the azeotropic
point. To answer this question it is necessary to carry out successive dosing with
A and thereafter with B.

The above procedure applies to positive binary azeotropes. If, instead, a negative azeotrope is examined the same procedure has to be used and the position
of the maximum boiling point has to be found on the appropriate isobar.

§ 25. Boiling Temperature Isobars of a Tangent or almost Tangent Binary Azeo-
trope. If a binary tangent or almost tangent azeotrope (A, B) is investigated,
the ebulliometric method would seem to be the most appropriate. The main aim
of the method is to establish the proper shape of the boiling temperature isobar
starting with pure lower-boiling component A and adding successively the higher
boiling compound B. In this way one can decide whether the isobar under investigation is tangent or almost tangent to the horizontal line drawn through the point
t_A (Fig. II. 5, § 21). If the boiling temperature isobar is tangent to the horizontal
line, a tangent azeotrope is formed. If a small minimum is observed, we are
dealing with an almost tangent azeotrope. On the other hand, if the curve is not
tangent to the horizontal line drawn through t_A, an almost tangent zeotrope (§ 26)
characterizes the system, and the symbol (A, B)$_z$ may be used in this case.

§ 26. Almost Tangent Zeotropes. It often happens that the isobar under in-
vestigation practically coincides with the relevant horizontal line along a section

with a concentration range from 0 to 2 or 3 per cent of component B. In this type system the addition of 50 per cent of B is often associated with a temperature increase of 3–3.5°C. Such a phenomenon has been observed by ANDERSON [36] for mixtures of benzene with isoheptanes and other hydrocarbons. Extensive research has been carried out on this subject by ZIĘBORAK [193] who examined mixtures of benzene with the hydrocarbons found in the 93–99°C gasoline fraction, used for ethanol dehydration. MAJEWSKA has found a similar effect when successive additions of naphthalene were made to the mixture of ortho- and para-cresols separated from carbolic oil [91].

In the last book of LECAT [15] a distinction was made between almost tangent binary zeotropes and azeotropes, compared with typical azeotropes. At that time however, the importance of this phenomenon for all kinds of azeotropes, including those in ternary and quaternary systems, was not known and, in addition, no attention was paid to the fact that both tangent and almost tangent boiling temperature isobars play a very important role in industrial problems.

§ 27. Classification of Negative Azeotropes.

For practical purposes it is convenient to divide negative azeotropes into three groups [37]. Azeotropes characterized by the inequalities

$$a_{AA} < a_{AB} < a_{BB},$$

where a_{AA}, a_{AB} and a_{BB} are the VAN DER WAALS forces between similar and different molecules, belong to the first group.

To the second group belong negative azeotropes the components of which are representatives of the series of weak acids and weak bases.

For instance, organic acids (Ac) and phenols (F) form numerous negative azeotropes of this kind. Azeotropes containing water and nitric acid or one of the hydrogen halides constitute a subgroup.

Recent experiments have shown that it is reasonable to consider that at least some aminehydrochlorides and pyridine-base hydrochlorides form negative azeotropes of the third group. In fact, if a pyridine base hydrochloride, for instance 2-picoline hydrochloride, is submitted to fractional distillation, the distillation starts with some decomposition of the hydrochloric salt, and a small amount of free base is collected in the receiver, together with the hydrochloride. Thereafter a negative azeotrope containing 1 or 2 per cent of hydrochloric acid is collected at a constant boiling point. Experiments have shown that this negative azeotrope is a powerful azeotropic agent forming ternary saddle azeotropes with a large number of substances (§ 69–87).

§ 28. Homozeotropes, Homoazeotropes and their Symbols.

A classification of systems into homozeotropes and homoazeotropes is given below. It should be emphasized that a transition from homozeotropes to homoazeotropes is always observed, if a series of homologues and their isomers are examined; this is shown by the existence of tangent and almost tangent azeotropes and zeotropes.

Homozeotropes	*Homoazeotropes*
1. Showing no deviations from Raoult's law	1. Positive
2. „ positive deviations from Raoult's law	2. I positive deviations
3. „ negative deviations from Raoult's law	3. II. negative „
4. Weak acid and base	4. III „ „
5. Tangent or almost tangent positive or negative zeotropes	5. Tangent or almost tangent positive or negative azeotropes

In LECAT's classification the group of homozeotropes is divided into two sub-groups showing larger or smaller deviations from RAOULT's law. Such a division is important if polyazeotropic mixtures containing two or several series of homologues and their isomers are examined (§ 40, § 108, § 109).

In view of the fact that the number of different kinds of azeotropes continues to increase, symbols are given below for positive and negative azeotropes and zeotropes. It seems moreover reasonable to establish general symbols for zeotropic mixtures as follows:

Type of homoazeotropes	*Type of homozeotropes*
1. (A, B) binary positive	$(A, B)_z$ binary positive
2. (A, B, C) ternary positive	$(A, B, C)_z$ ternary positive
3. (A, B, C, D) quaternary positive	$(A, B, C, D)_z$ quaternary positive
4. $[(-)A, B]$ binary negative	$[(-)A, B]_z$ binary negative

According to the proposed symbols the brackets with subscript letter z indicate that two, three or four components form zeotropes. The sign $(-)$ means that a negative binary azeotrope is formed. No sign $(+)$ is used for designating positive azeotropes, except in the case of saddle azeotropes (§§ 69–88).

Chapter III

HETEROAZEOTROPES AND HETEROZEOTROPES

§ 29. Binary Two-Liquid Phase Systems. A relatively large number of systems of two liquid compounds exhibit limited mutual solubility, and most of them form positive heteroazeotropes. The number of the latter will steadily increase with further development of our knowledge on azeotropy and zeotropy in general. Consider a binary system composed of compounds A and B having at a pressure p_c and temperature t_c a critical solubility point E (Fig. III. 1). It has long been known that within a certain range of p and t the mixture boils at a temperature lower than the boiling temperature of A and B at the same pressure. This means that the total vapour pressure of the two coexisting phases is higher than the sum of the vapour pressures of the pure components examined at the same pressure. The fraction

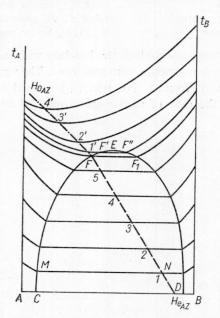

FIG. III. 1. Heteroazeotrope-homoazeotrope transition caused by pressure change. F is the transition point. At higher pressures the homoazeotropic point $1'$ is successively shifted to the left. Points $2'$, $3'$ $4'$ indicate the concentration and temperature changes.

collected in the course of fractional distillation has the same composition as the vapour coexisting with the two liquid phases. Consequently, the systems resemble binary positive azeotropes, and because of this LECAT in his first monograph, published in 1918, called such systems pseudoazeotropes.

The present author, taking into consideration the direct transition of many constant boiling two liquid phase systems to typical homoazeotropes, proposed [12] the name heteroazeotropes. This suggestion has been accepted by LECAT. Further developments of azeotropy have meant that supplementary distinctions for the systems under consideration are required.

The scheme in Figure III. 1 shows all of the stages of the transition from heteroazeotropes (e.g. *1*, *2*, *3*, *4*, *5*) to homoazeotropes (*2'*, *3'*, *4'*) with the transition points *F* and *1'*. The latter require some explanation. Point *F'* represents the composition of the liquid phase which is in equilibrium with the second liquid phase *F'* and of the homoazeotrope coexisting with the horizontal section *E* of the boiling temperature isobar which is or could be obtained from the two components under the appropriate pressure. Point *1'* is an azeotrope, the composition of which lies outside the two-phase section on the curve, almost tangent to the prolongation of the horizontal section *F'F''*.

It has to be pointed out that for other heterogeneous systems point *1* may be found on the left hand side, not far from *M*, and point *5* may be shifted towards the right hand side of the mutual solubility curve. It may happen that the heteroazeotrope homoazeotrope transition point coincides with the critical solubility point *E*.

§ **30. Symbols for Hetero- and Homoazeotropes.** It seemed important to have simple symbols to represent the various situations, which could arise in partially-miscible systems when the temperature and pressure are varied above and below those associated with the critical solubility point. Symbols which appear suitable are listed in the table below. The symbol (*A, B*) should be used if the point *F* coincides with *E*, because at this point there is no horizontal section of the boiling temperature isobar.

No.	Symbol	Kind of azeotrope
1	$[A, B]_{Az}$	Heteroazeotrope
2	$(A, B : -)$	Homoazeotrope having the composition of the left liquid phase
3	$(A, B - :)$	Homoazeotrope having the composition of the right liquid phase
4	(A, B)	Typical homoazeotrope having no horizontal section (points *2'*, *3'*, *4'* in Fig. III. 1).

Further development of the theory of the transition of heteroazeotrope into homoazeotropes should lead to a more detailed elucidation of azeotropy as a peculiar phenomenon associated with specific interaction of molecules. It should be pointed out that so far no negative heteroazeotropes have been found. If a typical heteroazeotrope is cooled down crystals of one of the components are formed in one of the liquid phases until, with decreasing temperature, the liquid phase reaches the eutectic composition, after which the second component begins to solidify.

The formation of clusters precedes the formation of submicro- and microcrystals. The condition:

$$a_{AA} > a_{AB} < a_{BB}$$

causes the formation of one-component clusters.

§ 31. **Azeotropes and Eutectics.** Analogous phenomena should characterize any positive homoazeotrope. Consequently, the probability exists that the formation of positive azeotropes is more or less closely associated with the formation of *eutectics* at a relatively lower temperature. No extensive experimental observations have been ever carried out on this subject, and so it is not known whether or not exceptions may be found among the numerous positive azeotropes thus far examined.

Negative azeotropes are formed due to the condition:

$$a_{AA} < a_{AB} > a_{BB}$$

so that a tendency exists at low temperatures to form complexes characterized by higher melting points than those of the pure components A and B.

In the case of positive azeotropes some exceptions are known. They consist of the formation of complexes at relatively low temperatures. In most of these cases water is one of the components of any kind of positive azeotrope. For instance, water forms complexes with pyridine bases which crystallize at temperatures below $0°C$.

So far as the author knows, ternary azeotropes formed by water, a pyridine base and a neutral third component usually form eutectic systems, in which the water-pyridine base complex constitutes one of the solid phases. Therefore, the formation of eutectics by azeotropes at temperatures below $0°C$ occurs in spite of the formation of water-pyridine base complexes.

Further systematic investigations should be carried out to establish the relation between the formation of azeotropes and eutectics. The history of chemistry and physical-chemistry contains many examples of the importance of the finding of analogy or similarity between the properties of polycomponent systems. In the case considered, such an analogy may lead us to the correlation of phenomena which seem to be quite different from each other.

§ 32. Transition of Heterozeotropes into Homozeotropes. In this paragraph and the previous one, two component systems are considered. The transition of a heterozeotrope into a homozeotrope may be observed if a sufficiently high pressure is used to raise the boiling point to a higher temperature than that corresponding to the critical solubility point of the components. No extensive experimental studies have been carried out in this field. STECKI, ZIĘBORAK and the author published two papers dealing with the classification of binary systems with limited solubility of the components [121, 123]; in addition, STECKI and the author [140] gave a general scheme of series of binary mixtures with limited mutual solubility. The latter will be discussed in the second part of this book (§ 132).

§ 33. General Remarks. The mutual transformations of hetero- into homoazeotropes and hetero- into homozeotropes should stimulate the development of a general theory of the liquid state, whether one-liquid or two-liquid phase systems are examined. In addition, it is desirable to collect more data in order to give an answer to the question whether mixtures forming positive azeotropes are those which after cooling form eutectics containing in their solid phase pure constituents. The new experimental material will be useful in any case to check if further theories may be proposed.

Chapter IV

SERIES OF BINARY AZEOTROPES

§ 34. Series of Binary Positive Azeotropes Formed by an Agent with Homologues. In § 5 VREVSKI's rule [13] expressing the change in the composition of a homoazeotrope with change in pressure was mentioned. This rule is based on a thermodynamic equation. In 1912 MERRIMAN [39] pointed out that a qualitative indication of the azeotrope composition change may be based on the comparison of the coefficients $\dfrac{dp}{dt}$ of the pure components of any binary azeotrope. In 1931

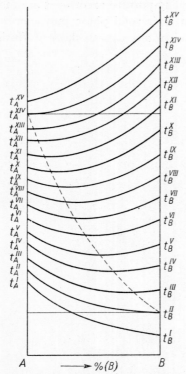

FIG. IV. 1. Composition changes of a binary positive azeotrope (A, B) with pressure change.

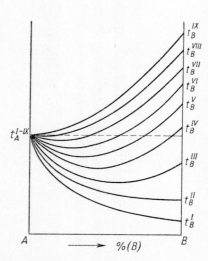

FIG. IV. 2. Rearrangement of the scheme shown in Fig. IV. 1. All the points $t_A^I - t_A^{IX}$ are represented by the common point $t_A^I - IX$. The points $t_B^I - t_B^{IX}$ are unchanged (Fig. IV. 1).

KAMIEŃSKI [22] published a modification of VREVSKI'S expression applicable to azeotropes which do not obey the simplified VREVSKI rule [62].

Usually it is more convenient to work with the coefficient $\dfrac{dt}{dp}$ than with $\dfrac{dp}{dt}$ and the rule then takes the form: *an increase of pressure produces in a binary positive azeotrope a concentration increase of the component having a lower* $\dfrac{dt}{dp}$ *value.*

In Figure IV. 1 it is shown how an azeotrope (A, B) changes its composition from $A = 0$ to $B = 0$, below the critical temperature of $A+B$ mixtures. It is easy to see that over a large range of pressure and boiling temperatures the coefficient $\dfrac{dt}{dp_B}$ is considerably larger than $\dfrac{dt}{dp_A}$.

At a low pressure the system has a boiling temperature isobar $t_A^{II} t_B^{II}$ tangent to the horizontal line through the point t_B^{II}. At lower pressures than this A and B form homozeotropes exclusively. At a sufficiently high pressure another tangent azeotrope is formed with the boiling temperature isobar $t_A^{XIV} t_B^{XIV}$ tangent to the horizontal line drawn through the point t_A^{XIV}, and at higher pressures, only zeotropes can be formed. The existence of such systems was predicted many years ago by VAN DER WAALS [17]. It should be emphasized that, under pressures close to the critical for $A+B$ mixtures, the curves representing the boiling temperature isobars may successively transform into straight lines. If this occurs, PAWLEWSKI'S rule will be observed [18]. No experiments in this direction have ever been made. It is possible that this phenomenon could not occur in systems forming binary positive azeotropes at low pressures.

Let us suppose that the following change is introduced in the graphical presentation: on the vertical line drawn through point A all the points starting with t_A^I and ending with t_A^{XV} are represented by one common point t_A^{I-XV} without any change on the vertical axis B. In this way Figure IV. 1 is transformed into Figure IV. 2. (The number of the series B is larger in Figure IV. 1 than in Figure IV. 2).

Figure IV. 2 is almost identical with Figure IV. 3, which was presented by the author [40] of this book at a time (1930) when the existing azeotropic data were insufficient for understanding the phenomena associated with what we now call *polyazeotropy.*

§ 35. Positive Binary Azeotropes Formed by an Agent (A) with a Series (B) of Homologues.

Let us suppose that a series of individual binary positive azeotropes (A, B_i) are formed by the agent A with the representatives, $B_1, B_2 \ldots B_{n-1}, B_n, B_{n+1}$ of the series B. In addition, suppose that there is a sufficient number of homologues to yield a large number of boiling temperature isobars as shown in Figure IV. 3. If the number of homologues is large, it is very likely that two tangent boiling temperature isobars $t_A t_{B_0}$ and $t_A t_{B_n}$ will occur. One of these isobars is tangential to the horizontal line drawn through the point t_{B_0}, the other is almost tangential to the line drawn through the point t_{B_n}. Below and above these two isobars binary positive almost tangent zeotropes for instance $(A, B_{n+1})_z$ are found.

In 1930 the opinion was often expressed, not unjustifiably, that azeotropes are most frequently encountered when the boiling temperature is below 170–

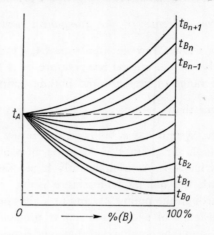

FIG. IV. 3. Binary positive azeotropes and zeotropes of type (A, B_i) formed by the agent A with representatives of the series of homologues (B).

200°C. More recently, series of azeotropes have been examined, but isomers of the homologues used to form the azeotropes were ignored. The importance of the existence of tangent or almost tangent azeotropes was not understood in the past. For this reason in the scheme described by the author in 1930 [40] no tangent boiling temperature isobars were shown on the diagram. At that time it seemed that the scheme shown in Figure IV. 3 might help in finding additional series of azeotropes, but nobody saw that it could also be used as a starting point for further classification and research into phenomena occurring in mixtures containing several series of homologues and their isomers (Chapts. XV and XVI). This is why in the two English editions of *Ebulliometry* the drawing shown in Figure IV. 3 was not reproduced [26].

In the monograph *Ebulliometric Measurements* (1945) [31] Figures IV. 2 and IV. 3 were reproduced in connection with the appearance of two papers published by J. R. ANDERSON [36]. The contents of these papers were known to the present author a long time before they were published.

ANDERSON proved by direct experiment that nitration benzene contains a relatively large number of higher boiling paraffins and naphthenes which form a bundle of almost tangent or tangent azeotropes and zeotropes with benzene. Consequently, some of these hydrocarbons cannot be removed even with a very effective distillation column. The contaminants are characterized by normal boiling temperatures of 96 to 99°C. At that time (1945) this finding was quite unexpected.

Owing to the close co-operation of the author with ANDERSON, the terms, tangent azeotrope and almost tangent azeotrope and zeotrope had often been used and the diagram published by the author in 1930 [69] had been discussed in detail. The drawings were published in *Ebulliometric Measurements* with the following remark: "It can be seen from the graph that, if the boiling temperature of the substance is too low or too high when compared with that of the azeotropic agent (*A*), no azeotrope can be formed. In the figure, homologue B_0 boils too low and homologue B_{n+1} too high. In between these two extreme cases the azeotropic concentration shows a distinct regularity. It starts at the point $C_A = 0$, increases gradually, and passes through the point $C_A = 50$ per cent. Finally, C_A reaches the 100 per cent point for the mixture of A with B_0. The latter one forms the lower tangent boiling temperature isobar in that series".

§ 36. **Series of Azeotropes Formed by an Azeotropic Agent with Homologues, their Isomers and Related Compounds.** LECAT, ŠKOLNIK [96] and other authors have used empirical equations expressing the relation between the boiling temperatures of binary azeotropes (A, B_i) and the parameter characterizing the members, B_i of a homologous series (B). The Polish group of scientists had in mind the general properties of the azeotropes formed in the course of a fractional distillation of a polyazeotropic mixture (§§ 106, 109, 119, 120). Therefore, the question had to be answered, whether binary positive azeotropes (A, B_i), (A, B_{i+1}) etc. differ considerably from those formed by the isomers of the same series and by other closely related compounds. For instance, if a paraffin B_i is replaced by a naphthene boiling at a temperature differing but slightly from t_{B_1}, it is important to know whether the boiling temperatures of the respective azeotropes, and their composition, will differ much from one another.

On the basis of investigations carried out by ZIĘBORAK [50, 52] and ORSZAGH [35] and for practical reasons, it seemed possible to include the isomers and some other chemically related substances in the series of homologues (B). Such a simplification was convenient when complicated polyazeotropic mixtures were being studied. In these cases the graphical presentation, similar to that shown in Figure IV. 3, included at least all the isomers and often chemically related substances as well. One of the first instances of such a procedure was associated with ANDERSON'S investigations into the typical contaminants of benzene.

§ 37. **Typical Contamination by Substances Forming Tangent or almost Tangent Azeotropes.** In 1945 ANDERSON [36] undertook an examination of the contaminants present in nitration benzene. The present author had the opportunity to follow these investigations closely. The results obtained were quite unexpected by many organic chemists; on the other hand, it was easy to conclude that the phenomena observed by ANDERSON could be easily explained with the help of the diagram shown in Figure IV. 3, since they represent the upper part of that diagram. In Figure IV. 4 the relevant section of the drawing shown in Figure IV. 3 is reproduced. ANDERSON proved that nitration benzene is contaminated with

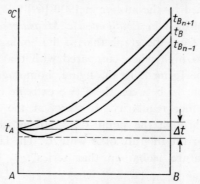

FIG. IV. 4. Tangent and almost tangent boiling temperature isobars formed by component A with higher boiling representatives of series (B). Δt — stands for the lowest temperature difference characterizing the efficiency of the distillation column.

several paraffinic and naphthenic hydrocarbons boiling considerably higher than benzene. All of them formed boiling temperature isobars tangent or almost tangent to the horizontal line drawn through t_A.

§ **38. Azeotropic Ranges.** In 1950 the author introduced the term azeotropic range [42] of an azeotropic agent A with regard to the series (H) of homologues and their isomers:

$$Z_A(H) = t_{H_k} - t_{H_e} \tag{1}$$

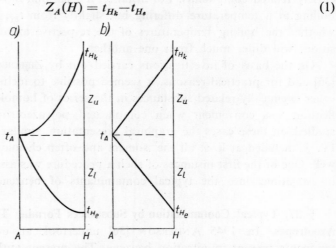

FIG. IV. 5 a, b. Azeotropic range $Z_A(H) = z_u + z_l$ of agent A with regard to the series (H) of homologues and their isomers. On the scheme (b) two tangent boiling temperature isobars are represented by straight lines.

H_k and H_e are the highest and the lowest boiling representatives of the series (H) which form two tangent boiling temperatures isobars as shown in Figure IV. 5 a, b.

MALESIŃSKI [158] in his extensive theoretical investigations on azeotropy has shown that the azeotropic range may be regarded as a physico-chemical constant characterizing the azeotropic agent (A) and the series of homologues and their isomers.

As shown in Figure IV. 5 a, the range $Z_A(H)$ is the sum of two values z_u and z_l

$$Z_A(H) = z_u + z_l, \tag{2}$$

where z_u and z_l are given by

$$z_u = t_{H_k} - t_A \text{ and } z_l = t_A - t_{H_e}. \tag{3}$$

In another chapter the azeotropic ranges of binary and ternary azeotropes are examined in more detail (§ 112).

In Figure IV. 5 a it is assumed that the number of representatives of the series (H) of homologues and their isomers is large enough for two representatives H_k and H_e, which form two boiling temperature isobars $t_{H_k} t_A$ and $t_A t_{H_e}$, to be found, one being tangent to the horizontal line drawn through t_A and the other to that drawn through t_{H_e}. In many cases the respective compounds H_k and H_e do not exist. In spite of this fact, the azeotropic range of an azeotropic agent expresses the possibility of the formation of azeotropes with a series of homologues and their isomers within a range, outside which zeotropes $(A, H_{e-1})_z$ and $(A, H_{k+1})_z$ are formed exclusively.

With regard to the z_u and z_l values, it should be pointed out that three different cases have been observed, namely:

$z_u = z_l$, symmetrical azeotropic range,
$z_u > z_l$, upper asymmetry of azeotropic range
$z_u < z_l$, lower asymmetry ,,   ,,   ,,

For convenience, the two curves representing the two tangent boiling temperature isobars may be replaced by two straight lines as shown in Figure IV. 5 b.

It is easy to see that for the same series (H) of homologues and their isomers and two different azeotropic agents A and A', boiling practically at the same temperature, the azeotropic ranges may be quite different:

$$t_A = t_{A'}, \quad Z_A(H) > Z_{A'}(H), \text{ or } Z_A(H) < Z_{A'}(H).$$

In Figure IV. 6 the difference in the azeotropic range values of two agents is shown. In Figure IV. 7 a, b lower (a) and upper (b) asymmetry of the azeotropic ranges are graphically represented. Both these cases are often encountered. Upper asymmetry is often associated with the decrease in solubility of the agent A in the higher boiling homologues, and indicates that at some lower pressure the possibility of binary heteroazeotrope formation exists (see Fig. IV. 12).

The lower portion $z_l = t_A - t_{H_e}$ of the azeotropic range indicates the limits within which the boiling temperatures of all the azeotropes lie. The larger the value z_l, the wider are the differences in boiling temperatures of the azeotropes belong-

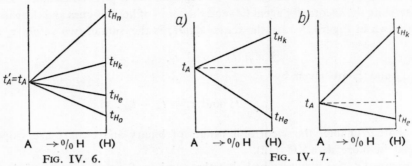

FIG. IV. 6.   FIG. IV. 7.

FIG. IV. 6. Azeotropic ranges of two agents A and A' characterized by equal boiling temperatures $t_A = t_{A'}$ and different azeotropic ranges $Z_A(H) > Z_{A'}(H)$.

FIG. IV. 7 a, b. Lower and upper asymmetry of the azeotropic ranges.

ing to the series (A, H_i). Consequently, for the separation of the azeotropes by fractional distillation a large z_l value is a favourable factor.

As has been pointed out in previous paragraphs two boiling temperature isobars $t_{H_k} t_A$ and $t_A t_{H_e}$ (Figs. IV. 3 and 5 a) separate the region of azeotrope formation from the upper and lower portions of the diagram where exclusively zeotropic mixtures exist. The successive transition from the zeotropy to the azeotropy region is quite obvious. In the past, however, more attention was paid to the question whether some arbitrarily chosen individual compounds could or could not form azeotropes. For this reason it seemed of great importance to examine a whole series (A, H_i) of azeotropes and also zeotropes, including those forming tangent or almost tangent boiling temperature isobars. ANDERSON'S work on typical contaminations of nitration benzene was considered rather as a peculiar case, not a phenomenon of general importance for understanding the nature of polyazeotropic systems and mixtures.

At present it is quite obvious that *there exists a gradual transition from lower boiling zeotropes to azeotropes and a further successive transition from azeotropes to zeotropes.*

The nature of agent A as well as that of series (H) and particularly of the number of homologues and their isomers are responsible for the number of almost tangent boiling temperature isobars accumulated on both sides of points t_A and t_{H_e} (Fig. IV. 3).

In spite of extensive investigations on this subject we are still far from a satisfactory development of azeotropy. More systematic investigations are required for obtaining all necessary azeotropic data. Polyazeotropic phenomena are closely associated with the development of researches dealing with series of azeotropes and not with individual, arbitrarily chosen, systems.

§ 39. Azeotropic Range Changes in Homologous Series of Azeotropic Agents.
In connection with studies on azeotropic ranges of agents forming series of azeotropes, the question has arisen, in what manner the azeotropic ranges undergo changes if the azeotropic agents A_1, A_2, A_3 themselves belong to series (A) of homologues. Experiments indicate that $Z_{A_1}(H)$, $Z_{A_2}(H)$, $Z_{A_3}(H)$ ... decrease with increase of CH_2 groups in the series of homologues.

The data collected by ORSZAGH [35] for paraffinic and naphthenic hydrocarbons, aliphatic alcohols, and two fractions of gasoline have confirmed the decrease of azeotropic range with increase of molecular weight in each series of homologues.

As early as 1955 MALESIŃSKI published a series of papers on the theory of formation of binary and ternary azeotropes examined under isobaric conditions [97]. It was assumed that these mixtures may be treated as regular solutions, and that each of the azeotropic agents is characterized by a symmetrical azeotropic range. MALESIŃSKI found that the azeotropic depression A with regard to agent A is given by:

$$\delta_A = z_l X_{H_i}^2, \tag{1}$$

X_{H_i} being the molar concentration of the representative H_i of series (H) and $z_l = t_A - t_{H_e}$ (Fig. IV. 3). If both sides of equation (1) are divided by z_l, we get the following expression [98]:

$$\frac{\delta_A}{z_l} = \delta_A^{(r)} = X_{H_i}^2, \tag{2}$$

in which $\delta_A^{(r)}$ is the reduced azeotropic depression, and equation (2) is the relation between reduced azeotropic depression value $\delta_A^{(r)}$ and $X_{H_i}^2$ expressed in general terms. For this reason, for any series (A_i, H_i) of binary positive azeotropes, the points $\delta_A^{(r)}$, X_{H_i} should lie on a common curve as shown in Figure IV. 8.

In Figure IV.8 the curve $\delta_A^{(r)}$, $X_{H_i}^2$ is plotted and the points for the six series (A_j, H_i) of binary positive azeotropes listed in Table IV. 1 are marked with small circles. Twenty-seven points out of thirty-two lie on the curve or very close to it. The points for the five azeotropes V.2, V.3, VI.8 and VI.7 show somewhat larger deviations.

In Table IV.1 are listed: 1—the number of the azeotropic agent A_j; 2— its name; 3—the numbers of the representatives of series (H); 4—their names; 5—the z_l values; 6—the mean z_l values; 7—δ_A; 8—X_{H_i}; 9—$\delta_{H_i}^{(r)}$.

Two of the six series of binary positive azeotropes are formed by non-associated or slightly associated azeotropic agents. Two remaining series, VII and VIII, containing methanol or acetic acid as agents were examined in the same manner; the results are given in Table IV. 2 and are plotted in Figure IV.9.

The symbols used in Table IV. 2 are identical with those employed in Table IV. 1.

The polar character of methanol and acetic acid produces relatively large deviations form regularity. In six series out of nineteen the points lie on the curve

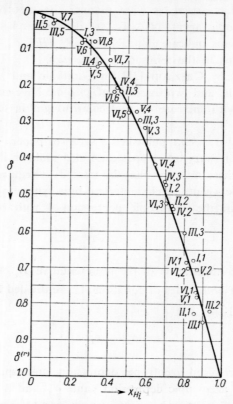

FIG. IV.8. The full curve obtained by plotting the reduced $\delta^{(r)}$ values against $X^2_{H_i}$ for series (A_j, H_i) of binary positive azeotropes.

or in its vicinity; the remaining points show two kinds of deviation. In the region from $X_{H_i} = 0$ up to $X_{H_i} = 0.6$ many points lie below the $\delta^{(r)}_A$, X_{H_i} curve. Within the range $X_{H_i} = 0.8$ to $X_{H_i} = 1.0$ most of them are found above the $\delta^{(r)}$, X_{H_i} curve.

It should be noted that the reduced equation (2) may be used for determining the z_l value:

$$z_l = \frac{\delta_A}{X^2_{H_i}}.$$

Consequently, the lower portion of the azeotropic range can be calculated if the depression δ_A and the concentration X_{H_i} for any representative H_i of the series (H) are experimentally determined. No compounds forming tangent boiling isobars $t_A t_{H_k}$ and $t_A t_{H_e}$ (Fig. IV. 3) are required for this purpose, since, for an arbi-

TABLE IV. 1

Reduced Depression against Concentration Values

No. of A	Name of A	No. of H_i	H_i	Z_l	Average Z_l value	δA	X_{H_i}	$\delta_A^{(r)}$
I	n-Propyl formate	1	2,3-Dimethylbutane	34		24.65	85	0.685
		2	n-Hexane	35	36.0	17.25	70.5	0.479
		3	n-Heptane	38		2.65	26.5	0.074
II	Acetone	1	2-Methylbutane	42		37.45	85	0.832
		2	n-Pentane	44		24.25	74.5	0.539
		3	2,3-Dimethylbutane	45	45.0	9.85	47	0.219
		4	n-Hexane	50		6.45	36	0.145
		5	n-Heptane	61		0.3	7	0.067
III	Amyl alcohol	1	n-Heptane	41		34.0	91	0.850
		2	Iso-octane	38		32.9	93	0.823
		3	2,4-Dimethylhexane	38	40.0	24.3	80	0.608
		4	n-Octane	37		12.1	57	0.303
		5	2,7-Dimethyl octane	33		1.1	11.5	0.028
IV	Phenol	1	Propylbenzene	34.5		23.7	82.8	0.687
		2	Mesitylene	33.5		18.7	74.7	0.542
		3	Pseudocumene	33.0	34.5	16.2	70.1	0.470
		4	Butylbenzene	35.5		7.2	45.1	0.209
V	Pyrocatechinol	1	1,2,3-Triethylbenzene	40.9		31.2	87.3	0.780
		2	Naphthalene	37.6		28.5	87.0	0.713
		3	2-Methylnaphthalene	36.7		12.65	58.7	0.316
		4	1-Methylnaphthalene	35.9	40.0	11.1	55.6	0.278
		5	Diphenyl	48.0		6.05	12.4	0.016
		6	Diphenylmethane	46.9		3.15	25.9	0.079
		7	Acenaphthene	42.2		0.65	12.4	0.016
VI	Resorcinol	1	2-Methylnaphthalene	53.8		41.35	87.7	0.769
		2	1-Methylnaphthalene	55.4		38.3	83.1	0.703
		3	Diphenyl	54.7		29.05	72.9	0.533
		4	Diphenylmethane	53.5	54.5	22.65	65.0	0.416
		5	Acenaphthene	56.9		15.2	31.7	0.279
		6	1,2-Diphenylethane	60.0		11.8	44.4	0.217
		7	Fluorene	42.0		7.4	41.9	0.135
		8	Stilbene	37.1		3.9	32.4	0.072

trarily chosen azeotrope (A, H_i), the values of $\delta_A = t_A - t_{Az}$ and concentration X_{H_i} expressed as a molar fraction suffice for the calculation of z_l.

A simple transformation of equation (2) gives:

$$\frac{X_{H_e}^2 z_l}{\delta_A} = \frac{X_{H_e}^2 (t_A - t_{H_e})}{t_A - t_{A_z}} = 1. \tag{3}$$

TABLE IV. 2

Reduced Depression against Concentration Values

No. of A	Name of A	No. of H_i	H_i	Z_l	Average Z value	δA	X_{H_l}	$\delta_A^{(r)}$
VII	Methanol	1	Isopropylethylene	53.4		46.65	93.5	0.933
		2	Methylbutane	48		40.1	91.5	0.802
		3	Isoprene	44		35.15	89.5	0.703
		4	n-Pentane	46		33.85	85.5	0.677
		5	2-Methylbutene-2	46		32.95	85.0	0.659
		6	3-Methylbutadiene-1,2	43		30.15	83.5	0.603
		7	2,3-Dimethylbutane	54		19.65	60.0	0.393
		8	Diallyl	54		17.60	57	0.352
		9	n-Hexane	59	50.0	14.15	49	0.283
		10	n-Heptane	107		5.65	23	0.113
		11	Iso-octane	131		5.25	20	0.105
		12	2,4-Dimethylhexane	142		3.65	16	0.073
		13	n-Octane	165		1.65	10	0.033
VIII	Acetic acid	1	n-Hexane	55		49.80	95	0.905
		2	n-Heptane	87		26.33	55	0.479
		3	n-Octane	123		12.35	32	0.225
		4	n-Nonane	181	55.0	5.25	17	0.096
		5	n-Decane	130		1.30	10	0.024
		6	n-Undecane	825		0.33	2	0.006

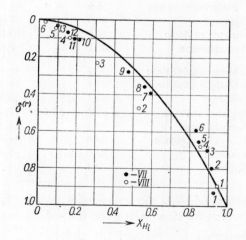

FIG. IV. 9. Plot of $\delta_A^{(r)} = X_{H_i}^2$ for methanol (●) and acetic acid (o) azeotropes.
(See Table IV. 2, Sections VII and VIII).

If we plot X_{H_i} as abscissa and $\dfrac{X^2_{H_i}(t_A - t_{H_e})}{t_A - t_{Az}}$, as ordinate we should obtain a horizontal line through the point 1.0. In Figure IV. 10 a graphical presentation is given for the eleven azeotropes listed in Table IV. 3. Large deviations occur at small concentrations of H_i.

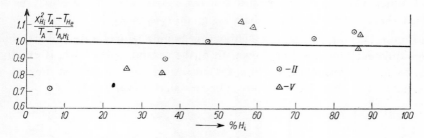

FIG. IV. 10. Deviations from relation (3) calculated for the eleven azeotropes listed in Table IV. 3 (series II and V).

§ 40. **Influence of Pressure Changes on the Shape of Boiling Temperature Isobars.** Since the physical properties change discontinuously on going from one member of a homologous series to the next, in general it will not be the case that each series of homologues (including their isomers) will have two components boiling exactly at t_{H_k} and t_{H_e}, so as to form the isobars $t_{H_k} t_A$ and $t_A t_{H_e}$, one of which will be tangent to the horizontal line drawn through t_A and the other to that drawn

TABLE IV. 3

No. of series	$(A_l\,H_i)$	$\dfrac{X^2_A(t_A-t_{H_e})}{t_A-t_{Az}}$	X_{H_i} mol.%
II	Acetone 2-methylbutane	1.07	85
II	Acetone n-pentane	1.02	74.5
II	Acetone 2,5-dimethylbutane	1.00	47
II	Acetone n-hexane	0.90	36
II	Acetone n-heptane	0.74	7
V	Pyrocatechol 1,3,5-triethylben-zene	0.98	87.3
V	Pyrocatechol naphthalene	1.06	87.0
V	Pyrocatechol 2-methylnaphtha-lene	1.09	58.7
V	Pyrocatechol 1-methylnaphtha-lene	1.11	55.6
V	Pyrocatechol diphenyl	0.83	12.4
V	Pyrocatechol diphenylmethane	0.85	25.9

through the point t_{H_e}. This is why the term, almost tangent, boiling temperature isobars has been often used in previous paragraphs.

However, under pressures higher or lower than atmospheric, strictly tangent isobars may actually be found, if the coefficients $\dfrac{dt}{dp_{H_k}}$ and $\dfrac{dt}{dp_{H_e}}$ are not equal to each other. Consequently, in most systems a particular pressure may be found at which the tangency of the isobars $t_{H_k} t_A$ or $t_A t_{H_e}$ may be observed.

In Figure IV. 11a, b, c three neighbouring boiling temperature isobars obtained at three different pressures are shown. In b, the central isobar $t_{H_2} t_A$ is exactly tangential to the horizontal line t_A. In a, the curves are those of almost tangent azeotropes, and in c they have become almost tangent zeotropes.

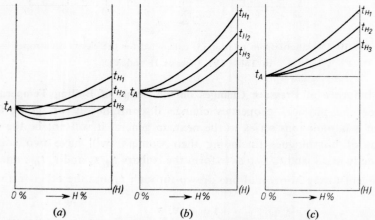

(a) (b) (c)

FIG. IV. 11 a, b, c. Three boiling temperature isobars obtained at three different pressures.

It should be pointed out that a relatively large change of pressure is required to cause any considerable change in the shapes of the boiling temperature isobars, especially if the boiling temperatures t_{H_1}, t_{H_2} and t_{H_3} differ only slightly from one another, and often under reduced pressure the changes of the boiling temperature isobars are very small. At pressures considerably higher than atmospheric the shapes of respective boiling temperature isobars undergo larger changes.

§ 41. Azeotropic Ranges of Binary Positive Azeotropes. The main difference between previous monographs devoted to the study of different kinds of azeotropes [14, 115] and the present one consists in a different approach to the phenomena taking place in the course of the fractional distillation of organic raw materials, containing one, two or more series of homologues, their isomers and closely related chemical substances.

According to the accepted definition, the azeotropic range of an agent A includes a bunch of normal boiling temperature isobars characterized either by a minimum or a maximum (containing the two tangent isobars), and separates them from those systems which have no extrema and, consequently, are classified as zeotropes. This new approach to the examination of azeotropy and zeotropy leads us to the determination, by direct experiment or by theoretical calculation, of the azeotropic ranges of a very large number of chemical compounds. A large number of experiments are needed to examine completely the azeotropic ranges of various agents with different homologous series and their isomers but fortunately it often suffices to find two representatives of a homologous series forming either tangent or almost tangent limiting azeotropes.

The collection of numerical data is made easier by the fact that most of the organic raw materials are composed of saturated, unsaturated and aromatic hydrocarbons. In addition, if the experimenter has to examine a given raw material, he can use a less precise, yet in many cases sufficiently precise method of azeotropic range determination. This method is described in § 121. There is also a series of papers published by MALESIŃSKI [85] which give a method of theoretical calculation of azeotropic ranges. Some experiments have also been made by KURTYKA [90] who determined the azeotropic range of acetic acid with normal paraffins by the ebulliometric method.

In Figure IV. 12 six normal boiling temperature isobars are shown starting with the lowest boiling hexane (I) and ending with undecane (VI). The azeotropic range is characterized by a distinctly pronounced upper asymmetry. A peculiar feature of the whole system of isobars is the unusual shape of numbers V and VI. These two curves are typical for mixtures of substances which at lower temperatures form two liquid phases, and this case may be considered as a typical example of the behaviour of systems lying close to the transition point of a homoazeotrope either into a heteroazeotrope or a heterozeotrope. Recently, KURTYKA found that a heterozeotrope was formed by acetic acid and n-octadecane [173].

An observation may be made for the case of the two practically symmetrical sections lying on each side of the azeotropic point t_{A,H_0} (Fig. IV. 13) formed by acetic acid and octane (H_0). If a mixture containing either a small excess of acetic acid or of octane as compared with (A, H_0) is submitted to fractional distillation, on an effective multiplate distilling column, it may happen that no pure azeotrope is obtained. The main fraction may contain a small excess of acetic acid or octane due to the fact that near the point t_{A,H_0} a small excess of one of the constituents produces a very small change in boiling temperature. Usually, the ebulliometric method of examining the boiling temperatures of mixtures, after successive additions of small amounts of one of the components, enables the boiling temperature changes to be measured with an accuracy of $\pm 0.002°C$. This is the limit of the precision with which it can be established whether the composition of the mixture is identical with that of the point t_{A,H_0} or is shifted slightly towards the left or towards the right side of that point (see § 21, 22, 23).

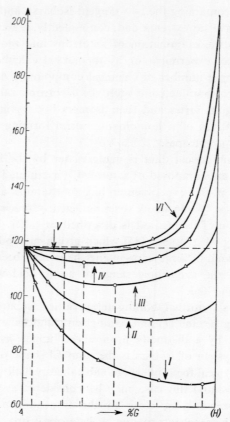

FIG. IV. 12. Normal boiling temperature isobars of mixtures of acetic acid with
the normal paraffins: hexane—*I*, heptane—*II*, octane—*III*, nonane—*IV*, decane—*V*
and undecane—*VI*.

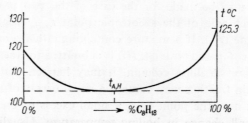

FIG. IV. 13. Boiling temperature isobar of acetic acid and octane; $t_{A,H}$ is the
boiling temperature of the azeotrope.

§ 42. **Large and Small Azeotropic Ranges.** The ability to form binary azeotropes
has long been the subject of discussion by many authors. Before the development of the electronic theory of organic compounds, and before the experimental
and theoretical investigation of substances characterized by strong dipole moments

or by formation of hydrogen bonds, there was no basis on which to found a theoretical explanation, but during the last two decades such a basis for a theory of binary azeotrope formation has been established. It might be expected that the azeotropic range values of an agent forming binary positive azeotropes with different homologous series will vary to a large extent. It was believed that isomers belonging to the same series of homologues are not able to form binary azeotropes with one another. Unexpectedly, CALLINGAERT and WOJCIECHOWSKI [44] proved that two isomeric hydrocarbons slightly differing in their boiling temperatures could form a negative azeotrope over a very small range of temperatures and pressures. With the change of pressure the mixture became homozeotropic. Azeotropes formed by benzene with paraffinic and naphtenic hydrocarbons, or by naphthalene with one-ring homologues of benzene were known long ago, but it is surprising that the azeotropic ranges are relatively large in the first case and small in the second. Recently, BRZOSTOWSKI, MALANOWSKI and ZIĘBORAK [174] proved that 3-picoline and 2,6-lutidine form a positive azeotrope with a depression of 0.6°C, although no such azeotrope had been anticipated.

The azeotropic ranges of paraffins in relation to the olefin series present an interesting case. They undergo a sharp decrease with increase of molecular weight of the saturated hydrocarbon. It has been proved that the azeotrope formed by butane and butene has a relatively large azeotropic depression. The latter decreases rapidly with increase in the number of CH_2 groups in the molecule [43]. No experiments have been carried out to show whether mixtures of high molecular weight paraffins and olefins can form azeotropes.

Alcohols are typical agents forming a large number of azeotropes with a large variety of substances. With increasing molecular weight, their azeotropic range decreases. Glycol belongs to a series of powerful azeotropic agents, especially as regards paraffinic hydrocarbons. Phenols and low-molecular weight organic acids have similar properties, and their azeotropic ranges also decrease with increase in the number of CH_2 groups in the molecule.

Phenols form azeotropes even with some aromatic hydrocarbons, their azeotropic range, however, decreases rapidly with the increase of CH_3 groups both in phenols and in aromatic hydrocarbons.

Aromatic amines, and to some extent pyridine and quinoline bases, show relatively small azeotropic ranges, which decrease with the increase of methyl groups substituting hydrogen atoms in the molecule.

In general it is quite evident that the ability to form binary positive azeotropes is strongly influenced by the dissimilarity of the structure of the components. In a series of azeotropes formed by one azeotropic agent and a series of homologues and isomers, the differences in structure and the presence of polar groups exert a large influence on the azeotropic range values.

Chapter V

THE INFLUENCE OF PRESSURE ON AZEOTROPIC RANGE CHANGES

§ 43. Changes of Azeotropic Ranges in Binary Positive Azeotropes. It has long been known that with change of pressure the composition of azeotropes changes [13, 118]. Consequently, a similar influence of pressure on azeotropic range values may be expected. Considering Figure IV. 3, it will be sufficient in the first instance to know in what direction the points t_A, t_{H_k} and t_A, t_{H_e} will be shifted with a pressure change. Experiments have shown [46, 175] that pressure changes which do not exceed ± 500 mm Hg are too small to produce such large shifts on the diagram as to replace the representatives H_k or H_e by H_{k+1} and H_{e+1}, or H_{k-1} and H_{e-1}. For pressure changes which exceed several atmospheres, the shift in the azeotropic range value may be associated with a replacement of the two substances H_k and H_e by higher or lower boiling representatives of the series. Some experiments at pressures of 19–20 atmospheres were carried out in 1934 by KAR-PIŃSKI [64]; they were not applied, however, to the problem of azeotropic range changes. Extensive measurements were carried out in the years 1929–1938 by ZMA-CZYŃSKI [46, 59, 47]. In most of these investigations the pressure did not exceed 2.75 kg/cm². In one series of experiments a pressure of 5914 mm Hg was reached and the change in benzene concentration in the benzene-ethanol azeotrope was from 67.6 to 41.0 %; this is equal to a decrease of 26.6 per cent. This shift was, at least qualitatively, in agreement with VREVSKI's rule.

The experiments conducted independently by KEUSSLER [60] and B. KARPIŃ-SKI [64], were carried out on the ternary system ethanol, benzene and water and will therefore be discussed in Chapters XII, XIII and XIV (§ 95–99 and § 106).

KRĘGLEWSKI [67, 141] made interesting observations on azeotropes examined under isochoric conditions near the critical states of binary systems. He found that the physical value called azeotropic range retained its meaning in the critical state region. However, the experimental data are not sufficient for the formulation of any broad generalization.

A remark should be made as regards systems of two components, the evaporation enthalpy curves of which cross each other before reaching the critical states of the pure constituents under consideration. A typical example is the system ethanol-benzene. The critical temperatures of benzene and ethanol are 288.5°C and 273.1°C respectively, and the molar evaporation enthalpies measured at atmospheric pressure are $H_{Et} = 9.22$ kcal and $H_B = 7.36$ kcal. It is obvious that, whatever the shapes of the two H,t curves, they should cross each other somewhere in the region between the normal boiling temperature and the lower critical point 273.1°C. One may therefore expect that at the crossing points of the curves under consideration the curve expressing the change in composition of the binary azeotrope will pass through an extremum and that above this point the ethanol concentration C_{Et} will undergo a steady increase instead of the decrease observed by ZMACZYŃSKI for the pressure range 760–5914 mm Hg.

In 1932 BYLEWSKI [45] found this type of turning point for the mixture water-isobutyl alcohol in the pressure range 2–4 atm. More experimental data are needed for selected substances in order to reach a properly motivated generalization. Such investigations require the use of adequately built apparatus and strictly comparative measurements. All the equipment used before World War II by Polish scientists was completely destroyed by the Germans.

Generally speaking, the azeotropic range of an agent A in a series of binary positive azeotropes (A, H_i) examined under atmospheric pressure

$$Z_A(H) = t_{H_k} - t_{H_e}$$

may be expressed for any other pressure as follows:

$$Z'_A(H) = t_{H_{k \pm m}} - t_{H_{e \pm n}},$$

m and n being whole numbers. They can be both positive or both negative and in particular cases may have opposite signs. No experimental results have been published thus far in this field. It is, however, easy to predict how the diagram shown in Figure IV. 3 (§ 35) will change, if the values of m and n are known. Any experimental work in this direction is associated with the determination of the coefficient $\dfrac{dt}{dp}$ for the substances examined.

§ **44. Tonometric Measurements.** Many methods have been devised for determining the change of vapour pressure with temperature. These tonometric measurements, are an essential part of any experimental work on azeotropes.

The ebulliometric method has often been used in the past and it continues to be applied. Precise determinations of $\dfrac{dt}{dp}$ or $\dfrac{dp}{dt}$ coefficients have been carried out at the International Bureau of Weights and Measures near Paris, in the National Bureau of Standards (USA); in the Bureau of Physicochemical Standards in Brussels; and in the pre-war German P. T. R. (Physikalisch-Technische Reichsanstalt), Berlin. ZMACZYŃSKI participated in all the experiments carried out in the above-mentioned European Bureaux [142, 46, 47]. WOJCIECHOWSKI took part in the work carried out in the United States of America [143, 44]. Most of the results obtained in the Bureaux mentioned above are summarized in the monograph *Ebullio-metric Measurements* [31]. ZMACZYŃSKI proved that the ebulliometers used by him in 1938 gave the highest possible accuracy in the value of $\dfrac{dt}{dp}$; it was, however, difficult to maintain a constant pressure in the ebulliometer which was directly connected to the manostat. Due to the advances in automation the desired pressure may be easily controlled within ± 0.02 mm Hg.

The application of strictly comparative measurements recommended many years ago by the International Union of Pure and Applied Chemistry [144] calls for the use of two ebulliometers, one of which is filled with the liquid examined, and the other with a suitable secondary standard. In 1938 water was established by the International Union (IUPAC) as the primary standard for ebulliometric and tonometric measurements.

Experiments have shown that in an isolated closed system it is more conve-nient to use a suitably chosen substance as secondary standard instead of water. Water is easily absorbed by many organic compounds, producing considerable errors in determination of $\dfrac{dt}{dp}$.

Chapter VI

BINARY NEGATIVE AZEOTROPES

§ **45. Series of Binary Negative Azeotropes.** The binary negative azeotropes formed by water with nitric acid or hydrogen chloride were known in the early years of the nineteenth century. The number of azeotropes of this type containing only organic substances is considerably smaller than the number of binary positive azeotropes.

It is convenient to use the symbol $[(-)A, H]$ for any kind of binary negative azeotrope, in spite of the fact that this symbol does not indicate the physicochemical nature of the components A and H which form a mixture having a boiling temperature isobar characterized by a maximum and an isotherm having a minimum. The present author made the proposal to divide the negative azeotropes into three groups, the formation of the first caused by the following inequality of the VAN DER WAALS forces:

$$a_{AA} < a_{AH} > a_{HH}. \tag{1}$$

The variety of compounds forming negative azeotropes belonging to this group is rather too large and diverse for division into subgroups.

The physicochemical character of the negative azeotropes belonging to the second group is more distinctly marked. All binary mixtures formed from a weak organic acid or from phenols or their homologues with weak bases such as amines, pyridine and quinoline and their derivatives are typical constituents of negative azeotropes.

In this group, series of azeotropes such as $[(-)Ac, Am]$, $[(-)Ac, P]$, $[(-)F, P]$, $[(-)F, Am]$ have been examined. Some of them are encountered in high and low temperature coal tars. The presence of neutral compounds, especially hydrocarbons, boiling at an appropriate temperature relative to the boiling temperature of the binary negative azeotropes, leads to the formation of large number of ternary bipositive-negative azeotropes which are described in § 69–88.

Recently, a sufficient number of experiments have been carried out to confirm the supposition of the author that pyridine hydrochlorides at least should be considered as binary negative azeotropes. In 1940 the observation was made by the author and another scientist, whose name has remained unknown to the author, that the hydrochlorides of pyridine bases may undergo fractional distillation. If the base is pure enough, an equilibrium is established in the column and the collected fractions may be distilled off in large quantities within 0.14°C. At the outset, however, a small excess of the free base is contained in the forerun, so that the main fraction does not correspond exactly to the equivalent amounts of the base and of the hydrogen chloride. At the end an excess of about 1–2% of the latter is still present in the distillate. For this reason, such hydrochlorides should be considered to be negative binary azeotropes. Experiments have shown that they are powerful azeotropic agents having a very large azeotropic range.

The azeotropes thus obtained belong to a specific type of ternary saddle heteroazeotropes (§ 88). Owing to the limited number of homologues and their isomers it is difficult to find tangent or almost tangent azeoropes in a series of binary negative azeotropes. In Figure VI.1 both tangent or almost tangent boiling isobars $t_{H_k} t_A$ and $t_A t_{H_e}$ are purposely shown to emphasize that the value of the azeotropic range

$$Z_A(H) = t_{H_k} - t_{H_e}$$

plays the same role as in the case of binary positive azeotropes, in spite of the fact that the whole scheme is reversed as compared with the latter.

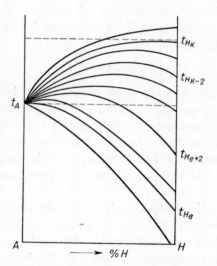

FIG. VI. 1. A series of binary negative azeotropes [(−) A, Hᵢ] in which H_i are the representatives of a series (H) of homologues and their isomers.

§ 46. General Remarks on Binary Negative Azeotropes. No extensive investigations have been carried out in the past on methods for the exact determination of the composition of binary negative azeotropes. Recently, much more attention has been paid to this problem. Most experiments, however, having in view the precise determination of both the composition and the normal boiling temperature of any kind of negative azeotrope, have been carried out using multi-plate distillation columns. No precise controlling measurements were made which could be regarded as proving that the main fraction collected actually had the exact composition of the azeotrope under examination.

The Polish group of investigators used combined distillation and ebulliometric methods in order to avoid any systematic errors associated with an exclusive use of the fractional distillation method. If the ebulliometric degree of purity of the main fraction is determined, and if afterwards, the boiling temperature isobars, obtained by successive addition, to the main fraction, of small quantities of the first and then of the second component, do not show any extrema (in this case maxima) it may be concluded that the main fraction really has the composition of the negative azeotrope.

Recently, precise determinations of negative azeotrope compositions were made by ORSZAGH and LELAKOWSKA [145] using binary azeotropes containing chloroform—isopropyl bromide or chloroform—ethyl formate. The ebullio-metric and distillation methods were employed and a satisfactory agreement of the data was obtained. These binary negative azeotropes formed the starting point for the discovery of two thus far unknown binegative-positive azeotropes. More details concerning the latter are given in Chapter X § 85.

Two interesting negative azeotropes were found in 1950 and 1953: COLLIN-GAERT and WOJCIECHOWSKI [44] proved that 2,2,3-trimethylbutane and 2,4-dim-ethylpropane form, at a pressure of 505.2 mm Hg a negative azeotrope with a boiling temperature increase 0.13°C (b.-pt. 67.58°C). PARVANT [120] found that some of the isomeric xylenols also form binary negative azeotropes. In the latter case, the assumption may be made that the hydrogen bridges could be responsible for the formation of negative azeotropes. Such an explanation is unacceptable in the case of two isomeric paraffinic hydrocarbons. The differences in the VAN DER WA-ALS forces should of course be very small.

It should be borne in mind that no negative heteroazeotropes have ever been found. This is in good agreement with the assumption that the inequality

$$a_{AA} < a_{AB} > a_{BB}$$

is responsible for the formation of the maxima in boiling temperatures and minima in vapour pressure which characterize negative azeotropes. In general, the forma-tion of maxima on the freezing curves is also a typical phenomenon in these sys-tems.

Chapter VII

TERNARY POSITIVE AZEOTROPES

§ 47. Historical Note. The first binary azeotropes, discovered by Dalton, belonged to the negative type formed by water and hydrochloric or nitric acids. Entraining by steam of numerous organic mixtures led to the discovery of binary heteroazeotropes a long time before this term was accepted. We recall that the positive ternary azeotropes discovered by YOUNG [10] contained water and formed mainly two liquid phase systems. The dehydration of ethanol, discovered and protected by patent claims by Young, was based on the removal of positive ternary heteroazeotropes containing water, a certain amount of ethanol and an azeotropic agent, for instance benzene. The mixtures collected in the receiver were typical ternary heteroazeotropes.

These facts show the role played by water as an important constituent of different kinds of heteroazeotropes. In LECAT'S first monograph (1918) on azeotropy it was stated that water may be an indispensable constituent of all positive ternary azeotropes. If this assumption were true, no ternary homoazeotropes would ever have been discovered. A rapid progress in this branch of physical chemistry has proved definitely that positive ternary homoazeotropes exist and that they are very often formed in the course of fractional distillation of different organic raw materials. If, instead of an azeotrope (A, B, C) composed of three suitably selected compounds, the series of azeotropes (A, B, H_i) formed by two azeotropic agents A and B and the representatives of a series (H) of homologues and their isomers is the subject of examination, the number of positive ternary azeotropes grows rapidly. Consequently, one may expect that the number of positive ternary homoazeotropes known will increase considerably as our knowledge of azeotropy and polyazeotropy increases.

§ 48. Water-Free Ternary Positive Azeotropes. The most common type of positive ternary homoazeotrope is that which occurs in mixtures of three substances which have an unlimited mutual solubility. If one, two or all three of the components formed series (A), (B), (H) of homologues, then, depending on the azeotropic ranges of the constituents belonging to each of the three series, a large number of ternary azeotropes would be formed.

Usually the component having the smallest azeotropic range has the greatest influence on the number of ternary azeotropes formed. This problem is discussed later (§ 106). Besides the examination of the azeotropic ranges of each of the components A, B, H separately, in relation to the three homologous series (A), (B) and (H), it is often important to examine the positive ternary azeotropes (A, B, H_i) formed by the two components A and B with a series (H) of homologues and their isomers. In this case the term azeotropic range of a binary azeotrope (A, B) refers to the series of binary azeotropes (B, H_i) and may be defined by the equation:

$$Z_{A,B}(B, H_i) = t_{B,H_k} - t_{B,H_e}.$$ (1)

The comparison of equation (1) with that defining the azeotropic range of the less active component A:

$$Z_A(H) = t_{H_k} - t_{H_e}$$ (2)

reveals the following differences. Firstly, when using equation (1) we are dealing with a series of binary azeotropes (B, H_i) and not with a series (H); secondly, the azeotropic range is given by the difference between the two boiling temperatures t_{B,H_k} and t_{B,H_e}. The first is practically equal to $t_{A,B}$ because it lies on the tangent boiling temperature isobar formed by mixtures of the two binary azeotropes (A,B) and (B, H_k); the second is practically equal to t_{B,H_e}, because it lies on the tangent boiling temperature isobar formed by mixtures of the binary azeotropes (A,B) with (B, H_e), and the concentration of A is practically zero: this isobar is a tangent to the horizontal line drawn through point t_{B,H_e}. In Figure VII. 1b the whole scheme is graphically presented and the azeotropic range of the azeotrope (A, B) with regard to series (B, H_i) of binary azeotropes formed by agent B with respective homologues and their isomers of series (H) is shown.

The two lines in Figure VII.1 represent the two tangent boiling isobars limiting the formation of positive ternary azeotropes (A, B, H_i). Below and above these two limits only ternary zeotropic mixtures of the binary azeotrope (A, B) with (B, H_{e-1}), (B, H_{e-2}) ... and (B, H_{k+1}), (B, H_{k+2}) ... can exist.

As mentioned above, the azeotropic range $Z_A(H)$ of the agent A is assumed to be smaller than $Z_B(H)$. In addition, we assume that

$$Z_B(H) = t_{H_{k+m}} - t_{H_{e-n}}$$ (3)

where m and n are whole *positive* numbers. This means that on the graph t_{H_k} lies below $t_{H_{k+m}}$ and t_{H_e} above $t_{H_{e-n}}$. This is graphically represented by Figure VII. 2 a, b, independently, whether the boiling temperature of the *main azeotropic agent* A is higher or lower than that of the *secondary agent* B.

The experiments carried out by ZIĘBORAK [193] and ORSZAGH [35] proved that series of typical ternary azeotropes which did not contain water could be easily obtained.

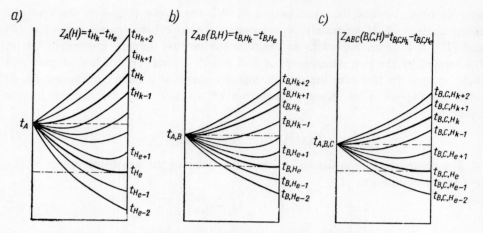

FIG. VII. 1. The azeotropic ranges $Z_A(H_i)$, $Z_{A,B}(B,H_i)$, $Z_{A,B,C}(B,C,H_i)$ of the binary, ternary and quaternary azeotropes.

§ 49. Peculiar Cases of Ternary Azeotrope Formation.

If the conditions (1) and (2) are not fulfilled, the formation of positive ternary azeotropes is restricted. It often happens that the two tangent boiling temperature isobars formed by the main and the secondary agent (§ 48) cross each other in the way shown in Figure VII. 2 *a, b* or VII. 3 *a, b*. If no crossing takes place, no ternary azeotropes can be formed, or if the existence of such an azeotrope has been proved, it should be regarded as an exceptional case. ORSZAGH [35] and ZIĘBORAK [193] have made a relatively large number of direct observations, and extensive theoretical considerations have been presented by MALESIŃSKI [165]. In some exceptional cases a theoretically impossible formation of ternary azeotropes has been noticed. As a rule in these cases the azeotropic depressions were very low and, tangent boiling isobars were found indicating that in these series the extreme limits of ternary azeotrope formation had been reached.

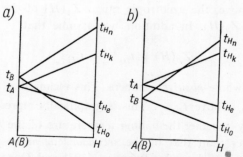

FIG. VII. 2 *a, b*. The azeotropic range $Z_A(H)$ of the main agent lies within that of the secondary agent $Z_B(H)$. In case (*a*), t_B is higher than t_A, and in case (*b*), t_A is higher than t_B.

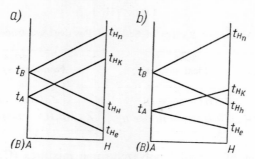

FIG. VII. 3 *a, b*. The tangent boiling temperature isobars t_3 t_{H_h} and $t_A t_{H_k}$ cross each other.

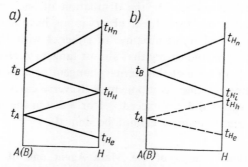

FIG. VII. 4 *a, b*. (a) Two tangent boiling temperature isobars $t_B t_{H_h}$ and $t_A t_{H_h}$ have a common point t_{H_H} (b). No crossing point is formed by the respective tangent boiling temperature isobars.

§ 50. **Ideal and Non-ideal Ternary Positive Azeotropes.** Let us compare the azeotropic ranges $Z_A(H)$ and $Z_{A,B}(B, H)$ in which A is the main azeotropic agent, B is the secondary agent and (H) is a series of homologues and their isomers. Suppose that the condition shown graphically in Figure VII. 2 is fulfilled. The question arises whether the following equations:

$$Z_A(H) = t_{H_k} - t_{H_e}, \tag{1}$$

$$Z_{A,B}(B, H) = t_{B,H_k} - t_{B,H_e} \tag{2}$$

are fulfilled, or whether, instead, of (2) the equation

$$Z_{A,B}(B, H) = t_{B,H_{k+m}} - t_{B,H_{e+n}} \tag{3}$$

is correct. In equation (3) m and n are whole *positive or negative* numbers. Experiments have shown that both systems exist. In many of them m and n do not exceed ± 1 or ± 2.

The suggestion was made by the author of this book that those systems should be called ideal, for which $m = 0$ and $n = 0$. Consequently, for series of positive ternary azeotropes, the following scheme may be presented.

TABLE VII. 1

Azeotropic Ranges of Series of Positive Azeotropes

Series of azeotropes	Ideal systems	Non-ideal systems
(A, H_i) (A, B, H_i)	$Z_A(H) = t_{H_k} - t_{H_e}$ $Z_{A,B}(B, H_i) = t_{B, H_k} - t_{B, H_e}$	$Z_A(H) = t_{H_k} - t_{H_e}$ $Z_{A,B}(B, H_i) = t_{B, H_{k+m}} - t_{B, H_{e+n}}$

The examination of complex polyazeotropic mixtures (Chapt. XV, XVI and XVII) shows that this classification is very useful and it is often applied to explain the phenomena which occur during the distillation of such mixtures.

It should be pointed out that direct observations have shown that quite often the boiling temperature isobars of mixtures of either A with H_k or A with H_e were of the almost tangent type, indicating that almost tangent zeotropes, not azeotropes, were formed, but that, in spite of this, ternary tangent or almost tangent azeotropes were formed on adding the third component B. Reverse cases have also been found though the m and n values did not exceed ± 1 or ± 2. On the other hand, the existence of non-ideal ternary systems cannot be denied.

§ 51. Concentration Changes of the Main Agent and of the Homologous Series (H).

If the compositions of the whole series of positive binary azeotropes (A, H_i) are examined (Fig. VII. 1), it will be seen that at the point t_{H_e} the concentration C_{H_e} of H_e is 100%. At the point t_A concentration C_{H_k} becomes zero. Obviously if we move from t_{H_e} to t_A via the series of azeotropes, there will be successive replacement of A by one of the members of (H), until in the upper tangent azeotrope (A, H_k), the concentration of A is 100% [171].

Somewhat similar changes are found when a series (A, B, H_i) of positive ternary azeotropes is examined. Some peculiar phenomena, however, should be pointed out. In general, C_A reaches a maximum value, equal to the concentration of the main azeotropic agent A in the binary azeotrope (A, B). On the graph (Fig. VII. 1b), the latter is represented by the point $t_{A,B}$ (which may be replaced by the symbol t_{A,B,H_k}, since $C_{H_k} = 0$). In the successive azeotropes C_A steadily decreases, reaching zero at the point t_{B,H_e}, which may be replaced by t_{A,B,H_e}.

It may be asked in what way the concentration of B changes through the series of azeotropes. No strictly formulated answer can be given. First of all it depends upon the value of the azeotropic range $Z_{A,B}(B, H_i)$. If the difference $\Delta t = t_{A,B,H_k} - t_{A,B,H_e} = t_{A,B} - t_{B,H_e}$ is relatively small, it may be taken as a first approximation that C_B is constant for the whole series of azeotropes. On the other hand, if Δt is large, it depends upon the boiling temperature t_B. To a first approximation, it may be assumed that if C_B remains practically constant the conditions are favourable for the formation of an ideal series of positive ternary azeotropes. If concentration of B changes considerably there is a probability that a typical non-ideal system of azeotropes will be formed.

§ 52. **Ideal Ternary Positive System.** In Figure VII. 5 the variation of C_A in an ideal series of positive ternary azeotropes is shown. On the vertical axis the mol. per cent compositions of a series of positive ternary azeotropes (A, B, H_i) formed by the main agent A, the secondary one B and the series (H) of homologues and their isomers are plotted against the value of H_i for the series of azeotropes. It is assumed that the concentration C_B of the secondary agent B remains constant for the whole series. Because of this, the lower part of the diagram is an elongated rectangle. The triangles A and H show the mutual successive replacement of A by consecutive representatives of the series (H) of homologues and their isomers. It is assumed that, due to the constant C_B concentration throughout the series, an ideal azeotropic system is formed because t_B is much higher than t_A.

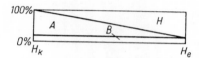

FIG. VII. 5. Composition change of the main agent A and the representatives of the series (H). It is assumed that C_B remains constant in all the positive ternary azeotropes of the type (A, B, H_i); B represents the lowest field.

MALESIŃSKI'S theoretical considerations are in agreement with the phenomena observed in a series of ideal positive ternary homoazeotropes. In 1956 he showed that a universal parabola may be obtained by plotting the value of δ_{Az} against X_{H_i}, where

$$\delta_{Az} = t_{Az_{23}} - t_{Az_{123}}. \tag{1}$$

In equation (1) 1, 2, 3 are the three components forming a positive ternary azeotrope and $t_{Az_{23}}$ is for the boiling temperature of the positive binary azeotrope formed by components 2 and 3, 2 being the main constituent, whilst 1 represents the homologous series (H) of the azeotropes (A, B, H_i). In Figure VII. 6 the parabola is drawn for the three series of ternary positive azeotropes formed by an alcohol, benzene and a light gasoline hydrocarbon group of homologues. The alcohols are methanol (I) isopropanol (II) and isobutanol (III). In the region from 0 to 35% of x_{H_i} the calculated values deviate by several per cent, but usually less than ten. With increasing of x_{H_i} not only do the deviations become much larger, but they are on both sides of the parabola. Moreover, some larger deviations are observed.

It would be desirable to examine a larger number homologous series of azeotropes in addition to the alcoholic one, because the presence of the latter does not favour the formation of regular solutions.

Concerning the probability of formation of either ideal or non-ideal series of positive ternary azeotropes, MALESIŃSKI's theoretical considerations seem to indicate that a large difference $\Delta t = t_B - t_A$ should lead to ideal systems (§ 51). Further examination of this problem is required, before a general rule can be formulated.

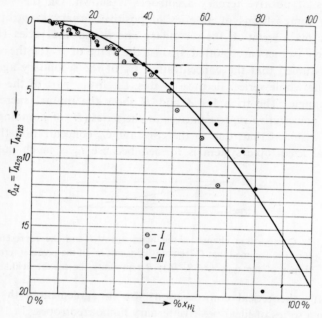

FIG. VII. 6. Parabolic dependence of $\delta^{Az} = t_{Az_{23}} - t_{Az_{123}}$ upon X_{H_i} observed for a series of positive ternary azeotropes (B, Al, H_i), B being benzene, Al, methanol, isopropanol or isobutanol, and H_i a close-boiling fraction of hydrocarbons (H) from low boiling gasoline.

§ 53. Transition of Ternary Positive Homo- to Heteroazeotropes.

As was mentioned in § 47, the discovery of positive ternary heteroazeotropes preceded the investigation of those which contained only one liquid phase. Nowadays some of the ternary heteroazeotropes are known which under a relatively small increase of pressure transform into homoazeotropes.

A large number of positive ternary heteroazeotropes are composed of two insoluble or partly soluble liquids A and W (water) and a component H which is soluble in both the other two components. H is often called the homogenizer because it produces an increase of the mutual solubility of the constituents. In Figures VII. 7 and VII. 8 two GIBBS concentration triangles are shown. In the first a heteroazeotrope $(A, W, H \, -\cdot-)$ is shown. The symbol $-\cdot-$ indicates that the point representing the composition of the azeotrope lies on the heteroazeotropic line RP (point Az). With increasing pressure and boiling temperature the mutual solubility curve is shifted downwards so that the azeotropic point Az is found in the one-phase region (as shown in Fig. VII. 8).

The two figures show the essential continuity of the two types of azeotropes; the possibility of a transition was long unrecognized.

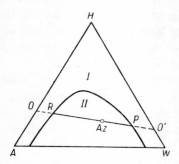

FIG. VII. 7. Positive ternary heteroazeotrope. I—homogeneous ternary region, II—heterogeneous ternary region, RP—heteroazeotropic line, Az—heteroazeotrope $(A, H, W$ $-\cdot-)$ composition.

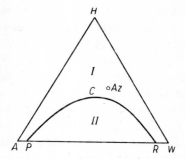

FIG. VII. 8. Ternary homoazeotrope; $Az-$ azeotrope composition.

§ 54. General Remarks. Two peculiar properties of positive binary and ternary azeotropes have been examined in the previous paragraphs which have been, at least to some extent, overlooked in the past. In fact, little attention was paid to the series of azeotropes formed by one and especially by two azeotropic agents with different series of homologues and their isomers and sometimes with other chemically related substances. Because of this, no azeotropic ranges have been examined in the past. The introduction of the terms ideal and non-ideal series of binary and ternary azeotropes (we will deal later with quaternary azeotropes as well) helps in the examination both of artificially prepared mixtures and of naturally occurring organic raw material fractions, such as those in coal tar.

Experimental and theoretical investigations have shown that in some cases it is more convenient to use the equations

$$Z_A(H) = t_{H_k} - t_{H_e}, \tag{1}$$

$$Z_{A,B}(B, H) = t_{B,H_k} - t_{B,H_e} \tag{2}$$

to designate the azeotropic ranges of binary (1) and ternary (2) series of azeotropes, or to examine exclusively the azeotropic ranges of series of binary azeotropes:

$$Z_A(H) = t_{H_k} - t_{H_e}, \tag{3}$$

$$Z_B(H) = t_{H_{k+m}} - t_{H_{e+n}} \tag{4}$$

In (4) m, and n are whole positive or negative numbers; MALESIŃSKI'S [97] theoretical examinations are based on the second method. The second novelty of the present work consists in taking advantage of the far-reaching analogy between homo- and heteroazeotropes on the one hand and homo- and heterozeotropes on the other. The transition of homo- into hetero-systems is a phenomenon which occurs in a wide variety of liquid mixtures and in spite of the fact that the theory of heteroazeotropes and heterozeotropes has not kept pace with the state of our knowledge [146], in the experimental treatment of these systems the analogy plays an important role and its significance cannot be overlooked.

Difficulty can arise, if low boiling representatives of the series are examined. MALESIŃSKI [97] has shown that, in the absence of representatives forming tangent or almost tangent boiling temperature isobars, the azeotropic range can be calculated. Such calculations, however, only yield approximate values of the ranges, and direct experimental data are then helpful. However, the lower boiling members are generally less important when it comes to examining organic raw materials. The main problems of azeotropy are still associated with liquid mixtures boiling within 70–250°C.

Chapter VIII

THE EXAMINATION OF TERNARY POSITIVE AZEOTROPES

§ 55. Ebulliometric and Distillation Methods. Some of the methods of determining the composition and the normal boiling temperatures of positive ternary azeotropes have been described in the monograph "Ebulliometric Measurements" [31]. Since then many improvements have been made, to reduce the systematic errors which may arise, due to the flatness of the boiling temperature surface surrounding the point representing the composition of the azeotrope under examination.

There are two types of methods and apparatus, suited to the examination of homoazeotropes and heteroazeotropes respectively.

Experiments have shown that the fractional distillation method may or may not yield correct results (See Fig. VIII. 1 *a*, points *M* and *M'*,). In the case of positive ternary homoazeotropes the error may be due to the very flat boiling temperature isobar surfaces, especially in the vicinity of the azeotropic point. For this reason, a combined method similar to that described in § 21, 22, and 23 should be employed. It consists in (*a*) using the fractional distillation method to prepare a main fraction collected within a very narrow temperature range, and thereafter, in carrying out three consecutive independent ebulliometric measurements and (*b*) in establishing the shape of three sections of the three boiling temperature isobars. Each measurement is carried out in a two- or three-stage ebulliometer filled each time with a new portion of the main fraction mentioned above. To each portion separately one of the three constituents is successively added so as to obtain a relatively small section of the respective boiling temperature isobar. In this way three sections are obtained. If no minima appear on these three isobars, it is a proof that the main fraction corresponds to the real composition of the ternary azeotrope examined. On other hand, if one or even two minima are found, an extrapolation should be made to find the real composition of the azeotrope. In § 83 more details of the extrapolation method are given.

§ 56. Ebulliometric Determination of the Composition of Homoazeotropes. If the amount of the components is not sufficient for using the combined distillation and ebulliometric methods, ebulliometric measurements may be applied exclusively. Generally speaking, they consist in examining the shape of the concave tridimensional boiling temperature isobaric surface lying in the vicinity or surrounding the azeotropic point. In Figure VIII 1*b*, a tridimensional model is shown with the point t_{Az} representing the minimum boiling point of the respective mixture.

In Figures VIII. 2 and VIII. 3 two different bunches of boiling temperature isobar sections are shown. They are appropriate to the "triangle" and "star" method respectively.

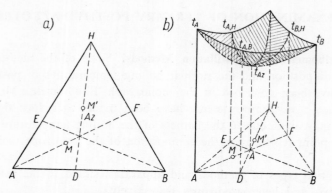

FIG. VIII. 1 *a, b*. Tridimensional model(*b*) and projection (*a*) of positive ternary homoazeotrope (*A, B, H*) are presented. *Az* in (*a*) and *A* in (*b*) show the composition of the azeotrope, t_{Az} is the normal boiling temperature of this azeotrope.

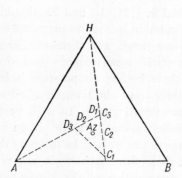

FIG. VIII. 2. Triangle method for determining the composition *Az* and the normal boiling temperature of the positive homoazeotrope (*A, B, H*); *Az* is the extrapolated value.

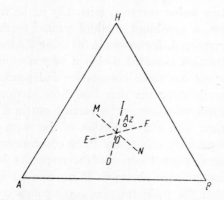

FIG. VIII. 3. Star method for determining the point *Az* representing the composition of the positive homoazeotrope (*A, B, H*); *Az* is the extrapolated value.

The main task of the experimenter is to prepare the three components in a state of high purity. It should be made a rule that the difference between boiling and condensation temperatures of the pure components should not exceed 0.020°C. This corresponds to the third degree of purity expressed in what is called the ebulliometric scale of purity [31, 32].

If the "triangle" method is used, the standardized differential ebulliometer similar to that shown in Figure II. 7 should be filled with the binary mixture. After determining the degree of purity of this sample, small amounts of the component H should be introduced successively and the points C_1, C_2, C_3 lying on the isobar section characterizing the respective boiling temperature changes, should be examined [31]. If a minimum in the boiling temperature is found, this indicates that we have bypassed the azeotropic point Az, in which case, small amounts of component A should be added. The point Az will be bypassed again and a minimum will be found on the isobar C_3D_3. The isobar D_3C_1 should then be examined, and the extrapolation will give the azeotropic composition.

It may be necessary to examine additional sections of the boiling temperature isobar to give the azeotrope composition more precisely.

The so-called "star" method consists in determining the shapes of several sections EF, ID and MN of three boiling temperature isobars lying not far from the point Az representing the expected composition of the positive ternary homoazeotrope (A, B, H). If these sections were suitably chosen two of them DI and EF would be characterized by minimum boiling temperatures. Interpolation then gives the composition of the ternary azeotrope Az. Due to the flat shape of the isobaric boiling point surfaces the boiling temperature of the azeotrope may be interpolated with relatively high accuracy.

§ **57. Influence of Contaminants.** It should be emphasized that in both the "triangle" and the "star" methods the examination of any section of the boiling temperature isobar is associated with the determination of one or two condensation temperatures depending upon whether two- or three-stage ebulliometers (Fig. II. 7) are used. Consequently, the smaller the difference $\Delta t = t_b - t_c$, t_b being the boiling and t_c the condensation temperature, the closer we approach the azeotropic point Az, since here the difference $t_b - t_c$ is zero for the pure azeotrope. However, owing to the presence of impurities, the difference Δt reaches a minimum and not zero, even when the point Az is reached. In the course of the study either by the "triangle" or by the "star" method Δt minima are observed, if this point lies in the vicinity of Az. It may be difficult to decide whether it is solely the contaminants which cause Δt to be > 0. For this reason, more attention should be paid to t_c changes. The interpolated t_b value corresponds to the point representing the boiling temperature of the azeotrope.

§ **58. Distillation of Ternary Heteroazeotropes.** In spite of the fact that many more ternary heteroazeotropes have been examined than ternary homoazeotropes, so far no general precise methods have been used for their examination. On the other hand, more theoretical generalizations are known for homo- than for heteroazeotropes.

BARBAUDY [176] was one of the earliest investigators to endeavour to obtain accurate data for binary and ternary heteroazeotropes, but at that time (1925) no ebulliometer which gave very accurate results was available.

Several years before the appearance of the Polish edition of *Ebulliometry* (1935), two modified ebulliometers were developed for examining the exact boiling temperature of coexisting two-liquid phase systems. Recently they have been found not to work properly, if the two liquids are practically insoluble in each other. In § 23 new devices are described which give better results than the apparatus previously used. Distillation columns should be provided with special heads to ensure that the liquid phases will undergo condensation without any change in the ratio of the denser and lighter phases. In Figure VIII. 4 one such head is shown.

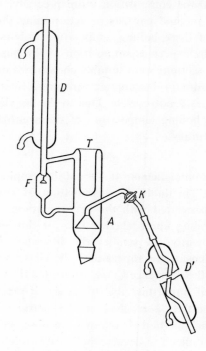

FIG. VIII. 4. Column head for collecting liquid phase condensate. The electrical heaters are not shown.

The vapours enter space where the thermometer well T is located. If the stopcock K is left open, part of the vapour will go through funnel A and the joining tube into condenser D'. This tube is heated electrically by heaters, which are not shown in the figure, so that condensation occurs only in D' and the condensate has the same composition as the vapour. When the desired amount of the two liquid phase fraction has been collected in a cylinder, the stopcock is closed.

After collecting several consecutive fractions, in a cylinder one is able to see whether, at constant temperature, the ratio $h_1 : h_2$ of the amounts of the two phases collected remains constant, h_1 and h_2 being the heights of the respective liquids in the cylinder.

The device described above, or a similar one, should be used for examining *homo-azeotropes* if the phase separation takes place at a sufficiently high temperature, even if it is lower than the boiling temperature of the homoazeotrope.

Most ternary heteroazeotropes contain water as one component. Some hete-roazeotropes which do not contain water are, however, hygroscopic, and it is essential to exclude moisture during the experiments, to avoid contamination.

§ 59. Use of Conventional Type Ebulliometers. It has been shown by direct experiment that in some cases any kind of differential ebulliometer may also be used for determining the composition and the boiling temperature of a positive ternary heteroazeotrope. This is the case with systems containing small amounts, (3–8 per cent) of water or any other component which has a relatively small solubility in the mixture of the other two components.

A classical example is the heteroazeotrope composed of benzene, ethanol and water. It contains about 7 weight per cent of water, and the concentration of ethanol is large enough to form two phases boiling at constant temperature without any fluctuation, in spite of the circulation of both phases in the lower portion of the ebulliometer.

§ 60. The Heteroazeotropic Line and its Location. In Figure VIII. 5 is shown the diagram of a typical ternary heteroazeotrope. If the liquids A and B are practically insoluble or slightly soluble in each other and H is soluble in A as well

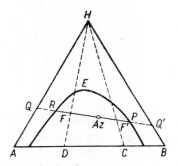

FIG. VIII. 5. Azeotropic point Az lies on the azeotropic line RP.

as in B, the component H is often called the *homogenizer*. Under the influence of the latter a typical mutual solubility curve is produced in the Gibbs concentration diagram. If the components A, B and H form a ternary heteroazeotrope (A, B, $H - \cdot -$), then its projection onto the concentration triangle lies on the so-called heteroazeotropic line *RP*, the points *R* and *P* representing the compositions of the two liquid phases in equilibrium with each other and with the vapour at the boiling temperature t_{Az}.

The author has recently proposed [177] the use of the symbol $(A, B, H\cdot-)$ for the case when the azeotropic point *Az* coincides with one of the liquid phases, for instance with *R*. In this case fractional distillation will yield a single phase condensate, because the azeotropic composition expressed by point *Az* is identical with that of the liquid phase *R*. (Fig. VIII. 6).

If, by changing the pressure, the azeotropic point can be shifted far enough to coincide with the mutual solubility curve *RP*, the signs—: or: —should be used according to whether the azeotropic point lies at the right or on the left-hand end of the heteroazeotropic line. In Figure VIII. 5 on GIBBS' concentration triangle the heteroazeotropic line *RAzP* is shown. The point *Az* represents the composition of the ternary azeotrope $(A, B, H - \cdot -)$. In order to find this composition it is necessary to find the location of the azeotropic line *RP*. To do this it is necessary to

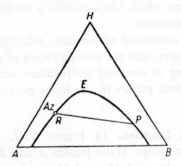

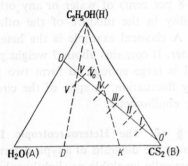

FIG. VIII. 6. The azeotropic point *Az* lies on the mutual solubility curve *REP*; its composition is equal to that of point *R*. The symbol of this azeotrope is $(A, B, H\cdot-)$.

FIG. VIII. 7. Ebulliometric determination of the location of the azeotropic line *OO'* Five sections of boiling temperature isobar were made after two isobars C_2H_5OH, *D* and C_2H_5OH, *K* had shown the location of the heteroazeotropic line in GIBBS' concentration triangle. In the other system ethanol was replaced by acetone.

examine the shapes of at least two boiling temperature isobars *HD* and *HC*. *D* and *C* should be adequately chosen. As a result of these ebulliometric investigations two minimum points *F* and *F'* should be found as projections on the GIBBS concentration triangle. If at the pressure established in the system, point *Az* coincides with point *R*, as shown in Figure VIII. 6 we are dealing with a $(A, B, H\cdot-)$ homoazeotrope (see Fig. VIII. 5 and 6).

Heteroazeotropes having an inclined heteroazeotropic line similar to that shown in Figure VIII. 7 are also known. Two of these heteroazeotropes formed by ethanol, (or acetone) carbon disulphide and water [99] have been examined in detail.

In order to show how flat the tridimensional surface is some details are given below of the boiling temperature changes produced by successive addition of water to a mixture V_0. The measurements were made along the line OO' (isobar section V_0-V) in Figure VIII. 7 [31].

The mixture V_0 used for this experiment was composed of 47.758 g of carbon disulfide, 40.456 g of ethanol and 14.390 g of water. The difference between the boiling temperature of this mixture and that of the heteroazeotrope was very small ($0.024-0.006 = 0.018°C$). The boiling temperature surface was so flat that the addition of several grams of water only altered the boiling temperature by about one hundredth of a degree.

TABLE VIII. 1

Successive Dosing of Mixture V_0 with V

Wt.% water, g	Boiling temperature changes °C
14.390	0.024
16.008	0.013
17.704	0.006
20.101	0 006
24.074	0.010
27.277	0.022

It was not easy to fix the composition of the mixture having the minimum boiling point, because the changing in water content by 2.497 g did not produce any measurable change in the boiling temperature near to the minimum.

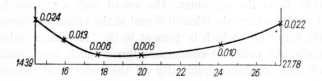

FIG. VIII. 8. Section of the boiling temperature isobar.

In Figure VIII. 8 the results given in Table VIII. 1 are plotted to show the shallowness of the minimum in the neighbourhood of the heteroazeotropic line.

It should be mentioned that the points R and P (Fig. VIII. 6) represent the composition of the two co-existing liquid phases at the boiling temperature of the heteroazeotrope. On cooling to room temperature, the composition of the two phases may change. Care should be taken to make the appropriate correction [31].

Chapter IX

QUATERNARY POSITIVE AZEOTROPES

§ 61. Discovery of Quaternary Positive Azeotropes. In 1918 LECAT predicted the existence of quaternary azeotropes without any specification of their type or their constituents. He remarked that with increase of the number of components the probability of formation of a multicomponent azeotrope would decrease. In 1936 the author described the method to be used for proving the existence of a positive quaternary azeotrope [31]. In 1949 ZIĘBORAK [52] discovered positive quaternary heteroazeotropes. The first paper appeared in 1950 [50].

The discovery of positive quaternary azeotropes was associated with the explanation of the phenomena taking place in the course of dehydration of ethanol according to the process described by GUINOT in his patent claims.

LECAT's idea was to find four adequately chosen pure chemical compounds forming a quaternary azeotrope, but ZIĘBORAK pursued the more fruitful line having in view the explanation of physico-chemical processes taking place in the course of fractional distillation of a mixture of three pure chemical compounds: ethanol, water and benzene, to which a gasoline fraction had been added.

According to GUINOT [51], a gasoline fraction (H) collected within a very narrow temperature range of 101–102°C should be mixed with an adequate amount of benzene (B) to form the entrainer. The use of such a mixture has two advantages: firstly it removes from the ethanol found in the column bottom product practically all of the water (W) which is present in the "rectificate" (about 5% W and 95% E); secondly, the collected condensate forms much more readily two liquid phases. One of these contains practically all the water, and the other a mixture of ethanol, benzene and gasoline. There is no evidence, but it is very probable that GUINOT assumed that the hydrocarbons found in the gasoline fraction form positive ternary azeotropes similar to that (B, E, W) formed by benzene in the dehydration process discovered by YOUNG and published by him and FORTEY in 1902. Today we can easily understand that GUINOT's discovery was classified as an extension of YOUNG's idea consisting in adding to benzene some hydrocarbons found in the 101–102°C fraction of gasoline. It should be stated in connection with this wrong conclusion that no hydrocarbons boiling within the range 101–102°C exist. The fraction usually collected contained a mixture of hydrocarbons boiling somewhat lower and higher than the fraction indicated in the patent claim.

The proper explanation was given by ZIĘBORAK twenty six years later. It is that a series of quaternary heteroazeotropes (B, E, W, H_i— · —) which all boil within a very narrow range of temperature so that they are collected as one fraction, even if an effective continuous distillation column is employed.

Two other sets of observation should be mentioned in connection with quaternary azeotropes in order to give a complete picture.

In 1930 some simple experiments were made by the author and his collaborators [31]. A series of distillations of mixtures containing gasoline and 10, 20, 30, 40 and 50 weight per cent of ethanol, respectively were made. In Figure IX. 1 distillation curves obtained are shown.

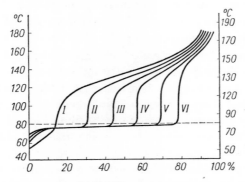

FIG. IX. 1. Distilling curves of gasoline with different amounts of ethanol.

It is easy to see that a series of almost tangent azeotropes (E, H_i) had been obtained, in spite of the fact that the boiling temperature of the gasoline fraction considerably exceeded 78.32° C, the boiling temperature of dehydrated ethanol. These experiments were taken into consideration by the author, when he presented at that time the diagram shown in Figure IV. 3 (§ 35).

In 1944–1945 J. R. ANDERSON carried out his very interesting experiments [148] which showed that all the hydrocarbons contaminating nitration benzene were characterized by boiling temperatures considerably exceeding that of pure benzene. A similar graph to that shown in Figure IX. 1 was obtained when ethanol was replaced by benzene. Tangent or almost tangent azeotropes formed by benzene with its main hydrocarbon contaminants have led ANDERSON to the above conclusion which had not been anticipated by organic as well as physical chemists.

These facts were known to Polish scientists at the time when ZIĘBORAK carried out his experiments intended to explain the ethanol dehydration by a mixture of benzene and an adequately chosen fraction of gasoline. ZIĘBORAK'S main concern was to find hydrocarbons which could form quaternary heteroazeotropes with benzene, ethanol and water. This work was completed in 1950 and a year later he completely accounted for the phenomena occurring in the course of ethanol dehydration by gasoline fraction not necessarily identical with those described and claimed in GUINOT'S patent.

In connection with LECAT's discussion [14] of the probability of the existence of quaternary azeotropes, the present author published in *Ebulliometric Measurements* [31] a paragraph entitled "Probability of Existence of Quaternary and Multicomponent Azeotropes", in which an ebulliometric method for proving the formation of a positive quaternary azeotrope was described. This method consisted in preparing the lowest boiling ternary azeotrope (*A*, *B*, *C*) and in establishing the shape of the boiling temperature isobar when successive small amounts of (*A*, *B*, *D*) are added to it. If a minimum is found on this isobar, the existence of the quaternary azeotrope (*A*, *B*, *C*, *D*) should be considered as proved or at least as being very probable. This method was employed by ZIĘBORAK to confirm the formation of three positive quaternary heteroazeotropes.

In Figure IX. 2 a typical example of the application of the method mentioned above is given. The boiling and condensation temperature isobars obtained by mixing the two heteroazeotropes: benzene-ethanol-water and n-heptane-ethanol-water were determined. They formed two typical curves, one lying above the other. Neither of the two minima represents the real composition of the quaternary azeotrope (*B*, *E*, *W*, *H*), but these two minima prove that without any doubt such an azeotrope exists.

A mixture of *B*, *H*, *E* and *W*, having a composition practically identical with that corresponding to the minimum on boiling temperature isobar shown in Figure IX. 2, was submitted to careful fractional distillation, and the main fractions collected were analysed. In Table IX. 1 the headings express: I—the compo-

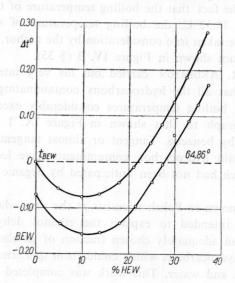

FIG. IX. 2. The boiling and condensation temperature isobars obtained by adding heteroazeotrope (*B*, *E*, *W* —·—) to the small amounts of the heteroazeotrope (*H*, *E*, *W*, —·—), *B* being benzene, *H* n-heptane, *E* ethanol and *W* water.

sition of the two phase quaternary azeotrope; II—the composition of the lower aqueous phase; III—the composition of upper (hydrocarbon) phase.

TABLE IX. 1

Composition of Heteroazeotrope (B, E, W, H — · —)

Component	I Total weight %	II Lower phase weight %	III Upper phase weight %
Benzene	62.4	11.8	73.5
n-Heptane	12.1	0.9	14.5
Ethanol	18.7	54.4	11.0
Water	6.8	32.9	1.0
	100.0	100.0	100.0

The data quoted in Table IX. 1 are obtained for the fraction when cooled to room temperature (20°C).

In Table IX. 2 the refractive indices and densities of the two liquid phases at 20°C are listed.

TABLE IX. 2

Densities and Refractive Indices of (B, E, W, H — · —) Heteroazeotrope

Measured value	Lower phase	Upper phase
Density d_4^{20}	0.8772	0.8385
Refractive index n_D^{20}	1.3789	1.4640

The volume percentage of the lower phase was 17.2%.

§ 62. Quaternary Heteroazeotrope Formed by Benzene, Iso-octane, Ethanol and Water.

In spite of the fact that 2,2,4-trimethylpentane (I), usually called iso-octane, has a slightly higher normal boiling temperature than n-heptane, it also forms a heteroazeotrope (B, E, W, I — · —) due, probably, to the branched carbon chain.

The experimental method used to establish the heteroazeotropic composition was the same as that used for n-heptane, but the iso-octane had a higher degree of purity so that the data are more reliable.

Numerical data for the azeotrope itself and for the two liquid phases at 20°C are listed below in the same way as in the case of the previous azeotrope.

Comparison of the two heteroazeotropes, having three identical constituents and either n-heptane or iso-octane as the fourth, shows that both the boiling temperatures and the respective concentrations are very similar. The normal boiling temperature of the heteroazeotrope $(B, E, W, H \; — \cdot —)$ containing n-heptane is 64.79°C, and that of the azeotrope containing iso-octane 64.68°C. The azeotropic depressions calculated by subtracting from the boiling temperature, 64.86°C, of the ternary azeotrope $(B, E, W \; — \cdot —)$ the respective boiling temperatures of the two quaternary azeotropes mentioned above are 0.07°C and 0.18°C. One peculiarity should be pointed out: the two boiling temperature isobars cross each other twice very close to the points $t_{B,E,I}$ and $t_{B,E,H}$ (Fig. IX. 4).

TABLE IX. 3

Composition of Heteroazeotrope $(B, E, W, I \; — \cdot —)$.

Component	I Total weight %	II Lower phase weight %	III Upper phase weight %
Benzene	61.5	11.5	72.2
Iso-octane	14.1	1.2	17.0
Ethanol	17.7	54.6	9.9
Water	6.7	32.7	0.9
	100.0	100.0	100.0

TABLE IX. 4

Densities and Refractive Indices of Heteroazeotrope $(B, E, W, I \; — \cdot —)$

Measured value	Lower phase	Upper phase
Density d_4^{20}	0.8766	0.8393
Refractive index n_D^{20}	1.3784	1.4595

§ 63. The Quaternary Heteroazeotrope with Cyclohexane. As regards the general properties of the third quaternary azeotrope examined by ZIĘBORAK, it is very similar to the two others described in § 61, 62. Notwithstanding this resemblance, one difference has to be stressed; this azeotrope contains a representative of the naphthene series instead of a paraffin. It is true that in certain circumstances the naphthene series may be regarded as if they belonged to the series of paraffins on account of their similar physico-chemical character. In complicated polyazeotropic mixtures (Chapters XV and XVI) such a similarity of behaviour plays an important role, and this analogy in ability to form ternary and quaternary azeotropes should not be overlooked.

In Figure IX. 3 the boiling and condensation temperature isobars of mixtures of the two ternary heteroazeotropes$(B, E, W \; — \cdot —)$ and $(C, E, W \; — \cdot —)$ are presented. As before, a differential ebulliometer was used for establishing the isobar shapes [31]. The minima observed do not give the proper composition of the quaternary heteroazeotrope under investigation, but they do prove beyond any doubt that it exists.

The total composition, taking into consideration both liquid phases, is given below for the main fraction collected close to the composition of the minimum found on Figure IX. 3 in the course of fractional distillation of the mixture $B+E+W+C$.

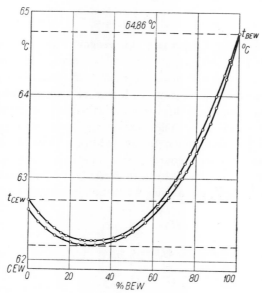

FIG. IX. 3. Boiling and condensation temperature isobars formed by mixtures of heteroazeotropes (B, E, W —·—) and (C, E, W —·—). All symbols except C, standing for cyclohexane, are the same as in Fig. IX. 2.

The difference between the boiling and condensation temperatures of the main fraction, representing the purest heteroazeotrope (B, E, W, C —·—) obtained by fractional distillation, was 0.006°C. This indicates a very high degree of purity (measured by the ebulliometric method). In spite of this, several years later the in-

TABLE XI. 5

Composition of Heteroazeotrope (B, E, W, C —·—)

Component	Weight %	Component	Weight %	Normal boiling point °C
Cyclohexane	54.3	Ethanol	19.4	66.99
Benzene	20.4	Water	6.1	

vestigation was repeated, because the determination of the water content could not be regarded as satisfactorily accurate. In fact, GALSKA [149] has found that the W value is lower in this azeotrope by 4 weight %. The azeotropic depression

$$t_{B,E,W} - t_{B,E,W,C} = 64.86 - 61.99 = 2.87°C$$

is considerably larger than those of the two quaternary azeotropes previously described. It may be seen that with the temperature decrease the concentration of the hydrocarbon increases considerably as compared with the two other quaternary heteroazeotropes.

§ 64. Series of Positive Quaternary Azeotropes. The experimental results obtained by ZIĘBORAK [193] and ORSZAGH [35] stimulated the author to give some kind of classification of positive binary, ternary and quaternary azeotropes formed by a common main azeotropic agent, with one or two secondary ones, and with a series (H) of homologues and their isomers as well as, in some cases, other chemically related substances [82]. The quaternary heteroazeotropes examined by ZIĘBORAK [50] gave the background for the addition of a third equation for calculating the azeotropic range characterizing positive ternary heteroazeotropes, for instance $(B, E, W — \cdot —)$, in relation to series (H) of homologues, their isomers and some other substances (naphthenes treated as belonging to the paraffins). Thus we may write:

$$Z_B(H) = t_{H_k} - t_{H_e}, \tag{1}$$

$$Z_{B,E}(E, H) = t_{E,H_{k+x}} - t_{E,H_{e+y}}, \tag{2}$$

$$Z_{B,E,W}(E, W, H) = t_{E,W,H_{k+x'}} - t_{E,W,H_{e+y'}}, \tag{3}$$

x, y, x' and y' being positive or negative whole numbers.

In Figure IX. 4 the boiling temperature isobars, with the minima slightly different from the real concentrations, of the positive quaternary azeotropes of the general type $(B, E, W, H — \cdot —)$ are shown.

It is easy to see that, if more representatives of the series (H) were used, a diagram similar to that shown in Figure IV. 3 would be obtained. Consequently, the azeotropic range (3) possesses a quite definite meaning and value, not only for an agent or its binary azeotrope but also for a series of ternary and quaternary azeotropes. Thus the existence of some other quaternary heteroazeotropes may be predicted on the basis of the graph in Figure IX. 4. In § 106–114 more details of this are given. In the Figure IX. 4 the upper boiling temperature isobars are almost tangent to the horizontal line drawn through the point $t_{B,E,W}$; consequently, n-heptane and isooctane are the two high boiling representatives of series (H) which limit the upper portion of the azeotropic range. No higher boiling paraffins or naphthenes would be able to form tangent boiling isobars in this region. In addition, no higher boiling paraffins or naphthenes are able to form ternary heteroazeotropes with ethanol and water. Their boiling points are too high for the formation of tangent boiling isobars with the heteroazeotrope $(B, E, H \; - \cdot -)$.

As regards the lower limit of the azeotropic range, it may be expected that the probability of finding a saturated hydrocarbon (H_e) capable of forming the ternary azeotrope $(E, W, H_e \; - \cdot -)$ is rather small. In fact, n-hexane is the only represen-

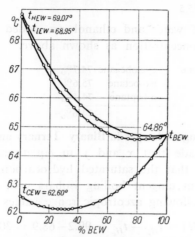

FIG. IX. 4. Boiling temperature isobars formed by the ternary heteroazeotrope $(B, E, W \; - \cdot -)$ with the three others $(H, E, W \; - \cdot -)$, $(I, E, W \; - \cdot -)$ and $(C, E, W \; - \cdot -)$. The symbols $B, E, W, H, I,$ and C are identical with those used in Figs. IX. 1, IX. 2 and IX 3.

tative which might have fulfilled this condition. Experiments carried out recently by GALSKA have proved that no ternary azeotrope composed of n-hexane, ethanol and water exists.

Mixtures of (B, E, W) and n-hexane do not give a tangent boiling isobar, but other, somewhat higher boiling hydrocarbons may exhibit such isobars, as is shown in § 112.

§ **65. Concentration Changes of Heteroazeotropes.** Below are listed the composition, in weight per cent, of the three quaternary heteroazeotropes so far discussed.

TABLE IX. 6

Concentrations of Components in $(B, W, E, H \; | \cdot \cdot -)$ Azeotropes

Component	Cyclohexane	Iso-octane	n-Heptane
Benzene	20.4	61.5	62.4
Ethanol	19.2	17.7	18.7
Water	6.1	6.7	6.8
Fourth component	54.3	14.1	12.1

If we assume that $(C_E + C_W)$ is approximately constant, it can be seen that in the series examined benzene is replaced by hydrocarbon.

Fourth component $C_E + C_W$ in weight per cent
Cyclohexane   26.5
Iso-octane   24.4
n-Heptane   25.5

If the percentages of water and ethanol are added together, the are values obtained for $C_E + C_W$ concentration as shown above.

Concentrations of benzene	+ cyclohexane	74.7%
" " "	+ iso-octane	75.6%
" " "	+ n-heptane	74.4%
Average value:		74.6%

§ 66. Azeotropic Range Changes in Binary, Ternary and Quaternary Azeotropes.
If the assumption is made that x and y in equations (1), (2) and (3) (§ 64) are equal to zero and that the saturated hydrocarbon H_e and its azeotropes (E, H_e), (E, W, H_e) form tangent boiling isobars with B, (B, E) and (B, E, W) respectively, then the following azeotropic range values are obtained:

$$Z_B(H) = t_{H_k} - t_{H_e} = 99.2 - 68.9 = 30.3°C,$$

$$Z_{B,E}(E, H) = t_{E,H_k} - t_{E,H_e} = 72.0 - 58.9 = 13.1°C,$$

$$Z_{B,E,W}(E, W, H) = t_{E,W,H_k} - t_{E,W,H_e} = 69.1 - 56.7 = 12.4°C.$$

The conclusion may be drawn that the azeotropic ranges

$$Z_B(H) > Z_{B,E}(E, H) > Z_{B,E,W}(E, W, H)$$

decrease with the increase of the number of components forming binary, ternary and quaternary azeotropes. It is to be expected that, if a quinternary azeotrope were found, its azeotropic range $Z_{B,E,W,H}(E, W, H, N)$ would be smaller than $Z_{B,E,W}(E, W, H)$.

§ 67. Composition of Quaternary Heteroazeotropes.
Considerable difficulties arise, if a precise determination of the quaternary heteroazeotrope composition is required. If the fractional distillation method is used for collecting the main fraction of the distillate, composed of two coexisting liquid phases, great attention should be paid to the proper functioning of the column head. It must collect the two liquid phases in a proportion corresponding exactly to the composition of the heteroazeotrope. In addition, the very flat surface of the boiling temperature isobar may be responsible for errors in obtaining the main fraction identical with the real composition of the heteroazeotrope.

For the performance of such experiments the following recommendations are made. First, a mixture of the four components should be submitted to careful fractional distillation with the column head adapted for collecting two phase distillates. Secondly, the main fraction thus obtained should be collected directly into a flask and submitted to a second distillation. A two or three stage differential ebulliometer may be used, if the amount of the water-containing phase is small enough. The ordinary ebulliometer, normally used for a one liquid phase system, gives correct boiling and condensation temperature measurements if the water concentration is small. If however, owing to the very small mutual solubility, the ordinary type of ebulliometer does not function properly, the special ebulliometer described in § 23 should be employed. Independently of the kind of ebulliometer used, for its successive filling, the necessary amount of the main fraction of the two liquid phase azeotrope should be collected directly into it during the course of the fractional distillation of the heteroazeotrope. For a quaternary heteroazeotrope four sections of the boiling and condensation temperature isobars should be examined.

In Figure IX. 5 the results of some experiments made by GALSKA [100] are presented. The object of investigation was the heteroazeotrope ($B, E, W, C - \cdot -$). No minima were found except the very shallow one in case I, and this is thought to

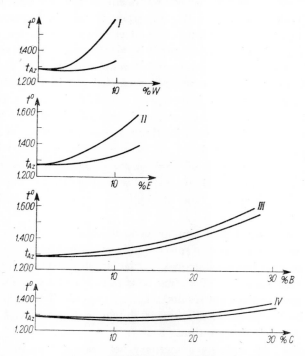

FIG. IX. 5. Four sections of boiling and condensation temperature isobars. The points t_{Az} on each of the four diagrams represent the main fraction distilled into the differential two stage ebulliometer. Curves I, II, III and IV represent the isobars obtained by adding: I—water, II—ethanol, III—benzene and IV—cyclohexane.

indicate that the main fraction contained somewhat less water than was required to get the real composition of the heteroazeotrope. The two boiling and condensation temperature isobars *III* and *IV* are also very flat, and the differences Δt between the boiling and condensation temperatures are also small. On the other hand curves *II* and especially *I* show large increases in Δt.

Because it might be expected that cyclohexane would be the most difficult component to remove from the quaternary heteroazeotrope by distillation, GALSKA purposely submitted to fractional distillation a mixture containing a 25% excess of cyclohexane and was able to obtain a main fraction having the composition of the azeotrope (*B, E, W, C* —·—). This result may be explained by the fact that during the distillation the excess of heat, due to some superheating of the lower phase, was given up to evaporate a relatively large amount of the upper phase, in which the excess of cyclohexane was found.

In this way, the thermal equilibrium in both liquid phases could have been established. If, however, the proper ratio of the lower and upper phases is to be attained with certainty, it is important to carry out a preliminary fractional distillation of any two liquid phase system. In the column some additional processes seem to occur, which favour the establishment of the thermal equilibrium between the two liquid phases. It is also important to use ebulliometers specially designed for two liquid phase systems. To collect more information on this matter, it would be useful if the observations made by GALSKA were to be extended to a larger number of ternary and quaternary heteroazeotropes. One fact seems to be undeniable; a large number of experiments carried out in the past by our group have confirmed that the ternary heteroazeotrope (*B, E, W* —·—), containing a relatively small amount of the denser water phase might have been used as a barometric ebulliometer liquid. No superheating was ever observed. On the other hand, the binary heteroazeotrope (*B, W* —·—) is one of the systems which cannot be examined in an ordinary type of ebulliometer due to a strong and irregular superheating observed in the thermometer well (Fig. II. 8). Good results were obtained, however, if a special type of ebulliometer for two liquid phase systems was employed.

A combined distillation and ebulliometric method, as used by GALSKA [100], seems to be the most convenient, if not the only one, for examining quaternary hetero- and perhaps also homoazeotropes. If the ebulliometric method of examining the shapes of a large number of boiling temperature isobars is used alone, much time is spent in getting the right results, whereas the examination of the main fraction collected, by fractional distillation as shown in Figure IX. 5, yields satisfactory results in a much shorter time.

Another method of studying quaternary heteroazeotropes has been developed by ZIĘBORAK [149]. In Figure IX. 6 *a, b* two schemes are presented. In scheme (a) the projections of three heteroazeotropic lines are shown. Scheme (*b*) shows the location of the heteroazeotropic line *HH'* in the tridimensional model. This scheme is based on the ratio B/C of weight per cent concentrations of benzene and cyclo-hexane found by direct analysis of the quaternary heteroazeotrope $(B, E, W, C$ $— \cdot —)$. Knowing the ratio B/C one is able to locate the horizontal plane drawn through point B/C. It is obvious from the model presented in Figure IX. 6, b that

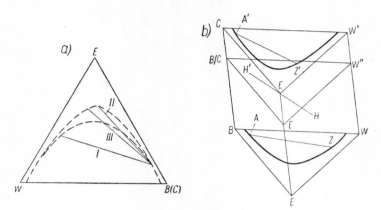

FIG. IX. 6 a, b. Comparison of the locations of the three heteroazeotropic lines: (a) I: $(B, E, W — \cdot —)$, II: $(B/C, E, W — \cdot —)$ III: $(C, E, W — \cdot —)$; B/C is the ratio of weight percentages of B and C in the quaternary heteroazeotrope $(B, E, W, C — \cdot —)$; (b) the tridimensional model of three- and four-component hetero-azeotropes.

the point where the line $H'H$ meets the horizontal plane drawn through point B/C represents graphically the composition of the quaternary heteroazeotrope under examination.

§ 68. **Further Investigations on Quaternary Positive Azeotropes.** It should be pointed out that all the experiments on positive quaternary azeotropes have been carried out exclusively with systems containing water as one of the compo-nents, probably because of ZIĘBORAK's discovery of quaternary heteroazeotropes whilst studying the course of the ethanol dehydration process. Of the same kind are the systems recently described by KOMINEK-SZCZEPANIKOWA [150]. She exam-ined the polyazeotropic ternary systems formed by toluene, isopropanol (and iso-butanol) and a series (H) of hydrocarbons found in the 100–125°C gasoline frac-tion. When the heteroazeotropes mentioned above were compared with the het-eroazeotrope benzene-ethanol-water plus one of the saturated hydrocarbons, some peculiar properties were observed [45]. It is certain that the whole series is not an ideal polyazeotropic system. At present any generalization laying down limits to the formation of ternary and quaternary heteroazeotropes could not be justified. It is certain, however, that in the course of fractional distillation of con-veniently chosen fractions of coal tar one may expect positive quaternary homo-azeotropes to be formed. So far quaternary homoazeotropes composed of highly purified compounds have not been examined owing mainly to the separation and purification difficulties encountered in this field. In addition, it seemed to be more important to extend our knowledge by further examination of new, hitherto unknown kinds of azeotropes.*

---

* Recently, at least one quinternary heteroazeotrope was found by Mrs. MALESIŃSKA.

Chapter X

SADDLE TERNARY AZEOTROPES

§ 69. Saddle Ternary Hetero- and Homoazeotropes. The existence of the so-called saddle ternary azeotropes was predicted a long time ago; the discovery, however, of such a kind of ternary system was made many years later. Those containing water as one component should be distinguished from the rest. The first saddle azeotrope to be found contained water and organic compounds slightly soluble in water, and were therefore heteroazeotropes. There has been little systematic work on series of azeotropes of this kind, and extension of our knowledge in this direction would be most useful.

In 1945 EWELL and WELCH [53] published an interesting contribution to the study of ternary systems characterized by the presence of a "top-ridge" line. Among these systems one ternary saddle azeotrope was also described. The latter contained chloroform (A) acetone (B) and methanol (H) as components. Two of these components, namely, chloroform and acetone, form a binary negative azeotrope [(−) A, B], and the existence of the two positive azeotropes (A, H) and (B, H) has been known for a long time. The existence of a saddle ternary azeotrope [(−)A, B(+)H] was confirmed five years later by LANG [54]. Some peculiar properties called distillation anomalies had been discovered by EWELL and WELCH and thereafter confirmed also by LANG. Since then, BUSHMAKIN and KISS [151] and MOLODENKO [152] have described two other saddle homoazeotropes obtained by replacing one of the constituents by another substance.

In 1950 a group of Polish scientists started the investigation of new kinds of saddle azeotropes, containing a hydrocarbon, a weak organic acid or phenol and its homologues and organic weak base, such as pyridine and its homologues.

The present author had investigated the separation of 3- and 4-picoline and 2,6-lutidine between 1941 and 1943, and so was aware that pyridine hydrochlorides could be regarded as binary negative azeotropes (§ 45) because after being distilled they contained an excess from 1 to 2 per cent of hydrochloric acid. He therefore suggested that bipositive-negative saddle azeotropes could be divided into three groups.

To the first group belong systems in which any negative azeotrope [(−)A, B], similar to that composed of acetone and chloroform, are formed due to the specific interaction of the components. To the second group belong systems containing a weak acid and a weak base, and to the third group those in which a pyridine base or amine hydrochloride series form negative binary azeotropes.

At the present time, a large number of saddle bipositive-negative azeotropes belonging to the second group are known. The large majority of them contain pyridine bases and acetic or other fatty acids, or pyridine bases and phenol or its homologues.

No extensive investigations on individual saddle azeotropes of the third group have been performed. Recently, however, 2-picoline hydrochloride has been used and found to be a very powerful azeotropic agent, forming heteroazeotropes with practically all the neutral constituents of carbolic or naphthalene oils [179]. These investigations have not as yet reached a point allowing an analysis of the phenomena thus far observed.

§ 70. Terminology and Symbols for the Designation of Saddle Azeotropes.

In §§ 45 and 69 the symbols $[(-)A, B]$ and $[(-)A, B(+)H]$ were used to designate binary negative and ternary bipositive-negative homoazeotropes. The term saddle azeotrope has been employed both for ternary homo- and heteroazeotropes, but although bipositive-negative azeotropes can be divided into three groups, to work out a complete classification and symbolism for ternary saddle azeotropes it is necessary to consider ORSZAGH'S and LELAKOWSKA'S investigations [145] in which a new type of saddle homoazeotrope has been discovered so that some revision of the terms used thus far is required.

Let us begin by analysing the shapes of the boiling temperature isobars of such ternary homoazeotropes as $[(-)A, B(+)H]$ or $[(-)F, P(+)H]$. The boiling temperature isobars formed by $[A+B]$ or $[F+P]$ mixtures are characterized by maxima, and the vapour pressure isotherms by minima. As regards the boiling temperature isobars of mixtures $(A+H)$, $(B+H)$ or $(F+H)$ and $(P+H)$, most of them have minima. There are, however, binary systems which have large positive deviations from RAOULT'S law without minima on their boiling temperature isobars, but in both cases we use the term positive for each of them. Consequently, the term bipositive-negative ternary homoazeotrope is adequate for both systems.

Let us return, however, to the new kind of saddle azeotrope recently discovered by ORSZAGH, LELAKOWSKA and BEŁDOWICZ [145]. One of the azeotropes of this kind is composed of chloroform (C), isopropylbromide (B) and ethylformate (E). The boiling temperature isobars of the mixtures $(C+B)$ and $(C+E)$ have maxima: consequently two binary negative azeotropes exist $[(-)C, B]$ and $[(-)C, E]$. The third isobar has a minimum boiling point due to the existence of a positive azeotrope (B, C). Carefully conducted experiments have shown that a ternary saddle azeotrope is also formed. It should be called a *binegative-positive homoazeotrope* and the symbol $[(+)B, E(-)C]$ should be used. One may expect too, that instead of the binary positive azeotrope (B, C) a zeotrope $(B, C)_z$ showing a large positive deviation from RAOULT's law may also take part in the formation, of this kind of azeotrope.

The existence of bipositive-negative and binegative-positive ternary azeotropes indicates that the term *saddle* does not give enough information on the nature of the azeotrope or of the tridimensional boiling temperature isobar surface. It should only be used if no doubt exists what kind of azeotrope is being considered.

Recently, ORSZAGH, LELAKOWSKA and RADECKI have described another binegative-positive azeotrope composed of phenol, phenyl acetate and glycol diacetate [145].

Finally, it should be emphasized that ternary water containing systems form, almost exclusively, heteroazeotropes. Consequently, their symbols should be supplemented by the sign $(-\cdot-)$. There exists, however, a peculiarity similar to that encountered in the pyridine base hydrochlorides which form a ternary heteroazeotropic system differing from the two other groups, due to the formation of a negative "azeotrope" PHCl and only one positive azeotrope in which the complex PHCl plays the role of a powerful azeotropic agent. The ternary system composed of a binary negative azeotrope $[(-)W, HCl]$ and one positive heteroazeotrope $[W, X]$, component X being an organic compound mostly insoluble or slightly soluble in water, possesses the same character. For the reasons mentioned above the symbol $[(-)W, HCl(+)X-\cdot-]$ should be used.

§ 71. Anomalous Distillation Phenomena.

EWELL and WELCH [53] described first, the anomalies observed when certain mixtures of chloroform, acetone and methanol were submitted to fractional distillation. (Figs. X. 6 and X. 7). The anomaly consisted of a sudden, relatively large, decrease of condensation temperature and then an increase. Because of this, the distillation curve consisted of three sections. First the usual condensation temperature increase was noticed, then a sudden temperature decrease section was observed on the distillation curve. Finally, an intermediate, relatively rapid temperature increase was observed before a new horizontal section was reached. As mentioned in § 69, five years later, LANG confirmed the observations of EWELL and WELCH.

Since the Polish group started investigations in 1950 on the second group of bipositive-negative azeotropes, containing a weak acid, a weak base and a neutral organic compound, we were interested in repeating the same experiment with a somewhat different bipositive-negative ternary system. These experiments were completed in 1956 by TRĄBCZYŃSKI [104], and details are given in § 76.

§ 72. General Characteristics of Bipositive-Negative Ternary Azeotropes.

Because of the large number of bipositive-negative ternary azeotropes $[(-)A, P(+)H]$ and $[(-)F, P(+)H]$ a relatively large number of them were examined in the period from 1950 to 1959 by our group. Some changes have been introduced compared with the presentation given in the Polish edition of *Azeotropy and Poly-azeotropy* as well as with that of EWELL and WELCH. In Figure X. 1 *a, b* the ear-lier and the modified graphical presentations are given.

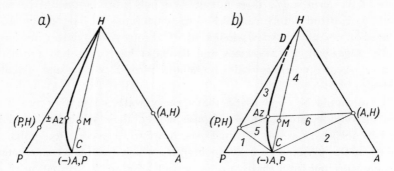

FIG. X. 1 *a, b.* Scheme (*a*) represents a bipositive-negative azeotrope formed by a weak acid *A* a weak base *P*, and a neutral compound *H*. Points *C* and $\pm Az$ corre-spond to the compositions of the negative azeotrope [(−) *A*, *P*] and of the biposi-tive-negative ternary azeotrope [(−) *A*, *P*(+) *H*]. *C*(±) *AzH* is the projection of the top-ridge line; CMH is called main line, the point M representing the compo-sition of the mixture of component H with the negative azeotrope [(−) *A*,*P*] which forms a minimum on the boiling temperature isobar. Scheme (*b*) differs from (*a*) by the shape of the top-ridge line. The latter does not reach the point *H* but only the point *D* lying on *PH*. Sometimes the top-ridge line disappears inside the triangle.

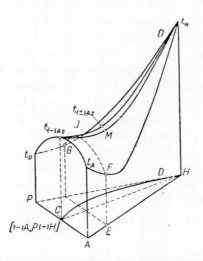

FIG. X. 2. Tridimensional model of the boiling temperature isobar; the isobar section $t_H M t_{(-)Az}$ shows that a minimum at *M* exists on the main line. The projection of the top-ridge line $t_H t_{(\pm)Az} t_{(-)Az}$ lies in the triangle *PCH*. The point $t_{(\pm)Az}$ is the ternary saddle azeotrope.

The modification introduced in the drawing requires an explanatory remark. Hitherto no ebulliometric investigations have been carried out on the ternary system examined by EWELL and WELCH. In the EWELL and WELCH scheme presented (§ 76) H is the end point of the top-ridge line $C(\pm)AzH$. Numerous experiments carried out by our group have shown that the top-ridge line reaches a point lying on the triangle side HP (or HA), and in extreme cases it was found close below the point H. In some cases, the top-ridge line disappears earlier. It is to be expected that in the Ewell-Welch saddle azeotrope the prolongation of section $C(\pm)Az$ (Fig. X. 6) should also cross the side BH somewhere below point H. This supposition still requires a direct confirmation by the ebulliometric method. In Figure X. 2 a tridimensional model of a boiling temperature isobar is drawn. Figure X. 3 represents a cross-section of the model shown in Figure X. 2. Each point lying on the top-ridge line represents, for each vertical plane, a maximum boiling point. For instance, the point J is the maximum boiling point with regard to line $GJMF$. Obviously, the point $t_{(\pm)Az}$ represents the minimum boiling temperature on the top-ridge line $t_{(-)Az}t_{(\pm)Az}D$.

The experiments carried out by our group consisted of examining bipositive-negative ternary azeotropes composed of organic acids, phenol or cresols, of

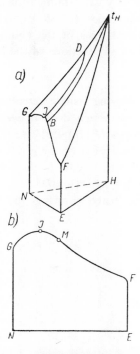

FIG. X. 3. (*b*) Cross section on plane $NGJMFE$ and tridimensional model (*a*) are shown. Points N and E lie on the triangle sides AH and PH (see Fig. X. 2.), and F and G on the boiling temperature isobars t_Ht_A and t_Ht_p.

pyridine bases and of hydrocarbons. Due to the hygroscopic nature, mainly of the pyridine bases, three-stage ebulliometers were used (Fig. II. 7) to see whether any moisture was left in the third stage of the apparatus.

§ 73. Surface Shape in the Vicinity of the Azeotropic Point. All observations made thus far indicate that the boiling temperature isobar surface in the vicinity of the point representing the composition of a bipositive-negative ternary azeotrope is very flat. This means that the application of the ebulliometric method is required to ensure that the composition of the azeotrope under investigation is determined accurately. For an azeotrope $[(-)A, P(+)H]$ both the boiling temperatures $t_{(-)A,P}$ as well as t_H have a predominant influence on the shape of the saddle surface near the point $t_{(\pm)Az}$. The points $Az_{P,H}$ and $Az_{A,H}$ representing the compositions of the two positive azeotropes (P, H) and (A, H) lie on the respective triangle sides PH and AH. The projections of the lines joining the point $(\pm) Az$ (Fig. X. 1 b) with $Az_{A,H}$ and $Az_{P,H}$ will be called *valley lines*. The location on the tridimensional model as well as on the triangular diagram indicates in a clear way their influence on the whole surface of the boiling temperature isobar.

Experiments initiated by Orszagh and carried out by LELAKOWSKA and BEŁDOWICZ [145] for examining a very flat tridimensional surface of newly discovered binegative-positive ternary azeotropes $[(+)B, C(-)X]$ may be considered as a classical proof of the great advantages of the ebulliometric method [31] offering the possibility of examination of any sections of the boiling and condensation temperature isobar surface.

§ 74. Peculiarities Characterizing Saddle Azeotropes. There are some bipositive-negative ternary azeotropes which do not necessarily require the formation of two positive binary azeotropes (P, H) and (A, H). Investigations have proved that under certain conditions one azeotrope, e.g. (P, H) and the zeotrope $(A, H)_z$, or even both zeotropes may play their part in the formation of the bipositive-negative ternary homoazeotrope $[(-)A, P(+)H]$.

Below several examples are listed showing the variations hitherto observed by our group.

TABLE X. 1

Saddle Azeotropes

No.	A or F	P	H
1	Acetic acid	Pyridine	n-Heptane
2	Phenol	2,6-Lutidine	Coal tar fraction
3	Mixture of p- and m-cresols	2,6-Lutidine	Naphthalene

Similar but less striking results were obtained by BOGUCKI [78] who used p-to-luidine (norm. boiling point 199.7°C). In fact, the temperature increase: $\Delta t = t_{(-)F,Am} - t_F$ was found somewhat lower than in the case of $\Delta t' = t_{(-)F,P} - t_F$.

System 1 (Table X. 1) is characterized by the formation of two positive azeotropes (A, H) and (P, H); in system 2, a series of positive binary azeotropes (F, H_i) can be formed, although no positive azeotropes containing 2,6-lutidine have been found with the coal tar fraction. In system 3 component H (naphthalene) forms a zeotrope with P and almost tangent boiling temperature isobars with p- and m-cresols.

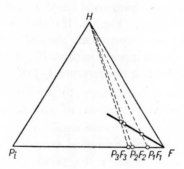

FIG. X. 4. Series of $[(-) P_i, F(+) H]$ azeotropes composed of naphthalene (H), cresol (F), and pyridine bases (P_i). The compositions are expressed in weight per cent.

Experiments carried out with different acids, different phenols and neutral or polar compounds (component H) have confirmed the peculiarities thus far observed with regard to the neutral component H in bipositive-negative ternary homo-azeotropes.

More experiments are required before generalizations about the binegative-positive homoazeotropes recently discovered by ORSZAGH and LELAKOWSKA [106]. Our information concerning binegative-positive azeotropes $[(+)B, C(-)X]$ is too restricted to allow the formulation of any rule. It is certain, however, that two negative azeotropes $[(-)B, X]$ and $[(-)C, X]$ should exist. As to the positive azeotrope (B, C), it might be expected that in some cases, instead of a positive binary azeotrope, a zeotrope $(B, C)_z$ characterized by a large deviation from RAOULT's law and by a suitable boiling point will suffice.

§ 75. Azeotropic Ranges of Bipositive-Negative Azeotropes. Our present knowledge of ternary saddle azeotropes composed of a weak acid, a weak base and a neutral or slightly polar third compound has led to the conclusion that the following equation:

$$Z_{(-)A,P}(H) = t_{H_k} - t_{H_e} \tag{1}$$

is the most suitable for expressing the azeotropic range of series (H) of homologues and their isomers, and the negative azeotrope $[(-)A, P]$. In some cases other, chemically similar, compounds may be included as members of the series H.

According to our previous considerations (§ 38) the upper and lower limits of the azeotropic range are two tangent (or almost tangent) boiling temperature isobars. The situation remains unchanged in the case of saddle azeotropes, except for two essential differences. In the first place, the upper tangent boiling temperature isobar should be formed at the point $t_{(-)Az} = t_{(-)A,P}$, that is, by the component H_i of the series (H) with the negative binary azeotrope $[(-)A, P]$. Secondly, the lower tangent isobar should be tangential to the horizontal line drawn through the point t_{H_e}, which is at variance with the diagram (Fig. X. 1b) and with the explanation given in § 72, according to which our experiments showed that the top-ridge line either crosses lines PH or AH, or disappears earlier. If we use equation (1), however, we must assume that the boiling temperature t_{H_e} of the lowest boiling member H_e is low enough to form the isobar tangent to the horizontal line drawn through point t_{H_e}. In this case the concentration of the negative azeotrope $[(-)A, P]$ should be zero: $C_{(-)A,P} = 0$. Under these conditions the discrepancy between the experimental observations and the theoretical considerations disappears. The real lower limit of the azeotropic range is the point $t_{H_{e+n}}$ not coinciding with the point H in the triangular diagram (Fig. X. 1).

Experiments thus far completed [43] prove without any doubt that the influence on the azeotropic range value $Z_{(-)A,P}(H)$ depends primarily upon the boiling temperature of the negative binary azeotrope $t_{(-)A,P}$ and upon that component of the latter which has the larger azeotropic range. For instance, in $Z_A(H)$, $Z_P(H)$, the predominant influence is exerted by A and not by P. Weak organic acids and the phenols have larger azeotropic ranges than organic bases like the aromatic amines, pyridine and their homologues.

More difficulties arise, if it is necessary to determine the lower limit of the azeotropic range. To do this, the difference:

$$\Delta t = t_{H_{e+n}} - t_{H_e}$$

between the normal boiling temperatures of the representatives H_{e+n} and H_e must be determined experimentally. The lack of representatives of any type of hydrocarbons with suitable boiling points very often makes the finding of a ternary saddle azeotrope which forms a tangent boiling point isobar impossible.

M. and K. ZIĘBORAK have examined the system formed by acetic acid, pyridine and n-heptane. They found that the bipositive-negative ternary azeotrope with a normal boiling temperature of 96.2°C had the composition:

acetic acid 2.0 weight per cent
pyridine   6.5   ,,   ,,
n-heptane 91.5   ,,   ,,

Its "saddle" depression was $138.1°C-96.2°C = 41.9°C$; $138.1°C$ is the boiling temperature of the negative azeotrope formed by acetic acid and pyridine.

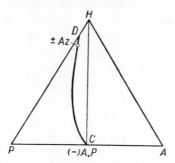

FIG. X. 5. Bipositive-negative ternary azeotrope formed by acetic acid, pyridine and n-heptane. The saddle point $(\pm)Az$ lies close to D.

If a more active representative of series A (or F) having an azeotropic range given by

$$Z_A(H) = t_{H_k} - t_{H_e} \text{ or } Z_F(H) = t_{H_k} - t_{H_e} \tag{2}$$

forms a negative high boiling azeotrope $[(-)A, P]$ or $[(-)F, P]$, with the amine the azeotropic ranges (2) are shifted toward higher boiling representatives of series (H);

$$Z_{(-)A,P}(H) = t_{H_{k+m}} - t_{H_{e+n}} \text{ or } Z_{(-)F,P}(H) = t_{H_{k+m}} - t_{H_{e+n}} \tag{3}$$

where m and n are positive whole numbers. The following typical example was examined by MAJEWSKA and ZIĘBORAK [56]. They found that a mixture of m- and p-cresols, in the same proportion as they occur in high temperature coal tar, forms an almost tangent boiling point isobar with naphthalene at $202°C$. If, however, to the cresol mixture a small amount of 2,6-lutidine, or the $142–145°C$ of pyridine base fraction (3- and 4-picolines and 2,6-lutidine) is added, a mixture of bipositive-negative ternary azeotropes is formed, which boils higher than the azeotropes formed by m- and p- cresols and naphthalene. Because of the very small boiling temperature decrease of the mixture of ternary saddle azeotropes, the mean composition of the latter $(\pm)Az$ lies in the vicinity of the points $[(-)F, P]$.

Special attention has been paid to another bipositive-negative azeotropes $[(-)A, P(+)T]$, where A stands for acetic acid, P for pyridine and T for toluene. The first experiments were carried out by ZMYSŁOWSKA. They were not published because we were not convinced that the toluene was pure enough. All the typical contaminants found in toluene always reduce its refractive index. In the course of the fractional distillation of toluene, similar phenomena take place to those described by J. R. ANDERSON for typical nitration benzene contaminants; all of them boil higher than benzene itself because they form tangent or almost tangent boiling temperature isobars. In TIMMERMAN's *Physicochemical Constants of Pure Organic Compounds* published in 1950 [124], the highest n_D^{20} value given is 1.49693. CHRÓS-CIELEWSKA succeeded in finding a slightly higher refractive index: 1.4970. The discrepancy between the two experiments of LECAT (1918) who found in his first observation that pyridine did not form an azeotrope with toluene and in his second experiment found that it really did, was resolved in favour of the second experiment. The composition and the boiling point of the positive binary azeotrope (P, T) were determined by the ebulliometric method, namely: 20.05 weight per cent of pyridine and 100.01°C (1 atm.)

The composition and the normal boiling temperature of the bipositive-negative saddle azeotrope are presented below;

Components	Weight per cent	Normal boiling temperature
Acetic acid	0.53	
Pyridine	7.47	110.20°C
Toluene	92.00	

According to our experiments the saddle azeotrope under consideration lies on the top-ridge line $(\pm)AzD$ in a similar way to that shown in Figure X. 5. The top-ridge line merges with the triangle side PH in the neighbourhood of the point $D=T$. We will return to this problem (§§ 126–129) in the course of the examination of polyazeotropic systems and mixtures.

§ 76. Ewell and Welch's Saddle Azeotrope. We mentioned in § 69 that the first ternary saddle azeotrope formed by chloroform, acetone and methanol was described in detail in 1945 by EWELL and WELCH [53], just ten years before MA-JEWSKA, ZIĘBORAK and BOGUCKI found the formation of an almost tangent bi-

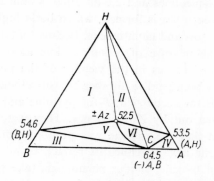

FIG. X. 6. Positive-negative (saddle) azeotrope described by EWELL and WELCH. $(-)A, B (\pm)AzH$ is the top-ridge line. *I, II, III, IV, V* and *VI* are distillation fields.

positive-negative azeotrope in the course of the fractional distillation of carbolic or middle oils. Since then a large number of saddle azeotropes formed by weak organic acids or phenol and various pyridine bases with a series of saturated hydrocarbons as the third component, have been examined by our group.

An essential difference between the methods applied by the Polish scientists and those used by EWELL and WELCH (and most other scientists dealing with ternary azeotropes) consists in the employment of differential ebulliometers, not only for testing what is called the "ebulliometric degree of purity" of an azeotrope, but also for examining the boiling temperature tridimensional surface.

EWELL and WELCH employed a very effective distillation column so that no irregularities were to be expected. As well, however, as horizontal levels on the distillation curve was reached, distillation anomalies were noticed, consisting in a sudden decrease of the temperature, after which the temperature increased to a new horizontal level. In Figure X. 7 one of the typical distillation anomalies is shown.

In Figure X. 6 the assumption is made that $H(\pm)Az$ is a straight line. Consequently, two triangles I and II are formed, each being a separate distillation field. This means that, if a mixture represented by any point inside either field I or II is submitted to fractional distillation three fractions will be collected with the compositions represented by the respective angle points; $H, \pm Az, B, H$ or A, H. The same phenomena characterize the fractional distillation of mixtures represented by points lying inside the fields III and IV. As regards the fields V and VI, separated from each other by the top-ridge line $(\pm)AzC$, EWELL and WELCH have found that it is in this region that distillation anomalies take place.

If the mixture was represented by a point lying inside triangle $C(\pm)Az(A, H)$, the distillation began by the appearance of the azeotrope (A, H), b.p. 53.5°C, then

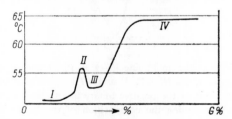

FIG. X. 7. One of the distillation anomalies observed by EWELL and WELCH.

some amount of the ternary saddle azeotrope $(\pm)Az$, condensing at 57.5°C was collected. Thereafter, a temperature decrease was observed due to the distillation of the azeotrope (B, H) boiling at 54.6°C. Thus two abnormal phenomena took place. First, there was a transition from one distillation field into the other, and secondly, a sudden temperature drop occurred after which a successive increase was noticed.

EWELL and WELCH succeeded in finding zeotropic systems, characterized by the presence of a top-ridge line; these systems, when submitted to fractional distillation, also showed distillation anomalies. Several years later, LANG repeated Ewell and Welch's experiments, using the same material. He confirmed the observations made by the American scientists. In 1957 KISS [151] working under the leadership of BUSHMAKIN [151, 152] replaced methanol by one of its esters. For this system also distillation anomalies have been found.

Initially our group was interested in examining the distillation phenomena taking place in the course of distillation of mixtures containing a weak acid, a weak base and a hydrocarbon. As mentioned above, in 1955 TRĄBCZYŃSKI [104] made experiments on the abnormal distillation of a bipositive-negative ternary azeotrope composed of a weak acid (A), a weak base (P), and a hydrocarbon (H). A system was chosen as different as possible from that examined by EWELL and WELCH: it was acetic acid, pyridine and n-octane. In Figure X. 8 the projections of the most interesting lines on the GIBBS concentration triangle are shown. Among them is the point M_p, lying on the maximum convexity compared with other points of the top-ridge line. The point $(\pm)Az$ representing the composition of the azeotrope $[(-)A, P(+)H]$ lies nearer to line HP and is found closer to H than to P (Fig. X. 1 a, b, § 72).

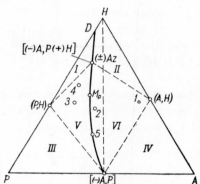

FIG. X. 8. Projections of the main line $[(-) A, P]$, H and of the top-ridge line $[(-)A, P]D$ are shown. I, II, III, IV, V and VI are the distillation fields, (P, H) and (A, H) the projections of the positive binary azeotropes. Point C (Fig. X. 6) coincides with that representing the composition of the binary negative azeotrope $[(-) A, P]$. Points 1, 2, 3, 4, 5 represent the compositions of five mixtures submitted successively to fractional distillation.

This is important because in the scheme representing the EWELL and WELCH azeotrope the saddle point $(\pm)Az$ (Fig. X. 6) is located near the end of the top-ridge curve and far away from the main line $[(-)A, B]H$. We draw attention to these differences between the EWELL and WELCH saddle azeotrope and that chosen by TRĄBCZYŃSKI, because the character of the top-ridge line and the location of the saddle point $(\pm)Az$ could play an essential role with regard to the distillation anomalies.

In Figures X. 9 and X. 10 the distillation anomalies are shown for two cases in which the starting mixtures are represented by points *4* and *5*. Point *4* lies on the left of the top-ridge line, whilst point *5* lies close to the top-ridge line and below M_p (Fig. X. 8).

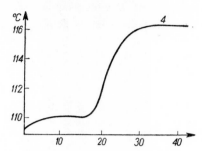

FIG. X. 9. Distillation curve observed when the mixture having the composition shown by point *4* (Fig. X. 8) was fractionally distilled.

The distillation curve was much more anomalous when the starting mixture had the composition represented by point *5* lying in field *V*, practically on the top-ridge line $[(-)A, P] D$. This agrees well with EWELL and WELCH'S observations.

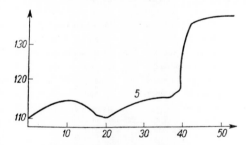

FIG. X. 10. Distillation anomalies observed when the mixture having the composition shown by point *5* (Fig. X. 8) underwent fractional distillation.

As regards the distillation anomalies, TRĄBCZYŃSKI carried out his experiments with a complete analysis of the fraction collected and the mixture found in the flask. Thus, a complete material balance was made. From this point of view his investigations differed to a large extent from those of EWELL and WELCH as well as of LANG [54].

In two Figures, X. 11 and X. 12, the results of the material balance obtained during fractional distillation of mixtures *4* and *5* are presented.

Let us examine the results obtained during the distillation of the fourth fraction. It is quite obvious that the first fraction collected in the receiver was equal or at least very close to the composition of the (P, H) positive binary azeotrope. Thereafter, the composition of the fractions changed almost linearly. The composition of the last fraction (point C in Fig. X. 11) was very close to the composition of the azeotrope $[(-)A, P(+)H]$, $(\pm)Az$ in Figure 8.

The composition curve of the mixtures remaining after each of the successive removals of the distilate shows a strong curvature (A) which rapidly disappears and a straight portion reaches point B which lies on another straight line joining point (P, H) with C. It is clear that the mixture B, if submitted to further fractional

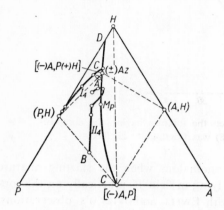

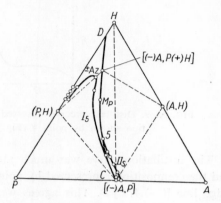

FIG. X. 11. Fractional distillation of the mixture having the composition shown by point *4* (Fig. X. 8). Curve I_4 indicates the changes in the composition of the fractions collected. Curve II_4 represents the successive composition changes of the mixture found in the flask after removal of each of the respective distillates.

FIG. X. 12. Fractional distillation of the mixture having the composition shown by point *5* (Fig. X. 8). Curve I_5 represents the composition changes of the fractions collected. Curve II_s indicates the successive changes in the composition of the mixture in the flask. The analysis was made after removal of each of the respective fractions collected.

distillation, would be separated into two azeotropes. The fraction collected would correspond to the composition of the positive binary azeotrope (P, H). The residue in the flask would have the composition of the negative binary azeotrope $[(-)A, P]$. Unfortunately, the amount of the mixture left as bottom product was too small to carry out a further fractionation.

The fractional distillation of mixture 5 (Fig. X. 12) yielded interesting results due to its location on the top-ridge line below the point M_p and far away from the saddle azeotrope point $(\pm)Az$. The first fractions collected in the course of this distillation were close to the point representing the (P, H) azeotrope composition. The next points lay on a line which approached point $(\pm)Az$ without reaching it. Then the curve changed sharply both its shape and its direction (curve I_5) and became almost parallel to the top-ridge line. It gradually merged with the top-ridge line and finally reached the point representing the composition of the negative azeotrope $[(-)A, P]$. As far as line II_5 is concerned, expressing the composition of the residue in the flask, the successive changes were represented by the curve lying on the right-hand of the top-ridge line. The composition of the last residue submitted to analysis was represented by the point lying on the right side of the top-ridge line, not far from the point $[(-)A, P]$. According to the analysis, more acetic acid was found in the bottom product than in the binary negative azeotrope. It may be that such a result was caused by analytical errors, which were relatively large, due to the difficulty of analysing small amounts of three-component mixtures, and more experimental work is needed to improve the analytical accuracy. Substantial improvement could be made by using larger quantities of purified materials so that the amount of the fractions collected could be increased.

In some experiments carried out recently by GALSKA attempting to obtain a quaternary saddle azeotrope, some abnormal distillation phenomena were observed. Quaternary mixtures, however, are too complicated, and they could not so far serve as objects for studying the mechanism of abnormal behaviour of saddle azeotropes as it concerns their distillation.

§ 77. Saddle Azeotropes Containing a Weak Acid, a Weak Base and a Neutral Third Component.

[58, 78]. All of them formed one liquid phase, and taken together constitute two series in which the weak acid and the weak base respectively remain unchanged. The neutral components belonged generally to the members of the series (H) of normal paraffins. The following symbols denote these types of ternary saddle azeotropes: $[(-)A_k, P_j(+)H_i]$ $[(-)F_k, P_j(+)H_i]$, A_k being an organic acid, F_k a representative of phenol, P_j a pyridine base, and H_i a normal paraffin.

In addition, as well as paraffins, other neutral or even polar compounds have been examined [101]. In some of the systems the pyridine base P was replaced by aromatic amines.

Due to the limited number of low boiling pyridine bases it was usually impossible to find tangent or even almost tangent boiling point isobars. Referring to previous considerations (§§ 69, 72, 73, 74), the three points $t_{(-)A,P}$ (or $t_{(-)F,P}$), t_H and $t_{(\pm)Az}$ on the tridimensional model (Fig. X. 2), form the basis of the whole scheme. The location of the point representing the composition of the negative azeotrope either on the tridimensional model or as a projection on the Gibbs triangle is important because it influences the shape of the top-ridge line.

Another important factor is, whether positive binary azeotropes (A, H) or (F, H) and (P, H) exist or whether zeotropes $(A, H)_z$ or $(F, H)_z$ and $(P_j, H)_z$, showing large deviations from RAOULT's law, are formed. Experiments have proved that three different cases may be observed: (a) two binary positive azeotropes, (b) two zeotropes or (c) one binary azeotrope and one binary zeotrope (Fig. X, 13 a, b, c, d).

We shall further discuss what kind of distillation fields are formed in each of the cases mentioned above.

§ 78. Distillation Fields Formed in Bipositive-Negative Systems.

EWELL and WELCH have shown that in the case of the ternary bipositive-negative azeotrope formed by chloroform, acetone and methanol six distillation fields are formed. If, however, only one positive binary azeotrope exists, the number of distillation fields is reduced to five, and if two positive binary zeotropes $(P, H)_Z$ and $(A, H)_Z$ characterize the systems, the number of distillation fields becomes four. In Figure

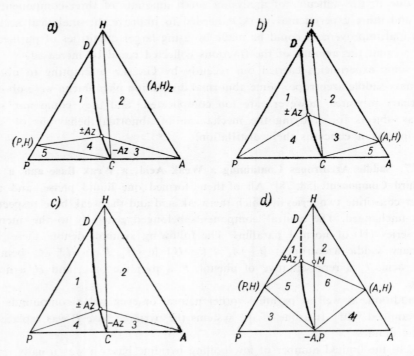

Fig. X. 13 *a, b, c, d.* Distillation fields characterizing systems having: (*a*) and (*b*)—one binary positive azeotrope (P, H) and one zeotrope $(A, H)_z$ or (A, H) and $(P, H)_z$ and (*c*)—two positive binary zeotropes $(A, H)_z$ and $(P, H)_z$, (*d*)—two binary positive azeotropes.

X. 1*b* and X. 13*a, b, c, d* the respective distillation fields are graphically represented. In cases *a* and *b* five distillation fields *1, 2, 3, 4* and *5* are shown and in *c* four fields characterize the system.

All the triangular diagrams previously used in our publications have been drawn anew, since experiments have shown that the top-ridge line never reaches the point t_H representing the boiling temperature of a pure neutral or slightly polar component *H*. In all the cases a space is found inside $(\pm)AzDH$ representing an additional distillation field. No detailed experiments have ever been carried out to decide what distillation phenomena take place, if a mixture represented graphically by any point inside the area $D(\pm)AzCH$ is submitted to fractional distillation.

§ 79. Ebulliometric Method of Bipositive-Negative Azeotrope Examination.
Experiments carried out by our group show the usefulness of the ebulliometric
method. Any section of the boiling temperature isobars may be examined with
considerable accuracy. As regards bipositive-negative saddle azeotropes any part
of the tridimensional surface may easily be examined. This applies not only to the
top-ridge line $C(\pm)AzD$ (Fig. X. 13 a, b, c) but also to the valley surfaces which
appear in all cases in which either one or two positive binary azeotropes (P, H)
(A, H) are formed. The valley surface lines join the binary azeotrope point (or
points) with the point $(\pm)Az$ (Fig. X. 13 d).

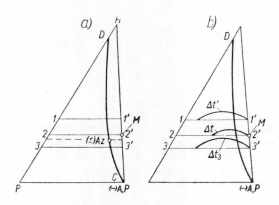

FIG. X. 14 a, b. Cross-section method for examining the shape of the top-ridge
line DC and establishing the location of the minimum boiling temperature M,
on the main line $H (-) A,P$. Cross-sections $11'$, $22'$ and $33'$ make it possible to
find the approximate location of the point $(\pm) Az$ representing the composition of
the ternary azeotrope $[(-) A, P(+) H]$.

To determine the shape of the temperature isobar surface, successive addition
of small amounts of one liquid mixture to another in a three-stage ebulliometer
is the best method. Such experiments are referred to subsequently as "dosage" or
"dosing" experiments. The experimenter should choose the compositions of the
dosed and dosing liquids so that an interesting part of the isobar surface is tra-
versed.

§ 80. Top-Ridge Line Shape Determination. The location of the top-ridge line
projection on the Gibbs concentration triangle is important in examining any kind
of ternary saddle homoazeotropes. As mentioned above the ebulliometric dosing
method offers good and precise results. The very flat boiling temperature isobar
surfaces practically exclude the use of any other method, because in most cases
the boiling and condensation temperature changes do not exceed a hundredth
of a degree. They vary very often in the vicinity of point $(\pm)Az$ within 0.009–0.005°C.

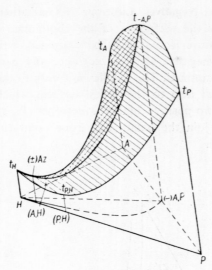

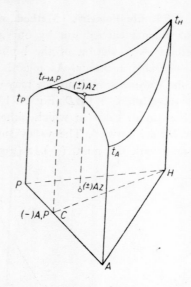

FIG. X. 15. A tridimensional model of the bipositive-negative ternary azeotrope formed by acetic acid (*A*), pyridine (*P*) and n-heptane (*H*) is shown. Both positive binary azeotropes (*P*, *H*) and (*A*, *H*) are found not far from *H*. The extrapolated top-ridge line is shown by dotted line on triangle plane.

FIG. X. 16. Tridimensional model of the bipositive-negative azeotrope formed by acetic acid, pyridine and hydrocarbon *H*.

In the first stage of development of the researches on saddle ternary azeotropes the following dosage method was employed. First the shape of the boiling point isobar obtained by successive dosing of $[(-)A, P]$ with the neutral component *H*, and vice versa, was examined. Then the point *M* on the main line $H(-)A,P$ (Fig. X. 14 *a, b*) corresponding to the minimum boiling temperature should be found. A number of bipositive-negative ternary azeotropes have been examined, in which the composition $(\pm)Az$ and the whole top-ridge line lie not far from the main line. In such cases the successive dosing of main-line mixtures as shown in Figure X. 14 in order to establish the shape of the sections *11'*, *22'*, *33'* of the boiling temperature surface is a very convenient method for examining the shape of the top-ridge line and for interpolating the composition $(\pm)Az$ of the saddle azeotrope.

There are, however, numerous cases in which the top-ridge, line lies closer to one of the triangle sides (*PH* or *AH*), In spite of this, the location of the top-ridge line and the extrapolation of point $(\pm)Az$ is carried out in the same way. The point $(\pm)Az$, however, lies well off the main line $H(-) A, P$, and therefore located where the minimum should be by establishing the shape of other sections of the boiling temperature surface.

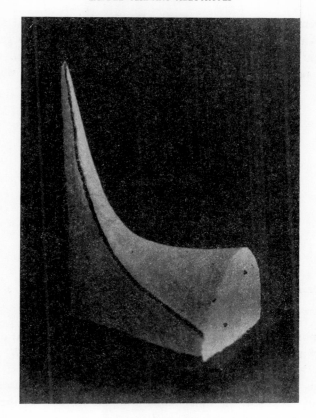

FIG. X. 17. Photograph of tridimensional model showing the location of point $(\pm)Az$ representing the mean composition of bipositive-negative azeotropes formed by a mixture of m- and p-cresols (F), a three degree (142–145°C) pyridine base fraction (P) and naphthalene (H). All the ternary saddle azeotropes are characterized by very small differences in their boiling temperatures.

§ 81. Crossing Boiling Temperature Isobar Method. With the development of our knowledge of bipositive-negative azeotropes an attempt was made to find other methods, more suitable for precise determination of the composition of these azeotropes. Among others the crossing boiling temperature isobar method was found useful and was described by TRĄBCZYŃSKI [103] and the present author. In principle, it resembles to some extent the method described in § 67 and used by GALSKA for the examination of quaternary positive azeotropes.

We start by collecting, in the course of a fractional distillation, the main fraction (F). Due to the very flat surface surrounding the point representing the composition of the azeotrope, composition of this fraction may or may not correspond exactly to the real azeotropic composition. The amount of the main fraction should be sufficiently large to carry out at least four successive and independent ebulliometric measurements. In Figure X. 18 boiling temperature isobar sections *1, 2, 3* and *4* are shown which should be selected in such a manner as to get two of them, *1* and *2*, tangent or almost tangent to the top-ridge line $C(\pm) AzD$, and the other two, *3* and *4*, tangent or almost tangent to the line of greatest slope.

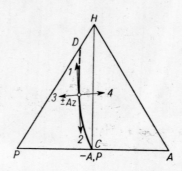

FIG. X. 18. Crossing boiling temperature isobars 1–2 and 3–4.

If the composition of the main fraction (F) is identical with that of the azeotrope $(\pm)Az$ as shown in Figure X. 19 each of the isobar sections *I, II, III* and *IV* are tangent to the horizontal line drawn through point t_F. Moreover, with increase of the amounts of *1* or *2*, the boiling temperatures of the mixtures rise steadily and Δt is always > 0. On the other hand, with the increase of the amounts of *3* and *4* added, a steady slope of curves *III* and *IV* downward is found.

In Figure X. 20 the case is presented in which the main fraction *F*, obtained by fractional distillation of a mixture of the components *A, P* and *H*, did not correspond to the composition of a bipositive-negative saddle azeotrope $[(-)A, P(+)H]$. Owing to this inequality, on curve *I* a minimum and on curve *IV* a maximum were found. On the other hand, no extrema were found in the course of dosing one part of fraction *F* with mixture *3* and another portion with mixture *4*. Below, curves *I* and *IV* are redrawn in such a way as to enable the most probable composition $(\pm)Az$ of the saddle azeotrope under examination to be extrapolated readily.

In some cases the crossing isobar methods require more than four independent successive dosings of the main fraction *F* with suitable mixtures. It sometimes happens that in the first run the location of the top-ridge and of the valley lines are unknown or an erroneous interpretation of the tridimensional model has led to four curves *I, II, III* and *IV* which clearly indicate that no tangent curves could be found. The experiment should be repeated after determining some additional isobar sections in the way shown in Figure X. 18. The flatness of the tridimensional surface surrounding the point $(\pm)Az$ means that very pure components must be used

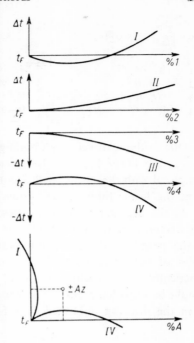

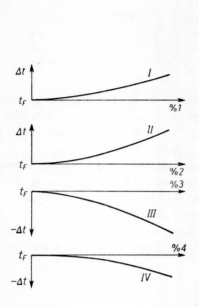

FIG. X. 19. Four sectional curves *I, II, III,* and *IV* obtained by using the method of crossing boiling temperature isobars. No minima or maxima are found on these curves. This means that the composition of main fraction *F* obtained by fractional distillation of the mixture is equal to the composition of the saddle azeotrope $F = (\pm)Az$.

FIG. X. 20. The composition of the main fraction *F*, characterized by the boiling temperature t_F, differs from that of the bipositive-negative ternary azeotrope. Due to this, curves *I* and *IV* are redrawn in a manner enabling the most probable composition $(\pm)Az$ of the azeotrope under examination to be found.

for preparing mixtures *1, 2, 3* and *4* (Fig. X. 18 and X. 19) to determine the four respective boiling temperature isobar sections.

§ 82. Typical Examples of Bipositive-Negative Azeotropes.

In the first stages of studies on saddle azeotropes of the type $[(-)A, P\ (+)H]$ it seemed to be important to examine systems characterized either by high concentrations of *H* or by unusual shapes of the top-ridge line. In azeotropes belonging to the first group the ternary point $(\pm)Az$ is found in the vicinity of the point *H*; in the second, the top-ridge line is found somewhere in the lower portion of the triangle declining either to the *PH* or *AH* side.

In Figure X. 21 the bipositive-negative saddle azeotrope of acetic acid *A*, pyridine *P* and n-heptane *H* is shown in detail. The system was described in 1954 by M. and K. ZIĘBORAK [102].

The following data characterize the three binary and the saddle azeotropes.

No.	Azeotrope	Composition in weight %		Normal boiling temperature
1	[(−)A, P]	A−51.0	P−49.0	138.1°C
2	(A, H)	H−69.5	A−30.5	91.9°C
3	(P, H)	H−74.7	P−25.3	95.6°C
4	[(−)A, P(+)H]	H−91.5	A−2; P−6.5	96.2°C

Due to the relatively high boiling temperatures of the binary negative azeotrope $t_{(-)A,P}$, the lower limit of the azeotropic range $Z_{(-)A,P}(H)$ is shifted upwards as compared with the acetic acid azeotropic range $Z_A(H)$, so that n-heptane is not far from the lower limit of azeotropic range $Z_{(-)A,P}(H)$.

At the beginning of our studies on bipositive-negative azeotropes we accepted the EWELL and WELCH scheme for the formation of the top-ridge line. It started at the point $(-)A$, P and terminated at angle H. More detailed examination of series of bipositive-negative azeotropes has convinced us that the top-ridge line practically never reaches the point H. If this happens in some particular case, it should be regarded rather as an exception. For this reason, Figure X. 5 was altered from the drawing published in 1954 [102].

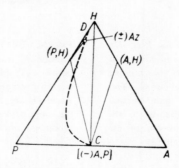

FIG. X. 21. Bipositive-negative azeotrope of acetic acid (A) pyridine (P) and n-heptane (H).

To use as an example a system encountered in the coal-tar industry, experiments were carried out in 1955 with a mixture of m- and p-cresols taken in the proportion found in carbolic oil, the three degree 142–145°C, pyridine base fraction, being a mixture of 3-picoline, 4-picoline and 2,6-lutidine, and naphthalene as the neutral component (H). The experiments were carried out by ZIĘBORAK and MAJEWSKA [56] (Fig. X. 4].

BOGUCKI repeated these investigations, replacing the pyridine base fraction by 2,6-lutidine. In both cases the mixture of bipositive-negative saddle azeotropes showed small temperature depressions as compared with the boiling temperature of the two close-boiling negative azeotropes formed by m- and p-cresol on one side and pyridine on the other.

Further experiments have confirmed the conclusion drawn from the previous investigations, which were carried out not only on laboratory equipment but also on technical installations. In fact, a bundle of tangent positive binary and bipositive-negative ternary azeotropes are formed with naphthalene being entrained by m- and p-cresols on one side and by organic bases with cresols on the other [89].

§ **83. Series of Bipositive-Negative Azeotropes.** Recently, a relatively large amount of experimental material has been collected. The object of the investigations were not individual azeotropes but mixtures obtained by the successive replacement of members of the hydrocarbons, weak acid and weak base homologous series by one another. The experimental work carried out in the period from 1955 up to the present time by ZIĘBORAK [154], WYRZYKOWSKA-STANKIEWICZ [159], GALSKA-KRAJEWSKA [155], BRZOSTOWSKI [156], KURTYKA [101], and other investigators belonging to the same group should also be mentioned.

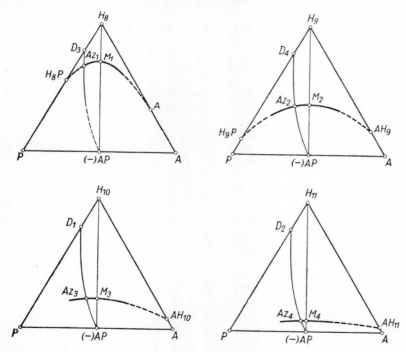

FIG. X. 22. The systems composed of 2-picoline (P), acetic acid (A) and n-paraffins from C_8 to C_{11} (H_8, H_9, H_{10}, H_{11}). The other symbols are: (P, H), (A, H_i) binary positive azeotropes, [(−) A, P] binary negative azeotropes, Az_i ternary positive-negative (saddle) azeotropes, M_i minimum points on the main lines [(−) A, P]H_i. The curves joining points [(−)A, P] with H_i through M are the projections of the main lines, and the curves having the points Az_i represent the projections of the respective top-ridge lines. The partly dotted lines represent the projections of the valley lines.

Theoretical work on ternary azeotropes in general and on saddle ones in particular has been published by MALESIŃSKI [158]. The results of MALESIŃSKI's studies will constitute a special monograph.

In Figures X. 22, 23 and 24 on the basis of the data in Table X.2, comprehensive diagrams are shown summarizing the investigations carried out thus far with series of bipositive-negative azeotropes. In the diagram, the compositions of negative binary azeotropes are given: $[(-)A_1, P_1]$, $[(-)A_1, P_3]$, $[(-)A_1, P_2]$, $[(-)A_1, P_4]$, $[(-)A_2, P_1]$, and $[(-)A_3, P_1]$; A_1 acetic acid, A_2 proprionic acid and A_3 butyric acid; P_1, P_2, P_3 and P_4 are the following bases: P_1—pyridine, P_2—2-picoline, P_3 2,6-lutidine and P_4 2,4-lutidine [159].

TABLE X. 2

Experimental and Calculated Compositions of Ternary Positive-negative Azeotropes

| No. | System | Boiling temp. °C | Composition in mol. per cent | | | | | | | | |
| | | | experiment | | Malesiński equation | | | improved method | | |
			% A	% P	% A	% P	d	% A	% P	d
1	Acetic acid-pyridine- n-heptane	96.5	5.0	12.8	4.7	18.2	5.3	5.3	18.3	5.35
2	n-Octane	115.7	16.6	24.6	15.0	27.1	2.2	18.4	29.3	5.7
3	n-Nonane	128.0	31.2	33.6	22.5	35.1	7.8	31.6	36.0	2.65
4	n-Decane	134.1	43.0	39.6	32.8	40.3	9.9	40.6	39.3	26
5	n-Undecane	137.1	48.2	42.4	39.3	44.9	9.5	49.3	41.7	0.8
6	Acetic acid-2-picoline- n-octane	121.4	6.3	27.9	0.2	41.8	11.3	04.2	42.6	12.9
7	n-Nonane	135.0	21.2	41.0	12.6	48.2	8.1	19.6	48.1	6.4
8	n-Decane	141.3	31.0	47.1	24.5	52.3	6.0	34.4	49.6	4.1
9	n-Undecane	143.4	42.6	49.7	31.4	55.1	5.7	44.0	49.5	1.1
10	Proprionic acid-pyridine- n-undecane	147.1	62.5	27.8	69.1	20.1	7.2	—	—	—
11	Butyric acid-pyridine— n-un- decane		—	—	92.1	1.4	—	—	—	—
12	Acetic acid-2,6-lutidine- n-decane	147.0	22.4	67.5	13.8	74.2	7.8	—	—	—
13	Acetic acid-2,4-lutidine- n-undecane	162.0	22.9	69.9	10.9	78.0	10.5	—	—	—

The experimental results lead us to the following conclusion. If in the series of bipositive-negative azeotropes $[(-)A, P (+)H_i]$ the organic acid (A) and the pyridine base (P) remain unchanged and the third component of the series (H) of paraffinic hydrocarbons undergoes a successive replacement by respective homologues of the series, the composition points of azeotropes obtained in this manner lie on one common top-ridge line, which never reaches the point H. In Figure X. 22 D_1, D_2, D_3 and D_4 are shown. They intersect the triangle side PH_i with the

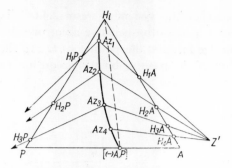

FIG. X. 23. Series of bipositive-negative azeotropes, composed of acetic acid
(*A*), pyridine (*P*) and n-heptane, n-octane, n-nonane and n-decane.

top-ridge lines. It is experimentally difficult to fix exactly the intersection points
mentioned above. Usually, very flat boiling temperature surfaces occur around
points D_1, D_2, D_3, D_4 (Fig X. 22). It is perhaps more reasonable simply to put
dotted lines in the places where the top-ridge line practically ceases to exist.

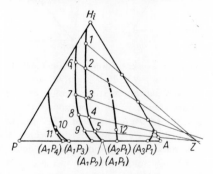

FIG. X. 24. Series of positive-negative azeotropes composed of: 1. acetic acid,
pyridine and normal paraffins: heptane (*1*), octane (*2*), nonane (*3*), decane (*4*),
undecane (*5*); 2. acetic acid and 2-picoline with: octane (*6*), nonane (*7*), decane
(*8*), undecane (*9*); 3. 2,6-lutidine, acetic acid and decane (*10*); 4. 2,4-lutidine, acetic
acid and undecane (*11*); 5. proprionic acid, pyridine and undecane (*12*); 6. butyric
acid, pyridine and undecane (the top-ridge line is drawn only) *A*, *P* and *H* stand for
aliphatic acid, pyridine base and hydrocarbon, respectively. The projections of the
top-ridge lines are drawn partly with dotted lines. The compositions are expressed
in mol. per cent.

The top-ridge line changes its shape considerably in cases where the composition point of the negative binary azeotrope, e.g. $[(-)A_1, P_4]$ or $[(-)A_1, P_3]$ (Fig.
X. 24) is shifted closer to either of points *P* or *A*. In some cases, the top-ridge line
merges with the triangle side *PH* without any minimum boiling temperature. A typical example is the ternary system acetic acid–2,6-lutidine–n-octane, although
in this case no ternary saddle azeotrope was found.

It should be noted that the system o-cresol–2,4,6-collidine–glycol, examined by KURTYKA [101], forms a bipositive-negative azeotrope. In Figure X. 25 a, b the projection of the top-ridge line and the point $(\pm)Az$ are shown. The point representing the composition of the positive binary azeotrope o-cresol–glycol lies not far from point $(\pm)Az$.

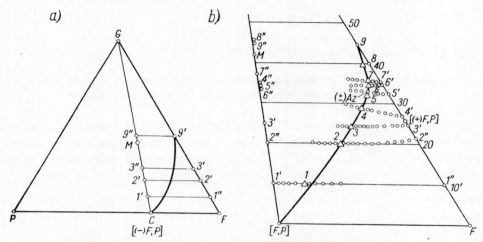

FIG. X. 25 a, b. (a) On the concentration triangle GFP the projections of the main line GC and of the sections $1'\ 1'', 2'\ 2'', \ldots 9'\ 9''$, corresponding to the boiling temperature isobars of different ternary mixtures composed of glycol, G, orthocresol, F, and 2,4,6-collidine, P, are shown. (b) A portion of the concentration triangle, limited by points G, F and $[(-)F, P]$ is presented. The projections of the sections of the boiling temperature isobars are shown by the dotted lines. The shapes of the boiling temperature isobars were ebulliometrically determined by mixing $1'$ with $1''$, $2'$ with $2''$ etc. The eight maxima found on these isobars lie on the projection of the top-ridge line and are represented by small triangles.

In Figure X. 26 typical changes in concentration of the components in the series $[(-)A, P(+)H_i]$, A being acetic acid, P pyridine base and H_i the representatives of the series (H) of normal paraffin hydrocarbons, are shown [159].

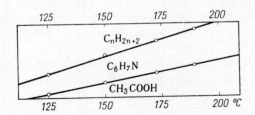

FIG. X. 26. Concentrations of ternary $[(-)A, P(+)H_i]$ azeotropes plotted against the boiling temperatures of homologues H_i.

The diagram shows (Figs. X. 23 and X. 24) that the acetic acid concentration is very low if the lowest boiling hydrocarbon, n-heptane, is the neutral component of the bipositive-negative ternary azeotrope $[(-)A, P(+)H_i]$. With increase of the boiling temperature of the successive hydrocarbons (n-nonane, n-decane, n-undecane) their concentrations decrease linearly, whilst the concentrations of the pyridine base (2-picoline) and of the acetic acid increase linearly.

MALESIŃSKI's theoretical considerations and formulated generalizations [158] are in quite satisfactory agreement with the experimental results hitherto obtained.

§ 84. Positive-Negative Quaternary Homoazeotropes.

The simultaneous development of investigations dealing with individual bipositive-negative azeotropes and their series as well as the physical chemistry of coal tar was associated with the idea that it must be possible to find quaternary positive-negative azeotropes expressed by symbols $[(-)A, P(+)Ar, H]$ or $[(-)F, P(+)Ar, H]$, A being an organic acid, P a pyridine base, F a phenol or its derivatives, Ar an aromatic hydrocarbon, and H a saturated hydrocarbon. LISICKI was the first [89] to collect in a differential two-stage ebulliometer an acid and base free coal tar fraction, and by successive addition of an adequately selected pyridine base, a cresol fraction and finally, naphthalene, he found that a positive-negative quaternary azeotrope was formed. Since then, several investigations with pure components have been carried out with a view to proving beyond doubt, whether positive-negative quaternary azeotropes are formed. The main difficulty consisted in finding two hydrocarbons Ar and H with adequate azeotropic ranges to render possible the formation of a positive-negative quaternary azeotrope.

The problem has been solved beyond doubt by ZIĘBORAK and GALSKA-KRAJEWSKA [160]. The components of the azeotrope are acetic acid (A), pyridine (P), normal nonane (H) and ethylbenzene (Ar). The experiments were carried out in three ebulliometers, two of which were of the three-stage type. All three units were located next to each other and in most experiments all worked simultaneously. As usual, a one-stage apparatus filled with water served for precise determination of any atmospheric pressure changes.

Four out of the six binary systems formed positive binary azeotropes. The two remaining, pyridine–ethylbenzene and ethylbenzene–n-nonane, were found to be zeotropes with large deviations from RAOULT's law.

As regards of bipositive-negative ternary azeotropes, two out of four such azeotropes exist. The remaining two, $(A, H, Ar)_z$ and $(P, H, Ar)_z$ are zeotropes characterized by large deviations from RAOULT's law.

To find the approximate composition of the quaternary azeotrope a relatively simple ebulliometric method combined with several fractional distillations was used. The boiling temperature of a positive-negative quaternary azeotrope lies within the limits of the boiling temperatures of the two ternary and the four binary azeotropes. In the case of zeotropes the boiling temperatures of the components forming zeotropic mixtures should also be taken into consideration. A tetrahedral model was used for orientation and clear presentation of the phenomena involved. In addition, the method previously employed [160] for examining quaternary positive azeotropes has been found useful after the introduction of some modifications.

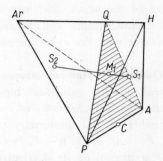

FIG. X. 27. Tetrahedron representing the positive-negative quaternary azeotrope. A—stands for acetic acid, P—for pyridine, H—for n-nonane, Ar—for ethylbenzene. Points S_1 and S_2 represent the composition of ternary saddle azeotropes: $[(-)A, P(+)H]$ and $[(-) A, P(+)Ar]$.

In Figure X. 27 the regular tetrahedron is shown with two of its faces formed by the two ternary systems $(A+P+H)$ and $(A+P+Ar)$. These systems show considerable similarity in their shapes and properties. Their saddle points are represented by the points S_1 and S_2. The common negative azeotrope $[(-)A, P]$ is represented on the drawing by point C. All the tetrahedral sections characterized by common axis PCA have the similarity that across any one the concentration ratio $C_H : C_{Ar}$ is constant, and both of them have saddle points lying on the tridimensional boiling temperature isobar surfaces.

If a positive-negative quaternary azeotrope really exists, the boiling temperature isobar S_1S_2 shown in Figure X. 27 ought to have a minimum M_1. To find whether there was such a minimum two ebulliometers were used, one being filled with azeotrope S_1 the other with azeotrope S_2. Two independent dosages (S_1 with S_2 and S_2 with S_1) were carried out to fix the extremum value exactly. The ratio $C_{Ar} : C_H = 1 : 2.1$ was found at the minimum. Consequently, the location of the APQ plane was fixed. There now remained the minimum boiling temperature of the systems represented by plane APQ to be examined, the concentration ratio $C_{Ar} : C_H$ being known.

The projection of the top-ridge line on triangle APQ was found and the composition X of the quaternary azeotrope under investigation was determined in the way previously employed for positive quaternary azeotropes (§§ 61–64).

For controlling the results of the ebulliometric measurements a mixture close to the composition X was submitted to fractional distillation and a sufficient amount of the main fraction (F) was collected to establish by successive and independent

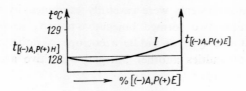

FIG. X. 28. Boiling temperature changes of the ternary bipositive-negative azeotrope acetic acid-pyridine-n-nonane (S_1) produced by adding azeotrope $[(-)A,$ $P(+)E]$, E being ethylbenzene. Points S_1 and S_2 show the projections of the two ternary saddle azeotropes in the tetrahedron Fig. X. 27.

dosages the shapes of four sections. This method is in principle identical with the crossing isobar method described in § 63 and shown graphically in Figures X. 19 and X. 20. The composition of the quaternary azeotrope is given below.

No.	Component	Weight per cent	Normal boiling temp.
1	Acetic acid	17 ⎫	
2	Pyridine	27 ⎪	
3	n-Nonane	38 ⎬	127.9° C
4	Ethylbenzene	18 ⎭	
		100	

More details are given in the paper [160].

§ 85. **Binegative-Positive Azeotropes.** Recently a new kind of ternary saddle azeotrope has been examined in detail by ORSZAGH, LELAKOWSKA and BEŁDOWICZ [145]. It has the following components: chloroform (C), isopropyl bromide (B) and ethyl formate (E), which form two negative azeotropes: (1) chloroform-isopropyl bromide $[(-)C, B]$ and (2) chloroform-ethyl formate $[(-)C, E]$; the remaining third pair forms a positive binary azeotrope (B, E). The ternary azeotrope $[(+)B, E(-)C]$ may be called a binegative-positive one [145].

Because of the very flat tridimensional surface, it was necessary to examine a very large number of boiling temperature isobar sections in order to locate and to determine the composition of this azeotrope. The ebulliometric comparative method was applied. In Figure X. 29 the concentration triangle with the main characteristic lines is shown.

The composition of the binegative-positive ternary azeotrope determined by the method of successive approximations is 76.6 mol. % chloroform, 14.8% isopropyl bromide and 8.6% ethyl formate. Its normal boiling temperature is 61.97° C.

It should be pointed out that EWELL and WELCH first examined the system chloroform-octane-diisopropyl ether, without finding a binegative-positive ternary

azeotrope. Nine similar systems were carefully examined by ORSZAGH and LELA-
KOWSKA, of which only two formed binegative-positive azeotropes. The authors
[145] concluded that this type of saddle azeotrope is rather a rare phenomenon.

In spite of the difficulties another binegative-positive azeotrope was recently
found by the same authors.

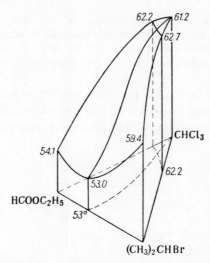

FIG. X. 29. Binegative-positive, saddle azeotrope composed of chloroform,
ethyl formate and isopropyl bromide.

§ 86. New Types of Azeotropes. It seems useful to state what kind of considerations have exerted their influence on researches into new kinds of azeotropes.
There were several factors which stimulated our group to undertake investigations
in this field. First of all, before the outbreak of World War II several modifications
of the standard one-, two- and three- stage ebulliometers proved to be very useful
for examining azeotropes and for determining the degree of purity of their components. With the increase of the number of components, combined fractional
distillation and ebulliometric methods have been proved a useful tool for examining
any kind of azeotrope, and with our present technique of ebulliometric measurement it is a very easy and simple task to examine any section of the boiling temperature isobars of any system. This is essential for any kind of azeotropes, but
is especially so for investigations of any kind of positive-negative azeotrope. As
concerns the terminology we prefer to use the term positive-negative rather than
saddle azeotropes, because the variety of ternary and quaternary systems is too
large for precise designation of the kind of saddle azeotropes we have in mind.

Besides the improved technique of azeotrope examination, other circumstances
have stimulated us to undertake investigations in a new branch of our knowledge,
the physico-chemical nature of organic raw materials. We know that most of these

contain two, three or more series of homologues and their isomers. These homologues and their isomers form, with the representatives of other series, numerous azeotropes and the number of components varies mostly from two to four. The probability exists that azeotropes containing five components may also be formed.

Low-and high-temperature coal tars contain, besides other series of homologues, phenols and organic bases, and constitute the main sources of positive-negative azeotropes.

Our group has started work on azeotropy and polyazeotropy with a view to examining the field of natural materials in which azeotrope formation is one of the most common phenomena. The variety of azeotropes formed in the course of fractional distillation of organic raw materials is so large that we have been stimulated to find methods which will enable us to give a proper interpretation of what is going on in the distillation of the multi-component mixtures which are now called polyazeotropic.

§ 87. **Azeotropic Ranges of Positive-Negative Azeotropes.** Experiments have shown that the expression (§ 75):

$$Z_{(-)A,P}(H) = t_{H_k} - t_{H_e} \tag{1}$$

has meaning for azeotropic ranges of negative binary azeotropes and series (H) of homologues and their isomers. In connection with equation (1) several remarks may be made. The influence of the location of the point $[(-)A, P]$ or $[(-)F, P]$ on the triangle side AP (or FP) is very great. If the composition of the negative azeotrope expressed in mol. per cent is close to $C_F = C_P = 0.5$ the projection of the top-ridge line usually lies inside the triangle PHC and crosses almost the whole diagram, reaching either H or D as shown in Figures X. 13 a, X. 21 or X. 23. If C representing the composition of negative azeotropes $[(-)A, P]$ or $[(-)F, P]$ lies closer to A (or F) the top-ridge line is shifted toward the F (or A) side, as shown in Figure X. 25 b. If, however, C lies closer to point P, the top-ridge line is shifted towards the side PH, as shown in Figure X. 24 (curves 10 and 11, § 83), for the azeotropes $(\pm)Az$ composed of acetic acid, 2,4-lutidine and undecane, and propionic acid, pyridine and undecane. Similar bipositive negative azeotrope is characterized by the formation of zeotropic mixtures in case of n-octane with 2,6-lutidine. Points $(\pm)Az$ and M representing the minima on the top-ridge line $(-)A,P \pm AzD$ and on the main line $(-)A, PMH$ are (Figure X. 13 d) found not far from angle HPC and from side PA.

We have described several typical locations of the top-ridge line and of the point $(\pm)Az$. There are, however, many other varieties of bipositive-negative azeotropes. More experimental work is required to give a better understanding of the conditions under which these kinds of azeotropes can exist.

§ 88. **Distillation of Mixtures Containing Weak Acids and Weak Bases.** Besides the anomalies described by EWELL and WELCH and confirmed by other inves-

tigators, some other peculiar phenomena are observed when mixtures of hydrocarbons, weak acids and weak bases are fractionally distilled.

We begin by asking whether it is possible to collect main fractions having the
composition of bipositive-negative ternary azeotropes. EWELL and WELCH'S experiments as well as those carried out by other authors have proved that in the
case of abnormal distillation with a sudden decrease and a sudden increase of the
condensation temperature, it is possible to obtain a fraction having a saddle
azeotrope composition.

WYRZYKOWSKA has fractionally distilled a mixture of two bipositive-negative
ternary azeotropes and she also found wellformed horizontal levels on the distillation curve.

In spite of these undeniable facts, other phenomena have been observed, e.g.,
when a ternary mixture containing a large excess of the neutral component H is
submitted to fractional distillation. In this and similar cases unexpected fractions
are often collected, which should be considered as proof that the ratio $C_A : C_P$
(or $C_F : C_P$) undergoes changes instead of remaining constant.

Much more complicated phenomena are observed when a polyazeotropic
mixture containing several pyridine bases, several representatives of the phenol
series and a mixture of homologues of paraffins and aromatic hydrocarbons is
submitted to fractional distillation. Some of these experiments are described by
LISICKI. More investigations are needed to make possible the prediction of what kind
of azeotropes will be formed in each particular case. The large azeotropic ranges
of the phenols and the relatively small ones of the pyridine bases are mostly responsible for the decomposition of ternary saddle azeotropes and for the formation
of positive binary azeotropes characterized by considerably lower boiling temperatures. Some practical applications may result from basic research in this field. The
behaviour of positive-negative quaternary azeotropes still remains an underdevel-
oped field of our knowledge.

Chapter XI

SERIES OF BINARY AND TERNARY HETEROAZEOTROPES

§ 89. Binary Series Formed by Methanol with Normal Paraffins. Hitherto no extensive investigations have been carried out of the gradual transition from binary heteroazeotropes to homoazeotropes and finally to heterozeotropes. The experiments resemble those described in § 29. The essential difference consists in the fact that, in the case of a system formed by two components A and B, a change of pressure is required in order to observe all the transition phenomena previously described.

If instead of two components a series (A, H_i) of azeotropes are investigated, a suitable constant pressure should be established for carrying out a series of experiments in which the representatives $H_1, H_2, \ldots, H_i, \ldots, H_n$ are successively replaced one by another.

Recently, ZIĘBORAK and MĄCZYŃSKA [194] published an interesting contribution dealing with the series (M, H_i) M being methanol and H_i any of the normal paraffins from n-heptane to n-undecane. An automatic electronic device maintained a constant pressure inside the system of two one-stage ebulliometers. One ebulliometer was filled with methanol and served as a barometric control for carrying out strictly comparative measurements. The second ebulliometer was filled with a mixture of methanol and the appropriate n-paraffin. One of the series of measurements was made at a pressure of 406 mm Hg and the other at 760 mm Hg. The results obtained in both series are very similar. No heteroazeotropes $(A, H_i - \cdot -)$ were found. The boiling temperature isobars obtained for mixtures of n-heptane or of n-octane with methanol show distinctly that the azeotropic compositions coincide with the composition of the remaining liquid phase, containing a relatively small amount of n-heptane or n-octane. Consequently, the symbol $(A, H:-)$ should be used [177]. The composition of the next azeotrope formed by methanol with n-nonane lies within the single-phase region, rich in methanol. This indicates that a typical homoazeotrope is formed. It lies on the boiling temperature isobar characterized by a horizontal two liquid phase section.

The two other isobars belong to typical heterozeotropes. Consequently, the symbol $(M, H_i \cdot -)_z$ is an appropriate one.

In Figure XI. 3 a, b, a more general scheme is shown in which homoazeotropes are formed with high boiling representatives $t_{H_{k-1}}, t_{H_k}$ of series (H), and one homozeotrope with boiling temperature isobar $t_A, t_{H_{k+1}}$.

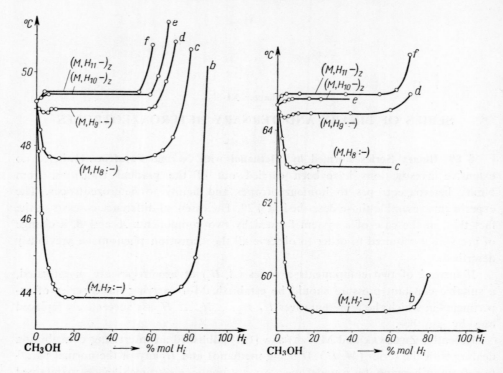

FIG. XI. 1. Series of boiling temperature isobars at 406 mm Hg formed by methanol (M) with normal paraffins: n-heptane (7) n-octane (8), n-decane (10) and n-undecane (11) are shown. The successive formation of hetero- (7,8), homoazeotropes (9), and heterozeotropes (10, 11) has been proved.

FIG. XI. 2. The same system presented graphically in Fig. XI. 1 were examined at atmospheric pressure. The existence of one heteroazeotrope $(M, H_7 \cdot -)$ and of two homoazeotropes $(M, H_8 \cdot -)$, $(M, H_9 \cdot -)$ and of two heterozeotropes $(M, H_{10} \cdot -)z$ $(M, H_{11} \cdot -)_z$ have been found.

The azeotropic range

$$Z_A(H) = t_{H_k} - t_{H_e}$$

covers all the varieties of hetero- and homoazeotropes. This is, however, a formal solution of the problem. Neither experiments nor theoretical calculations have been made to prove the usefulness of the value $Z_A(H)$ in both one and two liquid phase systems.

Recently, STECKI [123] published several papers on the theory of binary heteroazeotropes. He proved that a rule similar to VREVSKI's may be employed for predicting the displacement of the heteroazeotropic point caused by pressure changes. For more accurate calculations the heat of mutual saturation of the two phases should be taken into account.

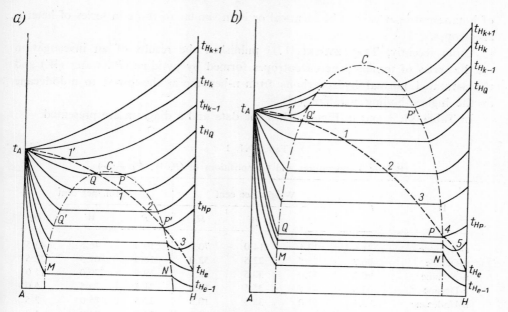

FIG. XI. 3 *a*, *b*, (*a*) Diagram of series (*A*, H_i) showing the formation of hetero- and homoazeotropes with transition points P' and Q. The normal boiling temperature t_A lies above the critical solubility point *C*. (*b*) Diagram of series (*A*, H_i) showing the formation of hetero- and homoazeotropes with transition points *P* and Q'. The normal boiling temperature t_A of *A* lies below the critical solubility point *C*.

§ 90. Ternary Positive Heteroazeotropes. In § 53 the transition of positive ternary homoazeotropes into heteroazeotropes by change of pressure was described. It is often observed that, if two components, *A* and *B* miscible with each other in all proportions are mixed with water or any other solvent characterized by low solubility both in *A* and in *B*, a ternary heteroazeotrope is formed. Water or other solvents having similar properties of splitting (*A*+*B*) mixtures into two liquid phases may be called dehomogenizers.

In some cases, if two components *A* and *B* are not soluble or slightly soluble in each other, a third component *H* may be added having a homogenizing effect. Component *H* is called homogenizer.

The variety of positive ternary heteroazeotropes is very large, but no extensive theoretical researches on this kind of azeotropes have been made.

STECKI has published several papers [162] with a view to finding some general rules embracing at least several adequately chosen ternary heteroazeotropes. He used some simplifications and showed that in a number of selected heteroazeotropes some regularities are observed.

The main conclusion which may be drawn from a direct comparison of positive ternary hetero- and homoazeotropes is that the regularities found in the series of homoazeotropes cannot be identical or even similar to those in series of hetero-azeotropes.

Quite recently, TRĄBCZYŃSKI [171] published the results of an investigation on the series of ternary heteroazeotropes formed by pyridine (P), water (W) and the saturated normal hydrocarbons from n-heptane as the lowest to n-dodecane as the highest-boiling paraffins (H).

In Table XI. 1 and in Figure XI. 4 the data and a diagram are presented.

TABLE XI. 1

Boiling Temperatures and Compositions of $(P, W, H_i \ -\cdot-)$

H	$t\,^\circ C$	Weight per cent			Mol. per cent		
		P	W	H_i	P	W	H_i
n-Heptane	78.6	12.5	14.0	70.5	10.0	46.5	43.5
n-Octane	86.7	25.5	22.5	52.0	16.0	61.5	22.5
n-Nonane	90.5	37.0	30.5	32.5	19.0	70.0	11.0
n-Decane	92.3	45.5	35.5	19.0	21.5	73.5	5.0
n-Undecane	93.1	51.0	38.5	10.5	22.5	75.0	2.5
n-Dodecane	93.5	54.5	40.5	45.0	23.0	76.0	1.0

TRĄBCZYŃSKI's diagram (Fig. XI. 4) shows that an almost straight line joins the points representing the composition of the ternary heteroazeotropes formed by pyridine, water and the respective representatives of normal paraffins. This

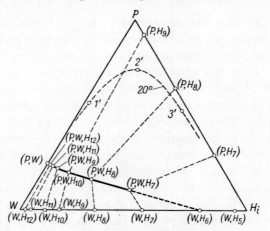

FIG. XI. 4. The series of ternary heteroazeotropes $(P, W, H_i \ -\cdot-)$ formed by pyridine (P), water (W) and representatives of n-paraffins (H_i) compositions being expressed in mol. per cent. The number of carbon atoms in the hydrocarbon molecule is used as a subscript, instead of "i". Points $1'$, $2'$ and $3'$ lie on the turbidity curve (at 20°C) of the system: pyridine (P)—water (W)—paraffin hydrocarbon fraction (H_i), boiling between 144.5 and 145.0°C·

experimentally established regularity is in agreement with STECKI'S theoretical predictions [162].

In Figure XI. 5 three curves are shown [171]. Two of them (I and II) show the boiling temperature changes of binary (W, $H_i—\cdot—$) and ternary (P, W, $H_i—\cdot—$) heteroazeotropes. Curve III represents the boiling temperature difference $t_{W,H_i}—$ $—t_{PWH_i} = \Delta t$. The Δt values ranging from 1 to 6°C are given on the right hand vertical axis.

In other series, larger deviations could have been expected. It is very probable that some systems are less and others more sensitive to simplifications introduced for deriving mathematical relations. The subject requires still more systematic research, firstly, by carrying out experiments with different series of ternary hetero-azeotropes, and secondly, in improving the background for theoretical considerations.

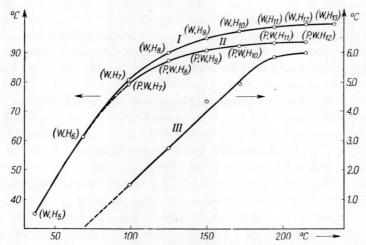

FIG. XI. 5. Curves I and II show the boiling temperatures of the azeotropes of the series (W, $H_i —\cdot—$) and (P, W, $H_i —\cdot—$). They are plotted against the boiling temperatures of the respective n-paraffins; curve III represents the boiling temperature differences $t_{W,Hi} — t_{P,W,H_i}$. The ordinates of curve III ranging from 1 to 6 °C are given on the right hand vertical axis.

§ 91. New Agents for Studying Polycomponent Heteroazeotropes. It is commonly admitted that there is a restricted number of agents which can form binary, ternary and quaternary heteroazeotropes. Amongst these, water is the most common heteroazeotropic agent. Due to the low boiling temperature of water, no interesting results can be obtained if the second, or generally speaking, other components of the heteroazeotrope boil much above 150°C.

Recent experiments have shown that there are other"heteroazeotropic" agents which boil within the range 210 to 240°C, and have very large azeotropic ranges. Amongst these are the pyridine base hydrochlorides. In § 27 the pyridine base hydrochlorides were classified as the third group of negative binary azeotropes and not as individual chemical compounds. This is due to the fact that the hydrochlorides, after being brought to the boil, undergo a partial dissociation and lose some of the base. There after, a constant boiling fraction is collected in the distillate containing an excess of 1–2% of hydrochloric acid.

Independently of the point of view accepted on the phenomena taking place in the course of fractional distillation of any pyridine base hydrochloride, owing to the very restricted solubility of the latter in most organic neutral liquid substances, typical heteroazeotropes are collected in the receiver, if mixtures of organic compounds with any pyridine base hydrochloride are fractionally distilled.

SOSNKOWSKA has shown that 2-picoline hydrochloride, melting-point 78–80 °C and boiling-point 238°C, forms heteroazeotropes with the neutral constituents of carbolic and naphthalene oils separated from high temperature coal tar. It is quite clear that polycomponent heteroazeotropes are collected in the receiver. With phenols negative azeotropes are formed with the 2-picoline hydrochloride.

These experiments are now under way and a precise examination of all the fractions is being made. In addition it is quite probable that some secondary phenomena take place in the course of distillation, under the influence of hydrochloric acid at temperatures exceeding 200°C.

Recently, W. MALESIŃSKI and B. MALESIŃSKA examined a series, where ternary heteroazeotropes (N, W, H_i—·—·—) are formed in three liquid phases, where N stands for nitromethane, W for water and H_i for a normal saturated hydrocarbon. The sign (—·—·—) indicates that three liquid phases are present at the boiling temperature. The azeotropic range of the heteroazeotropes (N, W—·—) was relatively wide, C_6H_{14} being the lowest and $C_{13}H_{28}$ the highest-boiling hydrocarbons.

The physico-chemical properties of the components W, N and the homologue of normal paraffins H_i seemed to be appropriate for finding other constituents which would be able to form a quaternary and even a quinternary heteroazeotrope composed of two liquid phases. In fact, a quaternary heteroazeotrope (N, W, Pr, H_8—·—), where Pr stands for n-propanol and H_8 (for normal octane) has been obtained and its composition examined. The quinternary heteroazeotrope (N, W, Pr, H_8, C_2Cl_4—·—) contained ethylene tetrachloride.

Chapter XII

AZEOTROPES AND THE CRITICAL STATE

§ 92. General Considerations. The problem of binary liquid mixtures approaching and reaching their critical state was discussed many years ago. Since then azeotropy has become one of the important phenomena in physical chemistry, and the question had to be answered whether azeotropes may exist in their critical state.

It should be mentioned that PAWLEWSKI's rule [18], predicting that the critical temperature of two liquids A and B changes linearly with the concentration, has only a restricted application. In most cases, instead of a straight line, curves showing positive or negative deviations are observed [66].

VAN DER WAALS [17] first predicted two phenomena which might have been expected in connection with binary liquid mixtures at their critical state. According to VAN DER WAALS either the extremum on the curve disappears before the critical state is reached, or it remains up to the critical point of the binary mixture under examination.

Most of the experiments were carried out with a view to either confirming or refuting PAWLEWSKI's rule. Few observations were made of the existence or non-existence of extrema on the critical curve of the mixtures examined. No ternary azeotropes have ever been examined.

KRĘGLEWSKI's experiments [67] began with the examination of the binary system with pyridine-acetic acid. He found that this binary system which at 138.1°C and 1 atm forms a negative azeotrope has a maximum of critical temperature. In Figure XII. 1 the relevant curve is shown. It should be emphasized that the experiments were carried out in sealed tubes, under isochoric conditions. The maximum, 348.5°C, is 3.5°C higher than the critical temperature of pyridine. The composition of the mixture at the maximum point is 75 ± 1 mol. per cent of pyridine.

An important contribution to the development of azeotropy and polyazeotropy was made in 1957 by KRĘGLEWSKI [67], who examined a series (A, H_i) of positive binary azeotropes formed by acetic acid with representatives of the paraffin series, namely n-hexane (*I*), n-octane (*II*), n-decane (*III*) and n-dodecane (*IV*). In Figure XII. 2 *a, b* the curves are presented. A series of binary azeotropes composed of pyridine with n-octane (*V*), n-decane (*VI*) and n-dodecane have also been examined.

Below is given a quotation from KRĘGLEWSKI'S paper: "Recently, the conclu sion has been drawn [164], that there exists a close analogy between the boiling temperature isobars and the critical temperature curves, and that MALESIŃSKI'S relations determining the azeotropic parameters could be directly applied to these

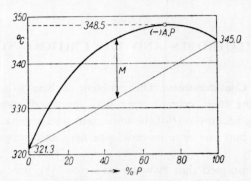

FIG. XII. 1. Critical temperatures of mixtures of pyridine and acetic acid.

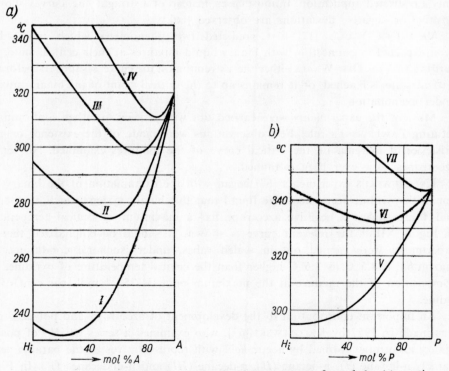

FIG. XII. 2 a, b. Critical temperatures in binary systems formed by (a) acetic acid A with n-paraffins, namely with n-hexane (I), n-octane (II), n-decane (III), and n-dodecane (IV), and (b) pyridine P with n-octane (V), n-decane (VI) and n-dodecane (VII).

curves. The azeotropic ranges $Z_A(H)$ of an agent A in relation to the homologous series (H), and the azeotropic depressions δ_A and δ_H are related by the equation:

$$(\sqrt{\overline{\delta_A}}+\sqrt{\overline{\delta_H}})^2 = 0.5\ Z_A(H). \tag{1}$$

This results from the two following equations:

$$\delta_A = 0.5\ Z_A(H)X_H^2 \text{ and } \delta_H = 0.5\ Z_A(H)X_A^2, \tag{2}$$

X_H and X_A being the molar fractions of the components in the azeotrope. Relations (1) and (2) are derived under the assumption that the azeotropic range $(Z_A H)$ remains constant for the whole series of azeotropes (A, H_i). Analogous quantities found on the basis of the critical curves:

$$\delta_A^C = T_A^C - T_{ex}^C \text{ and } \delta_H^C = T_H^C - T_{ex}^C,$$

T_A^C and T_H^C being the critical temperatures of the pure components and T_{ex}^W that of the extremum point, have been substituted in place of δ_A and δ_H (equation 1). It was found [164] that the value of $Z_A^C(H)$ thus calculated, for non-polar or moderately polar molecules is almost equal to $Z_A(H)$ corresponding to the boiling temperature isobars under atmospheric pressure."

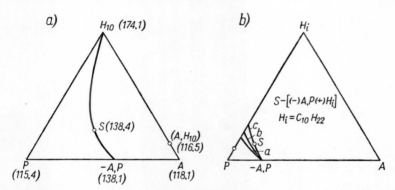

FIG. XII. 3 *a, b*. Curves (*b*) represent the top-ridge lines on the critical temperature surface for the systems composed of n-paraffins, pyridine and acetic acid; point *S* shows the extrema, the composition of the bipositive-negative ternary point. Scheme (*a*) is observed at 1 atm.

KRĘGLEWSKI succeeded in examining in detail a series of critical temperature surfaces under isochoric conditions for the ternary system n-dodecane-pyridine-acetic acid and in proving that the saddle point (*S*) exists in one bipositive-negative system. In that way, the existence of a ternary saddle point on critical temperature surface has been confirmed for the first time.

§ 93. **Azeotropic and Zeotropic Mixtures in their Critical States.** A series of binary mixtures formed by benzene, isopropyl, isobutyl and amyl alcohols examined by KRĘGLEWSKI are typical examples of azeotropes or zeotropes [164]. All KRĘGLEWSKI's papers are published in English.

§ 94. General Remarks. KRĘGLEWSKI's experiments show the importance of extending our knowledge on azeotropy to the region of the critical state of binary and ternary mixtures. A direct comparison of the phenomena observed at atmospheric pressure with those taking place at the critical state may lead to important generalizations.

KRĘGLEWSKI's investigations deal with problems which are not directly associated with the main subject of this monograph. For this reason, they are not fully dealt with in this short presentation of his achievement. For readers interested in the subject of critical states the full list of KRĘGLEWSKI's publications in the period from 1952 to 1957 is given [164].

Chapter XIII

SERIES OF POSITIVE TERNARY AZEOTROPES

§ 95. Ternary Positive Azeotropes Formed by Two Agents with Homologous Series (*H*). Two different approaches may be applied to the examination of the series of positive ternary azeotropes (*A*, *B*, *H*). One of them is based on direct experimental examination, whilst the other was developed in 1956 by MALESIŃSKI on the basis of thermodynamic considerations and the assumption that, to a first approximation, the azeotropes behave as regular solutions.

Let us present first the experimental approach to the problem. In conformity with the definition of azeotropic ranges (§ 38) of agents *A* and *B* in relation to the series of homologues and their isomers (*H*), we may write:

$$Z_A(H) = t_{H_k} - t_{H_e}, \tag{1}$$

$$Z_B(H) = t_{H_{k+m}} - t_{H_{e-n}}. \tag{2}$$

In equation (2) we assume that *m* and *n* are positive whole numbers. Consequently, from (1) and (2) we conclude that the following inequality exists:

$$Z_A(H) < Z_B(H).$$

Furthermore, we will call the agent *A* main azeotropic agent. It is always characterized by the smallest azeotropic range. Equation (2) shows that *B* also forms a series of binary azeotropes (*B*, H_i) with all compounds of the series (*H*) found within the limits $H_e \ldots H_k$, because the azeotropic range (2) includes the homologues which lie within much wider limits, from H_{e-n} to H_{k+m}, lying below and above the azeotropic range of agent *A*. Because of these relations we may define a new "azeotropic range" $Z_{A,B}(B, H)$ in relation to the series of binary azeotropes (*B*, H_i). In the ideal case, we may expect that

$$Z_{A,B}(B, H) = t_{B,H_k} - t_{B,H_e}. \tag{3}$$

In writing this we are postulating that the formation of the series of ternary azeotropes (*A*, *B*, H_i) will be limited by the same two representatives H_k and H_e which limit the formation of binary azeotropes of the type (*A*, H_i). As mentioned above, equation (3) represents an ideal scheme which will not apply to most actual systems. The general equation representing both the *ideal* and *non-ideal cases* is

$$Z_{A,B}(B, H) = t_{B,H_{k+x}} - t_{B,H_{e+y}}, \qquad (4)$$

x and y being either positive or negative whole numbers.

For simplicity, we have said that the azeotropic range $Z_A(H)$ lies within that of agent B (equations (1) and (3), but there are a very large variety of possible relative positions of the extreme lowest and highest $Z_A(H)$ and $Z_B(H)$ values on such diagrams as that shown in Figure XIII. 1.

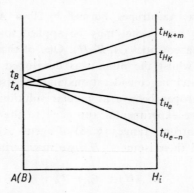

FIG. XIII. 1. Scheme showing the mutual dislocations of azeotropic ranges $Z_A(H)$ and $Z_B(H)$.

It is impossible to examine all the cases of reciprocal rearrangements of azeotropic ranges. Moreover, systematic researches on series of positive ternary azeotropes are still lacking, so that there is insufficient experimental material from which to start constituting a scheme of classification; such material would be of great help in accounting for distillation phenomena of polyazeotropic systems.

In 1955 MALESIŃSKI [165] started developing his theoretical considerations intending to deal eventually with all types of azeotropes. Positive ternary azeotropes have been examined in detail in the light of the large but still insufficient number of sets of azeotropic data thus far available. He assumed, as have other authors who have dealt with the thermodynamics of azeotropy, that the mixtures forming the azeotropes may be regarded as regular solutions. He proved that a very close and direct relation exists between the regular solution constants A_{12}, A_{23}, A_{13} and the binary azeotropic range values Z_{12}; Z_{13}; and Z_{23}.

Consequently two similar equations summarize his general conclusions:

$$A_{12} + A_{23} = A_{13} \text{ and } Z_{12} + Z_{23} = Z_{13}.$$

Two additional assumptions were made: first, that the evaporation entropies of all the substances involved are equal, and second, that all the azeotropic ranges are symmetrical. The latter assumption may be expressed by the equality of the lower and upper sections of the azeotropic range (Fig. IV. 5, § 38):

$$Z_u = t_{H_k} - t_A \text{ and } t_A - t_{H_e} = Z_l$$

remembering that:

$$Z_A(H) = t_{H_k} - t_{H_e}. \tag{1}$$

The symmetry makes it possible to divide the azeotropic range by a horizontal line drawn through the point t_A into two equal parts Z_u and Z_l; Z_u being the upper and Z_l the lower portion of the azeotropic range.

In Figure XIII. 2 the scheme given by MALESIŃSKI is shown.

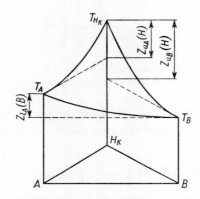

FIG. XIII. 2. Ternary tangent azeotrope having the limiting composition $X_B = 1$.

§ 96. Graphical Presentation of Series of Ternary Azeotropes.

In the above two somewhat different generalizations are made about the compositions of a series of positive ternary azeotropes (A, B, H_i). The first is based on a rather formal introduction of the term azeotropic range of an azeotrope (A, B) in relation to the series of binary azeotropes (B, H_i)

$$Z_{A,B}(B, H) = t_{B,H_{k+x}} - t_{B,H_{e+y}}, \tag{4}$$

where x and y may be positive or negative whole numbers characterizing a non-ideal ternary system (A, B, H_i). No limitation arises from any consideration of *the symmetry or asymmetry of the azeotropic ranges*. Experiment will show whether the system is ideal $(x = 0, y = 0)$ or non-ideal $(x \gtrless 0, y \gtrless 0)$. The equation gives no indication whether the points representing the compositions of the whole series of azeotropes (A, B, H_i), lie on a straight line or on a curve.

On the other hand MALESIŃSKI's theoretical conclusions are based on several assumptions and simplifications leading directly to important generalizations, which are approximately true. In a table given by MALESIŃSKI [165], for 67 out of 154 ternary azeotropes the $Z_A(H) = Z_B(H) - Z_A(B)$ values were given within $\pm 3°$C. For 49 azeotropes the deviations varied from 3 to 6°C, and in only 11 cases they did exceed 10°C.

§ 97. Lower Limit of the Azeotropic Range $Z_{A,B}(B, H)$. Returning to the

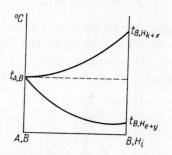

FIG. XIII. 3. Limits of the azeotropic range $Z_{A,B}(B, H)$ of the binary azeotrope (A, B) in relation to the series of binary azeotropes (B, H_i).

azeotropic range $Z_{A,B}(B, H)$ value discussed in § 95 (equation 4) the following conclusion results from MALESIŃSKI'S generalization. First, the y value in the equation:

$$Z_{A,B}(B, H) = t_{B,H_{k+x}} - t_{B,H_{e+y}} \tag{4}$$

should always be a whole positive number. If it is the lower limit of positive ternary azeotrope formations it is shifted upwards towards higher boiling representatives of the (H) series. If t_{B,H_e} is the lower limit, the inequality:

$$t_{B,H_i} > t_{B,H_e} \text{ or } t_{B,H_i} - t_{B,H_e} = \Delta t$$

characterizes this shifting. The value of Δt depends upon the molar concentrations C_B in the ternary azeotrope (A, B, H_i). The smaller C_B, the lower is the value of Δt.

Further systematic investigations dealing with a large variety of main (A) and secondary (B) components as well as with different homologous series may lead to more precisely formulated general conclusions. In addition, a thorough and detailed examination of the positive ternary azeotropes formed in the course of a fractional distillation of an organic raw material may lead to the discovery of new facts, unpredictable at present due to our restricted knowledge of the whole problem.

Chapter XIV

INFLUENCE OF PRESSURE ON TERNARY AZEOTROPIC COMPOSITION

§ 98. Influence of Small and Large Pressure Changes. As far as the author knows, no general rule has been formulated, which predicts the composition changes of positive ternary azeotropes whether the pressure changes are large or small.

In practice it is relatively easy to examine the changes in positive ternary azeotrope compositions produced by relatively small pressure changes; that is, those in the range between 300 and 2500 mm Hg. Direct determinations of dt/dp may, in this pressure range, be carried out in differential two-stage ebulliometers; the method of strictly comparative measurements should be applied.

ZMACZYŃSKI [46, 59] has carried out much research on the precise determination of dt/dp coefficients for water and a number of other pure substances. He worked at the Bureau International des Poids et Mesures at Sèvres, and later at Brussels, at the International Bureau of Physico-chemical Standards. Finally, in 1938 he and MOSER worked at the Physikalisch Technischen Reichsanstalt (PTR) in Charlottenburg, Germany. He compared the ebulliometric method directly with a static method described by MOSER in 1932. They remeasured the change of boiling temperature of water with pressure [47].

TABLE XIV. 1

Boiling Temperature of Water at Pressures from 680 to 800 mm Hg

P	0	1	2	3	4	5	6	7	8	9
680	96.9137	9541	9944	0347	0750	1152	1553	1954	2355	2755
690	97.3154	3553	3952	4350	4748	5145	5542	5938	6334	6729
700	7124	7518	7912	8305	8698	9091	9483	9875	0266	0651
710	98.1047	1436	1825	2214	2603	2991	3378	3765	4152	4538
720	4924	5309	5694	6078	6462	6846	7229	7611	7994	8375
730	8757	9138	9518	9898	0278	0657	1036	1414	1792	2169
740	99.2546	2923	3299	3675	4050	4425	4800	5174	5548	5921
750	6294	6666	7038	7410	7781	8152	8522	8892	9262	9631
760	100.0000	0368	0736	1104	1471	1838	2204	2571	2636	3301
770	3666	4031	4395	4758	5122	5485	5847	6209	6571	6932
780	7293	7654	8014	8374	8733	9092	9451	9809	0167	0525
790	101.0882	1239	1595	1951	2307	2662	3017	3372	3726	4080
800	4433	4786	5139	5491	5843	6195	6546	6897	7248	7598

In Table XIV. 1 the results obtained by ZMACZYŃSKI and MOSER are given. They have been accepted and recommended by the International Bureau of Pure and Applied Chemistry. These data agree with those obtained by OSBORN and MEYERS, who examined the same relations for water at the National Bureau of Standards, USA. The ebulliometric method has been also applied by SMITH and WOJCIECHOWSKI [167], who carried out their experiments at the National Bureau of Standards.

According to ZMACZYŃSKI'S data the error in determining the coefficient dt/dp is less than 0.1 per cent.

§ 99. Simplified Vrevski's Rule. As mentioned above, in spite of the progress made in precise determinations of dt/dp, we do not know of any systematic investigation of composition changes of positive ternary azeotropes produced by change of pressure.

For relatively small changes of pressure, VREVSKI'S rule enables qualitative conclusions to be drawn. The same rule has been used by many authors in connection with positive binary azeotropes. The rule is that an increase of pressure produces a concentration increase of the component having the lower dt/dp value.

The same rule may be used to predict positive ternary azeotrope composition changes produced by increase of pressure. In this case, however, one has to remember that there are three coefficients dt/dp. Several typical cases, which lead to some simplification of the problem, will now be considered.

First, let us assume that for a ternary azeotrope (A, B, C) we have the following relation between the dt/dp values:

$$(dt/dp)_C < (dt/dp)_A = (dt/dp)_B. \tag{1}$$

In Figure XIV. 1 the graphical presentation of the simplest case is given. Relation (1) shows that a displacement of point Az towards point C should be expected because the coefficients of A and B are equal to each other.

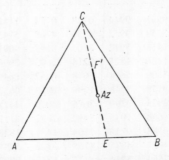

FIG. XIV. 1. Composition changes of positive ternary homoazeotropes caused by pressure increases. The two coefficients $(dt/dp)_A$, $(dt/dp)_B$ are equal to each other; $(dt/dp)_C$ is lower than the others.

In the reverse case, namely, if $(dt/dp)_C > (dt/dp)_A = (dt/dp)_B$ the change in composition of the positive ternary azeotrope (A, B, C) may be represented by the prolongation of line CAz as shown in Figure XIV. 1. Finally, if the dt/dp values of the three components differ from one another the azeotropic point Az is gradually displaced towards either point F or point F' (Fig. XIV. 2). If, due to a rare accident, the three dp/dt values were equal to one another, no change in composition may be expected.

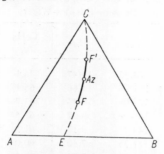

FIG. XIV. 2. Composition changes of ternary azeotropes. The three coefficients dt/dp are unequal to one another.

§ 100. Composition Changes of the Benzene-Ethanol-Water Heteroazeotrope.

Below an example is given which concerns not a ternary homo- but a heteroazeotrope. This system was examined by KARPIŃSKI [87] in 1934.

From 1924 onwards numerous ethanol dehydration plants were built, and generally GUINOT's patent claiming dehydration by a mixture of benzene and a 101–102°C boiling gasoline fraction was almost exclusively applied. In Germany efforts were made to circumvent the French patent claim. For this purpose a large

TABLE XIV. 2

Karpiński's Results for Azeotropic Concentrations under Increased Pressure

P atm.	t_{Et}	t_{Az}	δt_{Az}		Component I %	Component II %
			Azeotrope water-ethanol			
19.11	179.18	178.60	0.58		92.12	7.88
			Azeotrope benzene-ethanol			
18.62	177.90	176.40	1.50		68.40	31.60
			Heteroazeotrope benzene-water			
9.75	150.04	146.76*	178.26**	179.34***	85.7	14.3
20.63	182.68	180.02	214.62	225.03***	81.9	18.1

* Boiling temperature of the azeotrope.
** Boiling temperature of benzene.
*** Boiling temperature of water.

scale pilot plant was built for carrying out the dehydration under a pressure of about ten atmospheres. In view of these efforts, basic research was started at the Polish Institute of Industrial Research, Warsaw, with the aim of examining the relation between the concentrations of water, benzene and ethanol in the ternary heteroazeotrope and the pressure.

TABLE XIV. 3

The Effect of Pressure on the Composition of the Ternary Azeotrope
Benzene-Ethanol-Water

P atm.	t_{Et}	t_{Az}	δt_{Az}	C_6H_6 %	C_2H_5OH %	H_2O %
1	78.32	64.85	13.47	74.1	18.5	7.4
3.41	112.72	101.06	11.66	68.1	22.5	9.4
6.13	132.54	122.08	10.46	63.7	24.9	11.4
9.69	150.17	140.95	9.22	61.5	25.6	12.9
10.29	152.44	143.27	9.17	61.5	25.5	13.0
19.02	178.95	171.35	7.60	60.0	24.4	15.6
19.12	179.20	171.85	7.35	60.3	24.5	15.2

A special device, enabling strictly comparative measurements to be carried out, was built. The boiling temperature changes were compared with a chosen liquid as standard boiling under the same pressure at which the fractional distillation of the ternary mixture of ethanol, benzene and water was carried out.

Above are given two Tables, XIV. 2 and XIV. 3, showing the results obtained [87].

In Figure XIV. 3 the projection of the curve on the triangular diagram is given.

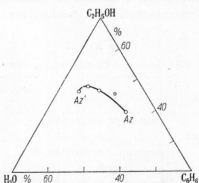

FIG. XIV. 3. Projection of the curve showing the composition change of the ternary azeotrope in the benzene, ethanol and water system produced by a gradual increase of pressure from 1 to 19.12 atmospheres.

Apart from the data of KEUSSLER [60] and KARPIŃSKI [64] there is no other material available on ternary azeotropes in general. No definite conclusions can be drawn because the experimental data are so very restricted.

Part II

POLYAZEOTROPY

Chapter XV

PHYSICO-CHEMICAL CHARACTERISTICS OF ORGANIC RAW MATERIALS

§ 101. Introductory Remarks on Polyazeotropy. The term *polyazeotropy* was nitroduced in 1952, but it is still practically unknown, or is not clear enough to many chemists and chemical engineers. In the history of the development of our knowledge of azeotropy, neither in LECAT's classical work, published in 1918, 1947 shortly before his death, nor in HORSLEY's *Azeotropic Data*, was any mention made of the urgent necessity of extending our knowledge on azeotropy by studying the phenomena taking place in the course of fractional distillation of organic raw materials, such as high and low temperature coal tars, products of coal hydrogenation by the BERGIUS method. Similar phenomena characterize the fractional distillation of petroleum and of other organic raw materials.

No publications are to be found which discuss the consequences of the fact that most organic raw materials contain one, two, three and even more series of homologues (and their isomers) belonging to different classes of organic compounds. Even in a large treatise such as H. H. Lowry's excellent fundamental monograph, *The Chemistry of Coal Utilisation*, published in 1945, in the large and thoroughly compiled subject index the terms *azeotropy* and *eutectic system* do not occur. If these terms, and the experimental and theoretical methods which go with them, had been applied in the examination of organic raw materials, and if it had been emphasized that the latter are polycomponent mixtures containing several series of homologues, our knowledge of a very large number of azeotropes formed in the course of fractional distillation of organic raw materials would have been developed many years ago, simultaneously with the progress made in the field of azeotropes composed exclusively of two, three or four pure componens. Investigations of much more complicated systems would also have beent carried out.

As regards coal tar, several papers were published dealing with the azoetropic phenomena. In 1939, in HALDENWANGER's doctorate thesis entitled "Über die Zusammensetzung der Methylnaphthalenfraction des Steinkohlenteers" the formation of azeotropes was discussed. In 1941 COULSON [74] pointed out the influence of bases and phenols on the formation of azeotropes in the course of the distillation of the methylnaphthalene fraction. The formation of negative azeotro pes owing to the presence of pyridine bases and phenols was also discussed by WILLE [192]. It seems, however, that the importance of these observations, in the distillation of the coal tar and other organic raw materials as well, was overlooked.

§ 102. Tangent or almost Tangent Boiling Temperature Isobars.

ANDERSON'S [36] investigation of the typical contaminants of nitration benzene did not stimulate anyone to extend the newly-discovered phenomenon to other similar systems. The azeotropes formed by benzene with its typical contaminants are now generally recognized as tangent or almost tangent azeotropes. They are important in all cases in which the homologues belonging to one series form tangent or almost tangent boiling temperature isobars with a lower boiling representative of another homologous series. We now call these isobars *lower limits of azeotropic ranges*.

It seems very probable that the development of our knowledge of *polyazeotropic mixtures* was held back because the formation of numerous azeotropes in the course of a fractional distillation of any complex organic liquid was considered an undesirable and harmful factor, which could not be usefully exploited industrially; certainly it was not thought capable of increasing the yield of some constituents of the mixture.

ANDERSON'S discovery that the main benzene contaminants boil at 17 to 20°C higher than benzene itself was regarded as an exceptional, rather curious and unexplained phenomenon, in spite of the fact that in 1930 a scheme was published [31] which gave a clear and natural explanation: all the contaminants forming tangent or almost tangent boiling temperature isobars distil with the *main component under examination at temperatures almost equal to the boiling point of the main component*.

In ANDERSON'S case benzene should be regarded as the *main component* and the contaminants as substances forming tangent or almost tangent isobars to the horizontal line drawn through the point representing the boiling temperature of benzene.

§ 103. Polycomponent Agents for Ethanol Dehydration.

There are direct proofs of the complete lack of close co-operation between physical chemists and inventors of azeotropic methods of ethanol dehydration. The following historical note may serve as a classical example of such a lack of co-operation.

Fundamental researches and inventions started by YOUNG in 1902 [10] (or perhaps one year earlier) on positive ternary heteroazeotropes such as benzene-ethanol-water, stimulated other inventors to improve the procedure of dehydration by adding to the benzene a gasoline fraction boiling, according to GUINOT'S [51] paper and patent claim, between 101 and 102°C. GUINOT'S discovery was and still is an industrially very important improvement, overcoming difficulties in separating the aqueous and the hydrocarbon phases forming the distillate collected in the receiver. If benzene alone is used it is difficult to separate these two liquid phases because of the small difference in their densities and because of unfavourable surface tension phenomena.

The addition of a fraction of gasoline favoured to a large extent the separation of the two phases collected as the top product of the distilling column.

The industrial realization of GUINOT's patent claim was simple enough and was so effective that within a short time 45 azeotropic installations had been built all over the world. In spite of this, neither GUINOT and his associates nor specialists in the field of azeotropy or in physical chemistry in general have ever carried out basic research to find a theoretical explanation of GUINOT's ethanol dehydration process.

There is also a particularly interesting misunderstanding with regard to the GUINOT patent claims themselves: it was a mistake to claim that the 101–102°C gasoline should be mixed with benzene, for there are no hydrocarbons boiling within the range from 101 to 102°C, and even if there were, they would not be the proper agents for the ethanol dehydration process. It will be shown in § 111 that the boiling temperature range of an appropriate gasoline fraction is 93–99°C, and that ethanol dehydration is an efficient operation owing to the formation of a series of positive quaternary heteroazeotropes expressed by the following formula: (B, E, W, H_i) where B stands for benzene, E—for ethanol, W—for water and H—for any paraffinic or naphthenic hydrocarbon boiling between 93 and 99°C.

§ 104. Pure and Applied Azeotropic Investigations.

In the previous paragraphs a short survey is given, explaining that from the beginning there has been a separation of everything associated with "pure knowledge" on azeotropy and the achievements in thermodynamics and general properties of individual binary and ternary azeotropes, from the investigation of more or less complicated polyazeotropic mixtures, whether found in organic raw materials or obtained purposely by mixing one, two or more substances with an organic liquid containing a relatively large number of hydrocarbons or other homologous series of compounds.

It is also a curious phenomenon that many suggestions and patent claims have been made relative to the utilization of azeotropy for the purification or separation of the products found in a more or less complicated liquid mixture. No direct contacts, however, existed between pure and applied knowledge on azeotropy.

§ 105. Typical Polyazeotropic Mixtures.

On the basis of the general considerations given in the previous paragraphs it is easy to conclude that the term *polyazeotropic mixture* may be formulated in the following way: *Any liquid containing representatives of several series of homologues and their isomers is a polyazeotropic mixture*. The term *homologue* leaves no doubt that we have in mind exclusively organic compounds. This definition embraces a very large number of mixtures differing from one another in their physical, chemical, and physico-chemical properties. For instance, if we purposely prepared a mixture in which the representatives of each of the series were not numerous and boiled at very different temperatures, it might happen that no azeotropes would be formed at all. We do not intend to consider such a peculiar and exceptional phenomenon. On the other hand, if we assume that the polyazeotropic mixture contains practically all the homologues and their isomers, then we may be sure that such a mixture will form a large variety and a very large number of azeotropes.

For the sake of clarity, let us examine two polyazeotropic mixtures: the low and the high temperature coal tars. These mixture contains at least the following series of homologues and their isomers; (H)—saturated hydrocarbons, (0)—olefins (Ar_1)—one ring aromatic hydrocarbons, (F)—phenol and its derivatives, (P)—pyridine bases, (Am)—aromatic amines.

For simplicity, we do not take into consideration the homologous series present in very small quantities in low temperature coal tar, because they do not change in any appreciable way the main processes going on during fractional distillation.

Generally speaking, we may expect that in the high temperature coal tar one of its constituents will occur in such quantity that in the course of distillation it will be able to form with the other constituents all the azeotropes within its azeotropic range in relation to each of the series of homologues, and an excess of it will still remain in the mixture undergoing distillation. If this happened, we say that the polyazeotropic mixture contains a *main distillation component*. It is easy to see that, if the mixture were submitted to a fractional distillation, the main distillation component would form in the first stage tangent and almost tangent azeotropes with suitable lower boiling homologues and their isomers.

In the fractions collected then we will observe in the first stages small amounts of the main distillation component "azeotropically entrained". In time, the amount of the main distillation component will steadily increase in the fractions collected and higher-boiling azeotropes will be formed containing, as a rule, larger quantities of the main component.

Finally, we will reach the distillation stage at which the upper limit of the azeotropic range has been reached. Thus the amount of the main component in the fractions collected will steadily increase until it reaches a maximum of almost 100 per cent. At the same time, the higher boiling representatives of the different series of homologues and their isomers will form almost tangent zeotropes, which have boiling temperatures close to that of the main component. They will soon be exhausted and the final stage of the main component distillation will be reached. This means that practically pure main component will be collected in the receiver. We may say that the "ceiling line of the main component" has been reached. At higher temperatures, if no almost tangent zeotropes were formed, no appreciable quantities of the main component would be found in the fraction collected.

This is, in general terms, what takes place, if besides relatively small quantities of representatives of several homologous series, a main component is present.

In the case of low temperature coal tar, opposite phenomena take place, because it contains no main distillation components.

Let us now examine the case of a low temperature coal tar, which, as often happens, does not contain any main distillation component.

The starting point will be the same. Any representative of a homologous series will start to form azeotropes boiling at a temperature corresponding to the lower limits of its azeotropic ranges. At this temperature, in the first stage, almost tangent zeotropes and tangent azeotropes will undergo distillation. Then somewhat higher boiling azeotropes will be collected in the receiver. Finally, the particular representative, which we are considering, will disappear in the polyazeotropic mixture undergoing fractional distillation at lower temperature than its normal boiling point.

We have not yet mentioned that, depending upon the number and nature of the homologous series present in the polyazeotropic mixture, neither the lower limit of the azeotropic range nor the number of components of the azeotropes or zeotropes collected in the receiver will be known precisely. For instance, it may happen that a tangent or almost tangent binary azeotrope (A, H_i), A being the main component, H_i—a representative of series (H) will distil first. It is possible that in the next stage a ternary azeotrope (A, Ar_1, H_i) will follow, Ar_1 being an aromatic hydrocarbon. The complexity of the distillation phenomena is so great that without the application of other methods no clear idea of the processes accompanying the fractional distillation of a polyazeotropic mixture can be obtained. The purpose of what follows is to describe the methods which may lead to a better understanding of the phenomena which take place when a typical polyazeotropic mixture undergoes fractional distillation.

Let us return to a more detailed examination of high temperature coal tar as another typical polyazeotropic mixture. It contains fewer saturated and unsaturated aliphatic hydrocarbons; in their place are several main distillation components, of which naphthalene is the most typical. It is found in high temperature coal tar in large quantities. In addition, other main components, such as 2-methylnaphthalene, acenaphthene and others, are present, distilling at much higher temperatures than naphthalene.

§ 106. Methods of Polyazeotropic Mixture Examination. We have chosen the low and high temperature coal tars as typical polyazeotropic mixtures. Besides the constituents mentioned in § 105 other homologous series are present in them. Among these, very important are acidic and basic compounds which form negative azeotropes with one another, for instance $[(-)F, P]$ or $[(-)F, Am]$ where F represents phenol or its derivative, P is a pyridine or quinoline base and Am is an aromatic amine. These acids and bases are able to form a relatively large number of saddle ternary azeotropes, and the formation of quaternary positive-negative azeotropes is very probable, since the possibility of their existence has been shown in the laboratory.

The presence of weak acids and weak bases is important and dictates the methods to be employed for a more detailed examination of such polyazeotropic mixtures as coal tars or oils obtained by their fractional distillation, since we may easily compare the behaviour of low or high temperature coal tar oils before and after chemically removing from them either the acidic or the basic constituents or both. A direct comparison of the resulting four distillation curves yields much information on what kinds of different azeotropes are formed in the presence or absence of the acidic and basic constituents. The absence of both these kinds of compounds makes it impossible to form negative and saddle (bipositive-negative) azeotropes. Consequently, positive binary, ternary and quaternary azeotropes are the only ones that can be formed in such mixtures.

We know also (§§ 72,75) that the azeotropic ranges of phenol and its derivatives are considerably larger than those of the bases. This is also useful information, which favours the solution of our problem. There exist, however, other effective methods for the examination of polyazeotropic mixtures. Some of these may be used almost exclusively for investigating polyazeotropic mixtures containing organic acids and bases. They consist in removing either all the acids or all the bases and in adding to the remaining mixture a known amount of a suitable acidic or basic constituent. Subsequently, we submit the mixture thus prepared to fractional distillation as we did before changing the composition of the initial mixture. After carrying out both distillations, we analyse the fractions collected. On the basis of the data obtained, we prepare diagrams of the two distillation curves and several curves of the analytical data. LISICKI and SOSNKOWSKA have shown the effectiveness of the methods described [70, 178, 179].

In Figures XV. 1, XV. 2, XV. 3 and XV. 4 some typical cases are graphically presented.

Each of the four figures shows some particular changes closely associated with the specific phenomena depending on the presence or absence of one or two acidic or basic series of azeotropic agents.

Let us start with Figure XV. 1. At the beginning of the neutral (curve 5) and basic (curve 4) components appear before any of the first low boiling acidic compound (exclusively phenol). This indicates that binary positive azeotropes of the type (P_j, H_i) are distilled first. The condensation temperature does not exceed 140°C. Thereafter, the neutral component curve 5 declines sharply and an abrupt fall in pyridine base concentration (curve 4) is observed. It is quite probable that some bipositive-negative (saddle azeotropes of the type $[(-)F, P(+)H]$ constitute the main distillation products. In the next stage, the phenol concentration (3) increases rapidly and the amount of neutral compounds (5) steadily decreases. Curve 4 representing the pyridine concentration falls rapidly, indicating that the concentration of bipositive-negative azeotropes is very low in this region.

In the next stage considerable changes are observed. First, the neutral compound concentration (5) falls more rapidly. On the other hand, large increases in the concentrations of the acidic and basic compounds are observed. This is an indication that relatively large amounts of negative and bipositive-negative (saddle) azeotropes are formed. In these fractions the saddle azeotropes contain large amounts of acidic and basic and a small amount of higher boiling neutral (mostly one ring aromatic hydrocarbon) compounds.

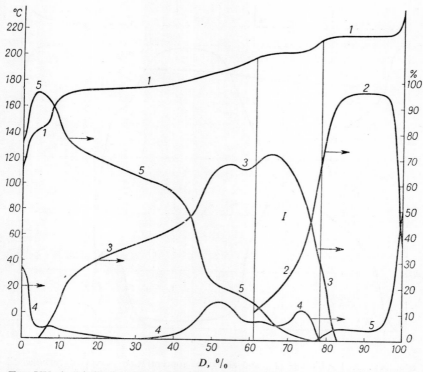

FIG. XV. 1. Distillation *(1)* and analytical concentration curves for the fractional distillation of carbolic oil. Curve *1* stands for the condensation temperatures of the fractions collected; *2* for naphthalene concentration in the samples; *3* for acidic compound (phenol and its derivatives) concentration; *4* for basic compound concentration; *5* for neutral compound (mostly one ring aromatics) concentration. The concentrations in weight per cent are shown on the right hand vertical scale. Region *I* corresponds to the distillation ranges where the formation of quaternary azeotropes becomes probable.

In the next stage of the distillation curve *2* appears. It represents the concentration of naphthalene which is becoming the main distillation (and crystallization) component. In this region the distillation phenomena become very interesting. The region *I* is characterized by the coexistence of four concentration curves *2, 3, 4* and *5*. In addition, curve *2* appears at the point at which the naphthalene concentration is approximately ten per cent and increases rapidly to about fifty per cent at the crossing point with curve *3*. The organic base concentration passes through a maximum in region *I*. All these changes indicate the probability of the formation of ternary and quaternary positive and perhaps positive-negative saddle azeotropes. Experiments carried out by LISICKI would seem to indicate that the formation of quaternary azeotropes is very probable.

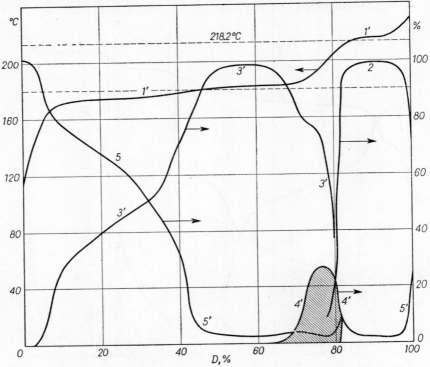

FIG. XV. 2. Distillation (*1'*) and analytical concentration curves of carbolic oil after the removal of all acids (phenol and its derivatives) and after adding a large excess of phenol.

The distillation phenomena observed after the removal of all acidic compounds and their replacement by an excess of phenol are also very interesting. The distillation curves are shown in Figure XV. 2, the curve numbers referring to the same substances as in Figure XV. 1. The first fractions collected did not contain any measurable amount of phenol. The latter appeared at 160°C and there was no doubt that it was as one of the components of binary azeotropes of type (F, H_i) or (F, Ar_1) where H_i and Ar_1 were the low-boiling representatives either of the saturated hydrocarbon series, or of one ring aromatics. In the next stage, curve 5 declines sharply and curve 3 climbs upwards. Fifty per cent of the oil having being distilled off, the phenol concentration rose to 98 weight per cent in the distillate and the remaining liquid in the flask contained almost exclusively aromatic neutral compounds.

Experiments have proved that under these conditions no ternary saddle azeotropes of the type [(−)F, P(+)H_i] or [(−)F, P(+)Ar_1] could be formed, and in the next stage of the fractional distillation, within the limits 62% to 82% all the organic bases underwent distillation, in general as binary negative azeotropes, and without any doubt several per cent of bipositive-negative ternary azeotropes were collected also.

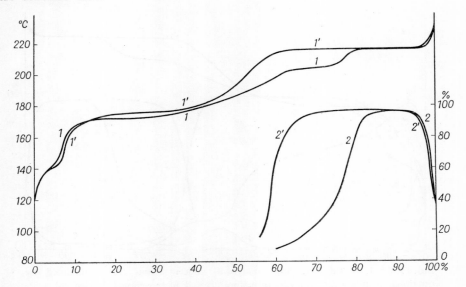

FIG. XV. 3. Distillation and analytical concentration curves obtained by fractional distillation of carbolic oil (1) before and (1') after removal of all acids and bases. Curves 2 and 2' are the concentration ranges of naphthalene.

Figure XV. 3 shows the shapes of the two distillation curves. One of them (1) represents the distillation of normal carbolic oil and is identical with that shown in Figure XV. 1; the other (1') shows the condensation temperature changes of carbolic oil from which all acidic and basic compounds were removed. It should be emphasized that the removal of approximately one third of the total amount of the carbolic oil makes a direct comparison of the two distillates impossible. One consequence of the change, however, is quite evident. The comparison of the two naphthalene concentration curves 2 and 2' shows that after the removal of the acidic and basic compounds fewer azeotropes of the types (H, N), (Ar_1, N) and (H, Ar_1, N) where N stands for naphthalene, are formed. This is because of the absence of the phenol series (F), which is a powerful azeotropic agent.

In Figure XV. 4 two distillation curves (1 and 1') are represented. The first one was obtained in the course of the distillation of normal carbolic oil; the second was found *after the removal of all organic acids*. Due to their absence no saddle ternary azeotropes could be formed. Consequently, curves of the same type, namely, *1* and *1'*, *5* and *5'* cross each other three times; in addition, curve *2'* is shifted backwards as compared with *2*. Each shift is associated with some change in azeotrope formation. More detailed investigations are needed to explain why such shifts occurred. In connection with these phenomena one general remark should be made. If we examine any section of curves *2*, *4* or *5* we may say that no azeotropes are formed by all constituents, the concentrations

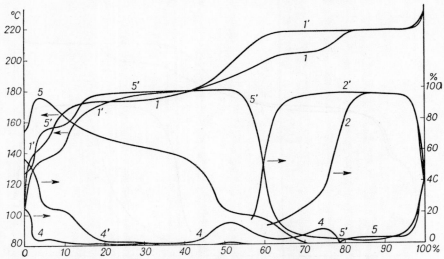

FIG. XV. 4. Distillation and analytical concentration curves obtained by fractional distillation of carbolic oil before (*1*) and after removal (*1'*) of all acids (phenol and its derivatives). All other numbers (*2*, *2'*, *4,4'* and *5,5'*) indicate the same groups of substances as in Fig. XV. 1 and 2.

of which are represented by the same concentration curve. For instance, curve *5* represents the concentration changes of neutral compounds. However, the latter may belong to the paraffinic, naphthalenic and other aromatic hydrocarbons. It is known that paraffins form positive binary azeotropes with some aromatic hydrocarbons. Even some xylenols are able to form azeotropes with one another. Recently, it has been proved by our group that 2,6-lutidine forms a binary azeotrope with 3-picoline. This is an indication that in complex polyazeotropic mixtures azeotrope formation is a much more complicated process than was ever admitted in the past.

LISICKI and SOSNKOWSKA [178] carried out a large number of experiments similar to those described in § 106. They removed either all the acidic or all the basic compounds and replaced them by an excess of phenol, cresols or pyridine derivatives, respectively.

Below two examples are given to show the difference between the infleunce exerted by ortho-cresol or a mixture of para- and meta-cresols and that of phenol (Fig. XV. 5 and 6).

In Figures XV. 5 and XV. 6 the respective distillation curves and concentration curves of naphthalene (2), acidic constituents (3), pyridine bases (4) and neutral compounds (5) are shown.

The replacement of phenol either by ortho- or by a mixture of meta- and para-cresols produces changes in accumulation, within the limits from 20 to 65 per cent of the fraction collected of the pyridine and small amounts of aromatic amines. This may be explained as being due to the formation of ternary bipositive-negative azeotropes in the earlier stages of the distillation. The formation of binary positive azeotropes of the type (P_i, H_j) is quite probable. The fractions which followed did not contain measurable amounts of organic bases. This means that

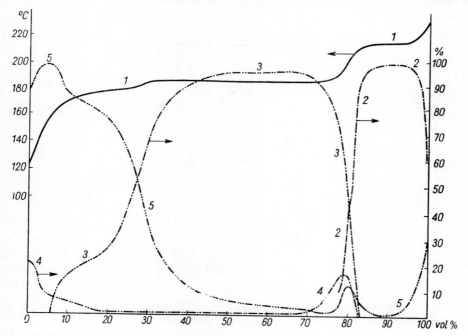

FIG. XV. 5. Distillation (1) and analytical concentration curves of normal carbolic oil after removal of acidic compounds and addition of an excess of ortho-cresol. The other curves show concentration changes: 2 of naphthalene; 3 of ortho-cresol; 4 of basic compounds (mostly pyridine bases) and 5 of neutral compounds.

in the next stage of the distillation neither negative nor bipositive-negative azeotropes were formed. Later, the basic compounds start to appear again in the distillate, which should be regarded as proof that binary negative $[(-)C_r, P_i]$ and ternary bipositive-negative $[(-)C_r, P_i(+)H_j)]$ azeotropes were collected. C_r stands for cresol isomers.

Similar experiments were carried out by LISICKI [112] in which, instead of replacing of the acidic compounds by an excess of phenol or its derivatives, all the organic bases were removed and replaced by one pyridine derivative, thus systematically applying the method of comparative measurements.

It should be pointed out that other methods of polyazeotropic mixture examination are still in their first stage of development.

All the foregoing analysis of distillation and concentration curves must be regarded as a first approximation. The phenomena have not been sufficiently investigated to assume without reservation that their interpretation is correct. In spite of this, a first step has been taken in the analysis of phenomena hitherto never discussed. We have made some progress though the final solution has not yet been reached.

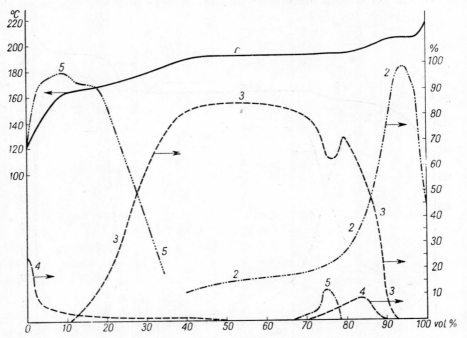

FIG. XV. 6. Distillation (*1*) and analytical concentration curves of normal carbolic oil after the removal of acidic compounds and the addition of an excess of a mixture of meta- and paracresols. The other curves show the changes in concentration: *2* of naphthalene; *3* of the mixtures of cresols; *4* of basic compounds; and *5* of neutral compounds.

As regards low and high temperature coal tars, as well as other organic raw materials containing four or a larger number of homologous series, an important condition must be fulfilled. Namely, it is necessary to collect large amounts of each of the fractions, especially those in which we suspect the formation of ternary and quaternary azeotropes, so as to have enough material for separating the samples into individual compounds. Chromatography and other new analytical methods are of great assistance here.

After the pure constituents have been obtained in satisfactory amounts, ebulliometric or other methods may be used to determine whether ternary or quaternary azeotropes are formed in the course of fractional distillation of some particular mixtures found in the polyazeotropic mixture under examination. As mentioned above, if four (or even more) "concentration curves" (Fig. XV. 1, curves 2, 3, 4 and 5) are carefully examined, in some region between two ordinates the formation of ternary and quaternary azeotropes may be found very probable (e.g. region I shown in Fig. XV. 1).

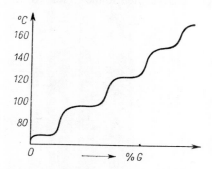

FIG. XV. 7. Distillation curve of a typical Fischer and Tropsch synthesis product.

There are, however, other organic raw materials, especially those which do not contain acidic and basic compounds, which are characterized by other peculiarities. One of these organic mixtures is the liquid product obtained by the FISCHER-TROPSCH synthesis. It is well known that this liquid product is composed mainly of normal paraffins with some amounts of their isomers and olefinic hydrocarbons. If such a mixture is submitted to fractional distillation relatively large horizontal sections are obtained on the distillation curves. This should be considered as evidence that the mixture examined contains a number of main distillation components. It must be stressed that no pure normal paraffins are obtained, because of the presence of olefins. Between each of the distillation levels transition fractions are also collected which are characterized by the presence of isomeric paraffins. In Figure XV. 7, a typical distillation curve of FISCHER–TROPSCH synthesis product is shown.

In many cases the opinion that the presence of numerous azeotropes in a fractional distillation is undesirable, is not quite justified. Investigations carried out since 1951 by the Polish group have proved [89] that azeotropy may often be exploited for getting a considerably larger yield of some high temperature coal tar constituents. For instance, the naphthalene yield may be increased from 35 to 90–93 per cent, taking its content in the coal tar as 100%. In this monograph we do not discuss many applications which are or might be used when dealing with complex polyazeotropic mixtures. It is too early to describe every such application.

The case of high temperature coal tar [89] may serve as an example of how physical chemistry may contribute to the development of the methods of rational industrial treatment of polyazeotropic mixtures. Further systematic research should be carried out to utilize to the utmost the processes occurring in fractional distillations due to the presence of two or several homologous series in most organic raw materials. The direct comparison of the curves 2, 3, 4, 5 makes it possible to observe the differences in the distribution of naphthalene, phenols, organic bases and neutral compounds when one type of compound is replaced by another in a fractional distillation. The curves mentioned refer to any figure shown in this chapter.

Part III

POLYAZEOTROPIC SYSTEMS

Chapter XVI

THE ETHANOL DEHYDRATION PROCESS

§ 107. Azeotropic Ranges of Polyazeotropic Systems. We will give the name polyazeotropic system to a mixture of one series (H) of homologues, their isomers and other chemically closely related substances, with one (A), two $(A+B)$ or three $(A+B+C)$ azeotropic agents. Such a mixture is considerably less complex than any polyazeotropic mixture containing two or any larger number of homologous series.

We have to extend our previous considerations (§§ 35, 38, 50) as shown below in Table XVI. 1.

TABLE XVI. 1

Azeotropic Ranges of Ideal and Nonideal Polyazeotropic Systems

Agent	Ideal systems	Non-ideal systems
A	$Z_A(H) = t_{H_k} - t_{H_e}$	$Z_A(H) = t_{H_k} - t_{H_e}$
A, B	$Z_{A,B}(B, H) = t_{B,H_k} - t_{B,H_e}$	$Z_{A,B}(B, H) = t_{B,H_{k+x}} - t_{B,H_{e+y}}$
A, B, C	$Z_{A,B,C}(B, C, H) = t_{B,C,H_k} - t_{B,C,H_e}$	$Z_{A,B,C}(B, C, H) = t_{B,C,H_{k+x'}} - t_{B,C,H_{e+y'}}$

The difference between ideal and non-ideal systems consists in the limiting boiling temperature of the azeotropes: t_{B,H_k}, t_{B,H_e}, t_{B,C,H_k} and t_{B,C,H_e} for ideal systems as compared with those non-ideal systems. In the latter the respective lower and upper limits are shifted by x, y, x' and y' members of series (H): x, y, x' and y' being positive or negative whole numbers.

In the considerations which follow, we will use a typical example which was examined in detail in 1951 by ZIĘBORAK [193] and his collaborator LEBECKA [68]. As mentioned above (§ 61) this example is associated with the strange history of the ethanol dehydration process by a benzene-gasoline mixture claimed by GUINOT [51] in 1923 in his patent. For a long time (1923–1951) no one knew that the dehydration of ethanol occurred by way of the formation of quaternary heteroazeotropes $(B, E, W, H_i - \cdot -)$ which differ slightly from the scheme of an ideal quaternary azeotrope presented in Table XVI. 1. One must not forget, however, that in defining the azeotropic ranges of positive quaternary systems, homoazeotropes (A, B, C, H_i) and not heteroazeotropes have been considered. However, sometimes in the scheme presented in Table XVI. 1 there are gradual transitions from hetero- to homoazeotropes. Further investigations may reveal whether such a treatment is correct, or whether basic changes are required in analysing series (A, H_i), (A, B, H_i) and (A, B, C, H_i) of azeotropes because some of them are homo- and others heteroazeotropes. Such a case is observed in azeotropes formed by benzene (B), ethanol (E), water (W) and the series (H) forming a close-boiling gasoline fraction. The binary azeotropes (B, E), (B, H_i) and (E, H_i), as well as the ternary one (B, E, H_i), contain only one liquid phase whereas $(B, W- \cdot -)$, $(B, E, W- \cdot -)$, $(B, W, H - \cdot -)$ and $(B, E, W, H- \cdot -)$ are typical heteroazeotropes containing from six to eight weight per cent of water. The azeotropes of the series (B, H_i), $(B, E, W- \cdot -)$ and $(B, E, W, H_i- \cdot -)$ will be discussed below together, as one polyazeotropic system.

Returning to the scheme shown in Table XVI. 1, benzene should be regarded as the *main component* of the whole system. Its azeotropic range is characterized by lowest value in relation to those of E and W. The inequality:

$$Z_B(H) < Z_E(H) < Z_W(H)$$

shows that in the series of ternary and quaternary azeotropes, with the boiling temperature increase of representative H_i, the latter is replaced almost quantitatively by B. On the contrary, the E and W concentrations undergo relatively small changes (§113) (Fig. XVI. 12).

§ 108. Dehydration Gasoline Characteristic.

Let us recall that in GUINOT's patent claim [51] a very narrow temperature range 101–102°C gasoline fraction was recommended for ethanol dehydration. GUINOT did not take into consideration that no saturated hydrocarbons—either paraffins or naphthenes—boiling within the range 101–102°C were known. We do not know exactly why the limits mentioned above were selected by GUINOT. Apparently, the patent claims were based on direct experiments without any scientific background. It is rather odd that a large number of ethanol dehydration plants were built and apparently no theoretical explanation required by those who spent money for running the process which was not confirmed by any basic research, explaining in detail the physico-chemical processes taking place in the distillation column. Perhaps this peculiar attitude towards GUINOT's patent licence was associated with the idea that his discovery did not change in principle the dehydration process claimed by YOUNG about twenty years earlier. To the chemical engineers one thing was clear: the addition of gasoline improved considerably the separation of the two liquid phases collected, one of which contained a large amount of water, and the other organic compounds, independently of whether there was a mixture of benzene with gasoline or benzene alone.

In ZIĘBORAK'S work the character of the gasoline fraction used for dehydration played a very important role. He started his investigations several years after two interesting papers were published by ANDERSON [36]. The latter proved that most typical nitration benzene contaminants boiled from 15 to 19°C higher than benzene itself but in spite of this temperature difference they could not be removed from benzene by fractional distillation. The present author took some part in ANDERSON'S investigations and discussed with him this phenomenon on the basis of his own diagram showing the formation of series of binary azeotropes (A, H_i) where A was an azeotropic agent and H_i one of the representatives of a series (H) of hydrocarbons forming azeotropes including the two tangent ones (A, H_k) and (A, H_e) [34].

This short historical survey of the development of the ideas associated with the consequences of the formation of tangent azeotropes and almost tangent zeotropes has been given with the intention of explaining why Zięborak started with the fractional distillation of a mixture of benzene and a narrow gasoline fraction prepared in a Polish petroleum refinery for replacing the gasoline fraction imported before World War II from Distillerie de Deux Sèvres, France.

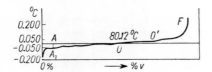

FIG. XVI. 1. Distillation curve of a mixture of benzene (B) with a narrow gasoline fraction (H): from the start to point O almost tangent azeotropes (B, H), and from O to O' almost tangent zeotropes are collected in the receiver. From point O' to F zeotropes are distilled off.

We were aware that the gasoline prepared by our petroleum refinery contained somewhat greater quantities of higher boiling hydrocarbons than that of French origin.

In Figures XVI. 1 and 2 the distillation curve of the benzene-gasoline mixture and the gasoline alone are presented.

The benzene-gasoline mixture contained 1370 g of benzene and 80 g (108 ml) of gasoline. Five hundred millilitres were collected within the temperature range from −0.050 to +0.50° expressed on an arbitrary Beckmann thermometer scale.

The next mixture submitted to fractional distillation contained 70.4% of benzene and 29.6% of gasoline.

For a proper interpretation of the phenomena which took place in the course of these three distillations the following facts should be remembered. First, the gasoline fraction contained about 60 per cent of paraffinic and naphthenic hydrocarbons boiling within the range 93–99°C. All of these were able to form almost tangent and tangent azeotropes (B, H_i) in complete agreement with ANDERSON'S observations [36]. For the formation of tangent and almost tangent azeotropes a large amount of benzene is required. This is the reason why, in Figure XVI.2,

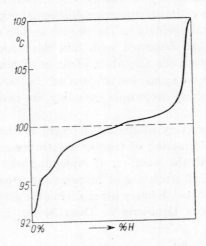

FIG. XVI. 2. Distillation curve of gasoline fraction. The starting point was 93° C and the highest boiling fraction was collected at 109° C.

a large section of the distillation curve has transformed into an irregular curve At the end the gasoline distillation curve transformed into a vertical curve and a steady temperature increase within the range 95 to 109° C has been observed.

The ZIĘBORAK experiment shown graphically in Figure XVI. 3 was performed with a large amount of a mixture containing 70.4% of benzene and 29.6% of gas-

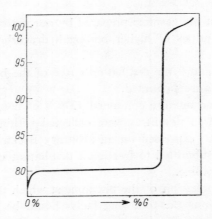

FIG. XVI. 3. Distillation curve of a mixture containing 70.4 weight per cent of benzene and 29.6 weight per cent of gasoline fraction.

oline. A relatively small amount of the condensate was collected before a temperature of 79°C was reached. The condensation temperature of the main fraction changes only from 79.9 to 80.1°C which is practically equal to that of technically pure benzene. We may also say that the ceiling line of the azeotropic agent (in this case benzene) was reached. As mentioned above, it is easy to explain the rapid temperature increase at the end of the distillation. Obviously, there was a lack of benzene. It should be remembered that tangent and almost tangent azeotropes often contain more than 99 per cent of the azeotropic agent. The latter boils at a temperature 13–19°C lower than the "contaminating impurities" [193].

Returning to the distillation curve of the narrow gasoline fraction shown in Figure XVI. 2. At the end of this distillation a sharp increase of the refractive index from 1.44 to 1.47 was noticed. This increase was produced by toluene (T) which distilled off with higher boiling saturated hydrocarbons forming binary azeotropes of the type (T, H_i).

There was no doubt that benzene, mixed with the gasoline fraction boiling between 93 and 99°C, boils at the beginning of the distillation at a temperature somewhat lower than that of pure benzene and at the end at its normal boiling temperature (80.1°C).

These observations exerted a predominant influence on the experiments carried out later by ZIĘBORAK. In fact, it has been concluded that the most suitable gasoline fraction for ethanol dehydration contains hydrocarbons boiling from 93 to 99°C. This fraction forms with benzene a bunch of boiling temperature isobars of the almost tangent or tangent azeotropes. It seems reasonable to expect that not only binary (B, H_i) but also ternary azeotropes of the type (B, E, H_i) will show similar phenomena.

§ 109. Series of Homoazeotropes (B, H_i) and (B, E, H_i). As mentioned in § 108 ZIĘBORAK undertook further examination by fractional distillation of mixtures containing: I—benzene and dehydrated ethanol; II—benzene, dehydrated ethanol and a 93–99°C gasoline fraction; III—dehydrated ethanol and 93–109°C gasoline fraction. In Figure XVI.4 the respective distillation curves are presented.

Curve I was obtained by distillation of the benzene-ethanol mixtures; a small amount distilled off below 68.02°C as fore-run. This is the boiling temperature of the azeotrope (B, E). Probably, small amounts of benzene impurities and water contained in the ethanol were responsible for the lower boiling fraction. Afterwards, starting with the point 0, pure binary azeotrope (B, E) formed the main fraction. A sharp temperature increase at the end of the distillation was due to the complete exhaustion of benzene. Curve II shows that each of the representatives of the saturated hydrocarbon series found in gasoline formed a binary azeotrope (B, H_i) which underwent distillation at its own boiling temperature. For this reason no horizontal section is found on curve III.

Curve *II* is the most interesting and should be examined in detail. It is composed of three sections. The first lies below the benzene-ethanol ceiling line 68.02° C; the next part, *OD*, indicates that a relatively large amount of the ternary zeotropes $(B, E, H_i)_z$ were formed, accompanied by a slight temperature increase, and influenced by higher boiling hydrocarbons still present in the 93–99° C fraction. The

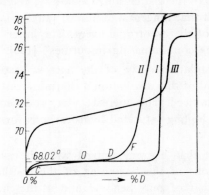

FIG. XVI. 4. Distillation curves of the mixtures: *I*—dehydrated ethanol and benzene; *II*—dehydrated ethanol, benzene and 93–99° C gasoline fraction; *III*—dehydrated ethanol and 93–109° C gasoline fraction.

third section, *DF*, appeared due to the exhaustion of the 93–99° C fraction of hydrocarbons found in the gasoline. In fact, as the distillation curve of the 93–109° C gasoline fraction indicates, the latter contained at least 40 to 45 per cent of hydrocarbons boiling above 99° C, including a relatively large amount of toluene. The latter must be considered as an undesirable constituent of any gasoline fraction for mixing with benzene, for the dehydration of ethanol containing about five per cent of water.

The conclusions based on the results obtained and presented in Figure XVI. 4 were important for the next step, namely, for carrying out experiments in which the fourth component, water, was added. It seemed to be most probable that after adding water to the mixture of benzene, ethanol and gasoline, the lower boiling hydrocarbons found in the latter would form quaternary heteroazeotropes $(B, E, W, H_i— \cdot —)$. To test this ZIĘBORAK compared four distillations, using in one the "inadequate" 93–109° C gasoline fraction and in the others three benzene-gasoline mixtures which had been previously recycled many times in three Polish ethanol dehydration plants.

§ 110. Positive Quaternary Heteroazeotropes. The existence of quaternary azeotropes was discussed independently by LECAT [14, 15] and the author of this book [26, 168]. The latter described a method based on ebulliometric measurements which could prove that four selected compounds do form a quaternary azeotrope. At the time when ZIĘBORAK started his experiments no one could have suspected that a polyazeotropic system in which a series of quaternary heteroazeotropes $(B, E, W, H_i - \cdot -)$ were formed had been applied in the course of ethanol dehydration. Nobody knew that GUINOT'S process was based on the formation of these azeotropes. Consequently, ZIĘBORAK had to find an undeniable proof that quaternary azeotropes are responsible for the efficient working of the ethanol dehydration process.

In Figure XVI. 5 the results of three distillations of the following mixtures are presented: *I*—benzene, ethanol and water; *II*—benzene and 93–109°C gasoline; *III*—ethanol, water and the same gasoline.

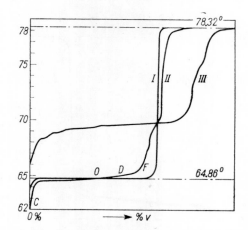

FIG. XVI. 5. Distillation curves of mixtures containing: *I*—benzene, ethanol and water; *II*—benzene and 93–109°C gasoline; *III*—ethanol, water and 93–109°C gasoline.

Curve I shows a typical distillation of the mixture identical with that used by YOUNG in his first experiments dealing with azeotropic dehydration of ethanol. As regards mixture II, it requires additional comment. On the basis of the experiments made thus far by ZIĘBORAK (distillation curve shown in Fig. XVI. 3) it was clear enough that 93–109°C gasoline contained a large amount of higher boiling hydrocarbons, including toluene, which did not play any part in the ethanol dehydration process.

These higher boiling constituents had to be removed in one way or another. It was obvious that the repeated recycling of the benzene-gasoline mixture in the dehydration plant would favour the spontaneous removal of all components of the gasoline fraction playing no positive part in the dehydration process. It seemed to be obvious that all higher boiling hydrocarbons, including toluene, would be removed, in the course of fractional distillation on the industrial scale, as bottom products and thus, in the fractions collected after each recycling, the concentrations of the higher boiling constituents will decrease with increase of the number of recycles of the benzene-gasoline dehydrating agent.

This phenomenon may be called *self-improvement* of the polycomponent azeotropic agent. This was the reason why ZIĘBORAK used three benzene-gasoline mixtures taken from three ethanol dehydration plants: to obtain a direct proof of the assumption mentioned above by direct experiment. Consequently, the following investigations were carried out. Each of the three "self-improved" benzene-93–99°C gasoline fractions was separately mixed with an adequate amount of ethanol containing five per cent of water. Each of them was fractionally distilled, and three distillation curves *I*, *II* and *III* obtained. They are shown in Figure XVI. 6.

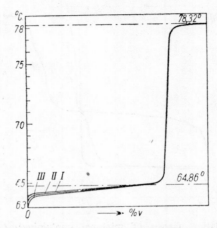

FIG. XVI. 6. Distillation curves of mixtures obtained by adding to ethanol and water, benzene-gasoline fractions *I*, *II* and *III* taken from three ethanol dehydration plants where these fractions had been recycled many times.

The small differences in the lower portions of curves *I*, *II* and *III* appeared to be due to different ratios of the amounts of benzene and gasoline used in each of the three ethanol dehydration plants. Dehydration of ethanol takes place within the temperature range 63 to 64.96°C. The latter temperature should be regarded as the ceiling line for the series of quaternary heteroazeotropes (B, E, W, $H_i - \cdot -$). The temperature 78.32°C is the boiling point of dehydrated ethanol.

§ **111. Polycomponent Azeotropic Agent.** In the previous paragraphs (§§ 109, 110) it has been pointed out that GUINOT [51] was the first inventor who recommended, without knowing what phenomena occurred during ethanol dehydration, the use of a polycomponent azeotropic agent. After a proper explanation had been given by ZIĘBORAK, the question arose as to what kind of narrow boiling gasoline fraction would give optimum results in the ethanol dehydration process. It should be remembered that, owing to the recycling of the benzene-gasoline mixture, a spontaneous self-improvement of gasoline took place and the hydrocarbons boiling above 99°C were collected with the dehydrated ethanol as the bottom product. If the benzene-gasoline mixture contained too much of the higher boiling hydrocarbons, then in the course of the self-improving process of the azeotropic agent the dehydrated ethanol would be contaminated with undesirable impurities, the removal of which would be an expensive procedure. Consequently, the gasoline fraction must contain as small a quantity as possible of hydrocarbons boiling above 99°C (not 101–102°C, as claimed by GUINOT). It would be advantageous to know what limit should be set on the lower boiling hydrocarbons present in the gasoline fraction so as not to increase the cost of the ethanol dehydration process. ZIĘBORAK'S experiments have proved that the gasoline boiling within the range 93–99°C gives quite satisfactory results, but do not show, however, whether saturated hydrocarbons boiling below 93°C might not have been used with success.

On the basis of the observations thus far made in ethanol dehydration plants, the conclusion may be accepted that the use of saturated hydrocarbons boiling below the limits 90 to 93°C should be avoided. This does not mean, however, that the lower boiling hydrocarbons exert an undesirable influence on the dehydration process. The real reason is that the lower the boiling points of the hydrocarbons, the lower is the percentage of water found in the two-liquid phase distillate. Consequently, a small increase in the dehydration costs will be noticeable, if hydrocarbons boiling much below 93°C are left in the ethanol dehydration gasoline.

§ 112. Azeotropic Range of Benzene-Gasoline-Ethanol-Water Mixtures.

The ethanol dehydration process is one of the most interesting and unique as an example of a polyazeotropic system containing three individual chemical compounds: benzene, ethanol and water, mixed with the 93–99°C gasoline fraction. For this reason it is important to answer the question whether or not the equation:

$$Z_{B,E,W}(E, W, H) = t_{E,W,H_k} - t_{E,W,H_e} \tag{1}$$

may be used for the determination of the azeotropic range of the ternary azeotrope (B, E, W) in relation to the series of azeotropes (E, W, H_i). In connection with this question we refer to Table XVI. 1 (§ 107) in which both ideal and non-ideal polyazeotropic systems were examined in general terms, including the equations expressing the azeotropic range values of ideal and non-ideal binary and ternary polyazeotropic systems.

In addition, referring to Figures XVI. 4, 5 and 6, obtained by ZIĘBORAK, it becomes evident that in using benzene and the 93–99°C gasoline fraction as a *complex polyazeotropic agent* we are still operating within a relatively small upper section of the azeotropic range expressed by equation (1). ZIĘBORAK'S main observations were graphically represented in Figure XVI. 6. In addition, his thorough examination of three individual quaternary azeotropes described in §§ 61–63 and shown in Figure IX. 4 gives more information on this polyazeotropic system. In fact, the latter diagram shows that the azeotropic range $Z_{B,E,W}(E, W, H)$ is to a large extent asymmetrical.

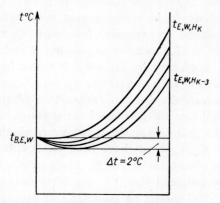

FIG. XVI. 7. Approximate portion of the azeotropic range within which quaternary heteroazeotropes $(B, E, W, H_i \ -\cdot-)$ are formed in the course of ethanol dehydration with a benzene 93–99° C gasoline mixture.

The distillation curves shown in Figure XVI. 6 prove that the azeotropic depressions observed by ZIĘBORAK, when he used the mixture of benzene with the previously "self-improved" 93–99° C gasoline fraction, did not exceed two degrees. Consequently, there is no doubt that the diagram shown in Figure XVI, 7, is at least approximately correct.

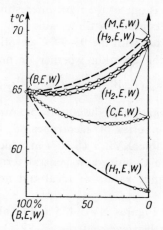

FIG. XVI. 8. Scheme showing the distinctly pronounced lower asymmetry of the azeotropic range of a series of ternary homoazeotropes (B, E, W). The line joining the point B, E, W with H_1, E, W shows the approximate lower limit of the azeotropic range $Z_{B,E,W}(B, H, W)$.

The results obtained have led to the examination of the azeotropic range of the positive ternary heteroazeotropes $Z_{B,E,W}(E, W, H{-}\cdot{-})$ which is graphically presented in Figure XVI. 8.

It was found that the upper part of the azeotropic range mentioned above is approximately equal to 4°C, whilst the lower is about 7.9°C. This conclusion is based on the experiments carried out recently by GALSKA [169]. She confirm edthat normal hexane H_1 boils at a temperature so low that it is not able to form a tangent quaternary heteroazeotrope with benzene, ethanol and water. If we assume that 7.9°C is the lower portion of the azeotropic range $Z_{B,E,W}(E, W, H)$, it follows that its most probable total range value is 11.9°C.

Consequently, the hydrocarbons found in the 93–99°C gasoline fraction form quaternary heteroazeotropes $(B, E, W, H_i{-}\cdot{-})$ boiling within a two degree range below the azeotropic ceiling line $t_{B,E,W} = 64.85°C$. The latter value is also the boiling temperature of the quaternary tangent azeotrope $(B, E, W, H_k{-}\cdot{-})$ because C_{H_k}, the concentration of H_k in this tangent azeotrope, is practically zero. This means that the boiling point of H_k must be 99°C. If we take into consideration that benzene and the H_k hydrocarbon also form a binary tangent or almost tangent boiling temperature isobar, as shown in Figure XVI. 1, we may conclude that the upper region of the respective quaternary heteroazeotrope behaves as an ideal polyazeotropič system (XVI. § 107).

We have mentioned above that a mixture of benzene and the 93–99°C gasoline fraction works well as a polyazeotropic ethanol dehydrating agent. Direct experiments confirm the supposition that the selection of the gasoline fraction is reduced to the choice of its higher boiling limit only. The upper point should be regarded as definitely fixed at 99°C by ZIĘBORAK's investigation. Iso-octane and n-heptane are the last hydrocarbons able to form quaternary heteroazeotropes $(B, E, W, H_i{-}\cdot{-})$. It seems also that the lower hydrocarbon boiling temperature limit should be as close as possible to 93°C, in spite of the fact that saturated hydrocarbons boiling within the range 91–93°C may also be admitted, after an experimental proof that the particular benzene-gasoline mixture favours the formation of two well-separated liquid phases in the condensate. It has now been proved, however, that there are no economic or other factors favouring the use of hydrocarbon fractions boiling below 93°C for ethanol dehydration purposes (§ 111).

§ 113. Asymmetry of Azeotropic Ranges. The ethanol dehydration process is an exceptionally suitable example for examining the asymmetry of azeotropic ranges of the following three series of azeotropes, two of them being ternary and one a quaternary one:

$$Z_{B,E}(E, H) = t_{E,H_k} - t_{E,H_e}, \tag{1}$$

$$Z_{B,W}(W, H) = t_{W,H_{x'}} - t_{W,H_x}, \tag{2}$$

$$Z_{B,E,W}(E, W, H) = t_{E,W,H_{y'}} - t_{E,W,H_y}. \tag{3}$$

ZIĘBORAK determined all of these assuming that the lowest hydrocarbon in each case is n-hexane with normal boiling point 68.9° C. As mentioned above ZIĘ-BORAK and GALSKA [169] have recently proved (Figure XVI. 8), that n-hexane does not form a ternary azeotrope with ethanol and benzene and that the quaternary system $(B, E, W, H_1 - \cdot -)_z$, H_1 being n-hexane, is an almost tangent quaternary *heteroazeotrope*. The real tangent heteroazeotrope $(B, E, W, H_x - \cdot -)$ cannot be found because of the lack of a hydrocarbon H_x having a slightly higher boiling temperature than n-hexane (H_1).

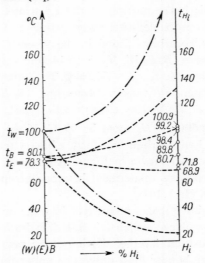

FIG. XVI. 9. Azeotropic ranges of three azeotropic agents: benzene (B), ethanol (E) and water (W) in relation to the series (H) of saturated hydrocarbons. Substances B, E and W mixed with suitable gasoline fraction form quaternary heteroazeotropes $(B, E, W, H_i - \cdot -)$.

In Figures XVI. 9, 10 and 11 the following diagrams are shown. First the azeotropic ranges of the three azeotropic agents, benzene (B) (main azeotropic agent), ethanol (E) and water (W) — secondary agents in the quaternary heteroazeotrope $(B, E, W, H_i - \cdot -)$. Owing to the very large azeotropic range of water neither the upper nor the lower limit on the diagram (Fig. XVI. 9) could be shown. In Figures XVI. 10 and 11 the azeotropic ranges of the binary positive azeotropes (see equation (1) and (2) in the same paragraph) are graphically represented.

It should be pointed out, that both series of binary $(W, H_i - \cdot -)$ as well as of ternary $(B, W, H_i - \cdot -)$ systems are typical heterozeotropes, whilst the series of binary (E, H_i) and of ternary (B, E, H_i) systems are typical homoazeotropes.

A direct comparison of the diagrams (shown in Fig. XVI. 10 and 11) leads to the conclusion that the azeotropic range $Z_{B,W}(W, H)$ is characterized by upper, and $Z_{B,E}(E, H)$ by lower asymmetry. In Table XVI. 2 the respective values are given.

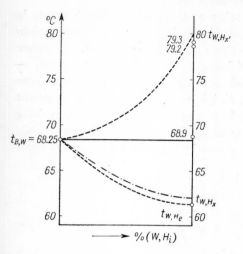

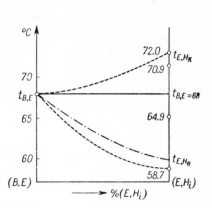

FIG. XVI. 10. Azeotropic range of binary positive heteroazeotrope $(B, W -\cdot-)$ in relation to the series of binary positive heteroazeotropes $(W, H_i -\cdot-)$. The formation of ternary positive heteroazeotropes $(B, W, H_i -\cdot-)$ takes place.

FIG. XVI. 11. Azeotropic range of binary positive homoazeotrope (B, E) in relation to the series of binary positive homoazeotropes (E, H_i). As a result, ternary positive homoazeotropes (B, E, H_i) are formed.

The comparison of the data presented in Table XVI. 2 leads to the following conclusion: benzene, being the main component of the positive binary azeotropes (B, H_i), shows the largest upper azeotropic range, namely 19.1°C (close to 60 per cent of the total azeotropic range.) In the binary azeotrope series the presence of ethanol reduces the upper portion of the azeotropic range (No. 2 in Table XVI. 2) to approximately 4.0°C. Its lower portion has the highest value, 9.3°C, or close to 70 per cent of the total azeotropic range $Z_{B,E}(E, H)$. If ethanol is replaced by water (No. 3 in the same table) the upper part of the azeotropic range is 11.7°C or 61 per cent of the total value of 19.0°C. It should be pointed out, that both binary $(B, W-\cdot-)$ and $(W, H-\cdot-)$ as well as ternary $(B, W, H_i-\cdot-)$ systems are typical heteroazeotropes. Finally, the azeotropic ranges of the ternary heteroazeotrope $(B, E, W-\cdot-)$ in relation to the series of ternary heteroazeotropes $(E, W, H_i-\cdot-)$ are characterized by a large lower asymmetry (7.4°C is approximately equal to 67 per cent of the total value 11.6°C).

Unfortunately, further experiments on the series of quaternary positive homo- and heteroazeotropes have not been completed. The variety of phenomena taking place in different quaternary systems, is too complicated for the formulation of any generalization. It takes a long time to complete the examination of a whole series of binary, ternary and quaternary azeotropes, because the combined distillation and ebulliometric methods should be applied to ensure that precise numerical data are obtained.

Most interesting, however, is the scheme (Fig. XVI. 8) obtained by ZIĘBORAK and GALSKA [169]. They determined the boiling temperature isobars formed by mixtures of a ternary heterozeotrope $(B, E, W—\cdot—)$ with two other: $(M, E, W—\cdot—)$ and $(H_1, E, W—\cdot—)$, M being methylcyclohexane and H_i — n-hexane. The first of these compounds boils too high and for this reason forms at point $(B, E, W—\cdot—)$ with azeotrope $(B, E, W—\cdot—)$ an almost tangent *zeotropic isobar*. On the other hand, cyclohexane boils too low; therefore it also forms an almost tangent boiling temperature isobar to the horizontal line drawn through point $(H_1, E, W—\cdot—)$ (Fig. XVI. 8). There are no hydrocarbons boiling just slight-

TABLE XVI. 2

Azeotropic Ranges of Binary and Ternary Homo- and Heteroazeotropes

No.	Azeotropic ceiling point °C	Lower portion °C	Upper portion °C	Total azeotropic range °C
1	t_B $= 80.1$	$80.1-68.9 = 11.2$	$99.2-80.1 = 19.1$	$99.2-68.9 = 30.3$
2	$t_{B,E}$ $= 68.0$	$68.0-58.7 = 9.3$	$72.0-68.0 = 4.0$	$72.0-58.7 = 13.3$
3	$t_{B,W}$ $= 68.3$	$68.3-61.0 = 7.3$	$80.0-68.3 = 11.7$	$80.0-61.0 = 19.0$
4	$t_{B,E,W}$ $= 64.85$	$64.9-57.5 = 7.4$	$69.1-64.9 = 4.2$	$69.1-57.5 = 11.6$

ly higher than n-hexane; for this reason it is not to be expected that the real lower limit of the azeotropic range will be found. As to the upper limit iso-octane and n-heptane form almost tangent heteroazeotropes $(B, E, W, H_3—\cdot—)$ and $(B, E, W, H_2—\cdot—)$, H_3 and H_2 being iso-octane and n-heptane respectively. The diagram shown in Figure XVI. 8 indicates without any doubt that all saturated hydrocarbons, i.e. paraffins and naphthenes, boiling within the range 70 to 99°C, form quaternary heteroazeotropes of the type $(B, E, W, H_i—\cdot—)$.

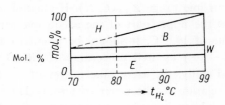

FIG. XVI. 12. Concentration changes of benzene (B), a representative of the series (H) of saturated hydrocarbons, ethanol (E) and water (W) as function of the boiling temperature of homologues.

In the publication [169] the projections on the triangular plane HWE of the heteroazeotropic lines two of them are given. A composition diagram for the whole series of quaternary heteroazeotropes of the type $(B, E, W, H_i—\cdot—)$ is presented in Figure XVI. 12, where the molar concentration of the components of the quaternary heteroazeotropes $(B, E, W, H_i—\cdot—)$ are plotted against the normal boiling temperatures of the respective saturated hydrocarbons. It will be seen that the water concentrations remain practically constant (22 mol. per cent). The ethanol concentrations starting from 80°C undergo small changes within the range 23.4 to 25 mol. per cent. As regards the molar concentration changes of benzene and the respective hydrocarbons it is quite evident that benzene replaces the respective hydrocarbons almost quantitatively from left to right in the diagram.

§ 114. Composition and Properties of the Self-improved Benzene-Gasoline Poly-azeotropic Agent. The discovery of the existence of a series of quaternary heteroazeotropes, two constituents of which—benzene and the 93–99°C saturated hydrocarbon gasoline fraction—have been recycled for a long time in ethanol dehydration plants, offered an exceptional opportunity to examine the self-improvement process of this polyazeotropic agent. Having this in view, ZIĘBORAK and LEBECKA [68] undertook a thorough examination of the problem. First of all, the gasoline fraction prepared by a petroleum refinery was compared with the gasoline fractions obtained after long recycling in three ethanol dehydration plants. To do so, it was necessary to remove benzene from all of the three samples of the self-improved dehydrating benzene-gasoline mixtures. The benzene was removed by distillation with acetone as entrainer. Experiments have shown that from 5 to 6 per cent of benzene still remained in the gasoline. Due to this fact, from the samples, *I*, *II* and *III* obtained after the removal of 94–95 per cent of benzene relatively large fore-runs were collected at temperatures lower than 90°C.

In Table XVI. 3 the data obtained are given. In the left hand column are given the condensation temperatures either of the original 93–109°C gasoline or of those samples which underwent self-improvement and were taken from three ethanol dehydration plants. In the next column the amount of the fractions collected expressed in weight per cent of the 93–109°C gasoline samples are listed. The data listed in the last three columns of Table XVI. 3 indicate that in spite of some differences in the distribution of the amounts collected, in particular gasoline fractions, the boiling temperature ranges are equal in all of them. As mentioned above, owing to the presence of several per cent of benzene the first fractions were collected some degrees below 93°C. The highest condensation temperatures were equal to 99°C in all the samples examined. As mentioned in previous paragraphs, isooctane and n-heptane, were the last hydrocarbons forming the highest boiling quaternary heteroazeotropes $(B, E, W, H_i - \cdot -)$.

§ 115. Boiling Temperature Isobars of Benzene-Iso-Octane and Benzene–n-Heptane Mixtures. For the better understanding of the phenomena taking place in a not too complicated polyazeotropic mixture the examination of the shape of the two boiling temperature isobars formed by benzene on the one hand and iso-octane or n-heptane on the other, has played an important role. The two isobars were examined by ZIĘBORAK [193], and are shown in Figure XVI. 13.

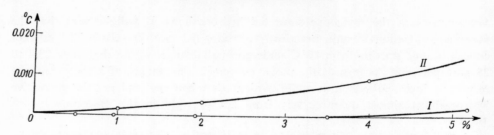

FIG. XVI. 13. Boiling temperature isobars obtained by dosing (*I*) benzene with 2,2,4-trimethylpentane and (*II*) benzene with n-heptane.

The boiling temperature isobar *I* obtained by adding benzene to 2,2,4-trimethylpentane is an ideal tangent one. Up to a concentration of 3.5 per cent of isooctane no temperature increases were noticed. On the other hand, isobar *II* shows that small increases of n-heptane content cause small temperature increases. The method of ebulliometric comparative measurements made it possible to examine

TABLE XVI. 3

Distillation of 93–109° C Original and Three Samples of Self-improved 93–99° C Gasoline Fractions

Condensation temperature ranges in °C	Per cent of 93–109° C	Recycled 93–99° C gasoline fractions		
		Sample I	Sample II	Sample III
Original gasoline fraction				
to 90	—	22.5	13.5	13.0
91–92	1.0	3.7	13.1	17.2
92–95	4.5	14.3	33.2	27.8
95–96	7.2	10.5	12.0	17.0
96–97	4.8	12.5	8.9	7.5
97–98	7.5	14.0	10.4	7.1
98–99	12.4	11.2	6.2	6.2
99–100	15.5	—	—	—
100–101	29.0	—	—	—
101–102	6.4	—	—	—
102–103	2.1	—	—	—
103–105	2.7	—	—	—
105–110	4.4	—	—	—

in detail mixtures containing one and two per cent of the respective hydrocarbons. The temperature increases did not exceed 0.002–0.004° expressed on the BECKMANN thermometer arbitrary scale. In spite of the formation of tangent and almost tangent boiling temperature isobars of the two hydrocarbons with benzene, after adding ethanol and water, a quaternary heteroazeotrope (*B, E, W, H_i*) is formed, where H_i stands in one case for n-heptane and in the other for 2,2,4-trimethylpentane. They are characterized by small temperature depressions which amount to $0.170°C$ for iso-octane and $0.070°C$ for n-heptane. No other saturated hydrocarbons exist so that the ternary heteroazeotropes $(B, E, W—\cdot—)$ might form tangent isobars with the ternary heteroazeotropes $(E, W, H_i—\cdot—)$. In spite of this, the whole series of quaternary heteroazeotropes $(B, E, W, H_i—\cdot—)$ may be classified as an almost ideal system (§§ 106, 107). The quaternary azeotropes formed in the course of the ethanol dehydration process is rather an exceptional case. First of all, the condition of azeotropic ranges inequality:

$$Z_B(H) < Z_E(H) < Z_W(H) \tag{1}$$

is fulfilled. In addition, the boiling temperatures of benzene and ethanol do not differ too much. The boiling temperature of water is also not so high as to exert an undesirable influence on the almost ideal system of the respective series of ternary and quaternary heteroazeotropes. In other series, the condition expressed by the inequalily (1) of azeotropic ranges, is very often not observed.

Observations regarding other ternary and quaternary systems made in the course of investigations conducted by our group, which are not yet completed, show a very large variety of phenomena. Most frequently non-ideal ternary and quaternary azeotropes are encountered.

Less information is available with regard to non-aqueous quaternary systems. The latter are formed mostly in the course of fractional distillation of organic raw materials. Thus far, they have not been examined in detail. Some difficulties are encountered in finding a series of ternary and quaternary heteroazeotropes containing two or three individual azeotropic agents, e.g. A, B and C and a representative of series (H) as third or fourth component. Extensive investigations should be conducted in this practically undeveloped branch of knowledge. The symmetry or asymmetry of the azeotropic ranges of binary (A, H_i), ternary (A, B, H_i) and quaternary (A, B, C, H_i) systems should also be examined in detail.

MALESIŃSKI'S theoretical considerations [158] may suggest new ways of choosing the azeotropic agents and the homologous series for the systematic collection of experimental material.

§ 116. Series of Ternary Azeotropes.

The knowledge of polyazeotropic systems has been considerably advanced by ORSZAGH'S investigations [35] carried out in the early stages of the polyazeotropy development. They were started as early as 1951 and were completed several years later.

ORSZAGH developed a method of examining ternary azeotropes in which two gasoline fractions boiling within the temperature ranges (H_1) 55.1–89.7°C and (H_2) 89.7–96.7°C were used. In addition, benzene was used as a constant constituent and representatives of the alcohol series (Al_j) as components which were replaced by one another. In this way, series (B, Al_j, H) of ternary azeotropes have been examined. Methyl-, propyl-, isopropyl-, and isobutyl-alcohols constituted the alcohol series.

ZIĘBORAK'S and ORSZAGH'S investigations have been utilized by the author of this book in writing the "Classification System of Azeotropes and Zeotropes" (1951) as well as a second paper entitled "Positive Polyazeotropic Systems" [76] (1953).

In ORSZAGH'S investigations the azeotropic ranges of alcohols underwent changes with the substitution of one representative of the series (*Al*) for another. In the equation:

$$Z_{A.}(H) = t_{H_{k+x}} - t_{H_{e+y}},$$ (1)

x and *y* are negative or positive whole numbers. It has to be remembered that benzene (*B*) still remains the main azeotropic agent characterized by the azeotropic range:

$$Z_B(H) = t_{H_k} - t_{H_e}.$$

In addition, we should take into consideration the azeotropic range value of binary azeotropes (*B*, *Al*):

$$Z_{B,Al}(Al, H) = t_{Al,H_{k+m}} - t_{Al,H_{e+n}}.$$ (2)

In equation (2), *m* and *n* are positive or negative whole numbers.
It was known that benzene does not form any azeotrope with n-butyl alcohol, but nevertheless, ORSZAGH proved the existence of a series of positive ternary azeotropes expressed by the general symbol (*B*, *Al_j*, *H_i*), where *Al_j* stands for one

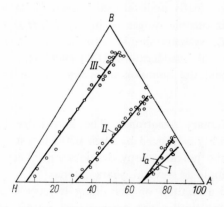

FIG. XVI. 14. Composition changes of ternary positive azeotrope series (*B*, *Al_j*, *H_i*), *B* being benzene, *Al_j* one of the following: methyl, n-propyl, iso-propyl or iso-butyl alcohol, and *H_i* one of a mixture of close boiling representatives of the series of saturated hydrocarbons.

of the alcohols of concentration varying in dependence on the boiling temperature of the saturated hydrocarbons found in the gasoline fractions H_1 and H_2.

In Figure XVI. 14 the results obtained by ORSZAGH are presented.

In the diagram four theoretically anticipated straight lines are shown for four series (B, Al_j, H_i) of positive ternary azeotropes. As mentioned above, Al_j stands for methyl- propyl- isopropyl- or isobutyl-alcohol.

Chapter XVII

CHARACTERISTIC PROPERTIES OF POLYAZEOTROPIC MIXTURES

§ 117. Azeotropic Ranges of Main and Secondary Constituents. Our knowledge of polyazeotropic mixtures and systems is too restricted to be able to give a satisfactory answer to many questions arising in the course of physico-chemical investigations on a very large number of complex organic liquids. The first step which should be taken consists in examining a series of individual azeotropes formed by one, two or three compounds with a series of homologues and their isomers. The next step consists in using a mixture of homologues and in examining the azeotropes formed during the distillation of such a mixture. The azeotropic ethanol dehydration agent containing a mixture of benzene and gasoline was an exceptionally appropriate object for these studies [193]. The change of one secondary azeotropic agent in the positive ternary azeotropes (B, Al_j, H_i) offered additional experimental material for a better understanding of the polyazeotropic systems characterized by the presence of only one homologous series [49].

In all these investigations the azeotropic range values both of the main and the secondary azeotropic agents played an important part. The azeotropic range values have been exploited in full by MALESIŃSKI [165] in his theoretical studies on azeotropy and their significance has been proved. For these reasons, the importance of the examination of series of azeotropes, instead of just one, became more evident than ever before. At present, the lack of our knowledge on azeotropic ranges is one of the obstacles to a proper understanding of azeotrope formation in complex polyazeotropic mixtures. Fortunately, MALESIŃSKI's theoretical method of calculating the approximate values of azeotropic ranges does not call for finding out by experiment which homologue or isomer forms a tangent or almost tangent azeotrope with a certain constituent of another series of homologues. Wherever possible, however, experiments should be carried out to establish the lower limit of azeotrope formation of the constituent under examination with the member of a homologous series (H).

§ 118. Secondary Phenomena in Polyazeotropic Mixtures. Experiments carried out thus far have proved that the presence of lower boiling constituents belonging to series (H) and found in a polyazeotropic mixture may change to a large extent the formation of higher boiling azeotropes with a representative of another series of homologues (H'). This is caused by the fact that one of the higher boiling components forms lower boiling azeotropes with the more volatile constituents of series (*H*). Taking into account our actual knowledge on polyazeotropy we assume, that if these phenomena occur they may lead to the removal of one of the components which might be able to form a bipositive-negative (saddle) azeotrope of the type $[(-)F, P(+)H_i]$. The probability exists that in the case of a similar type of quaternary azeotrope one component, most likely the weak bases (*P*) or weak acids (*A* or *F*), are entrained by one or several lower boiling constituents of the polyazeotropic mixture. If this happens the saddle azeotropes disappear entirely or at least partly from the fractions collected in the receiver. Similar phenomena have been observed when a saddle ternary azeotrope contained a small amount of a neutral compound and the fractional distillation was carried out in the presence of a large excess of another component. In this case, a binary lower boiling positive azeotrope was collected in the receiver. The composition of the mixture undergoes such changes that the top-ridge line of the saddle azeotrope transforms into the curve expressing the compositions of the successive fractions of the distillate.

The phenomena mentioned above should be taken into consideration in all cases when the polyazeotropic mixture contains some amount of weak acids and weak bases which are expected to form negative binary and bipositive-negative ternary azeotropes.

§ 119. Heterogeneous Polyazeotropic Mixtures. In many cases the presence of water is responsible for the formation of two phases, one of which represents a typical polyazeotropic mixture. Consequently, the transformation of binary and ternary homoazeotropes into ternary and quaternary heteroazeotropes is often observed. For instance, the water content in low and high temperature coal tars is responsible for the formation of two-liquid phase distillates. As the water concentration reaches zero, the fractions collected become homogeneous at a specifically higher temperature for each polyazeotropic mixture.

Recently, our group has found high boiling azeotropic agents which produce the appearance of heteroazeotropes over a large temperature range. 2-picoline hydrochloride is one of these "heteroazeotropic" agents.

It was known more than fifteen years ago that most pyridine base hydrochlorides undergo distillation. In the receiver a small excess (1–2%) of hydrochloric acid is collected. The excess of the free pyridine base is usually found in the forerun. The hydrochlorides form two-phase condensates with most of the carbolic and naphthalene oil constituents. The normal boiling temperatures of pyridine base hydrochlorides vary only within a relatively narrow temperature range (from 210 to 238°C or slightly higher). For this reason, the relatively low melting 2-picoline hydrochloride should be regarded as a most suitable "heteroazeotropic" agent. If it is submitted to fractional distillation with carbolic or naphthalene oil all the fractions containing neutral components form second liquid phase. This means that mainly heteroazeotropes are formed. Some coloured substances are also found in the receiver. It should be pointed out that the molar concentrations of pyridine base and of hydrogen chloride are not equal. As mentioned above, a small amount of the free pyridine base is removed in the fore-runs because of the partial dissociation of the pyridine base hydrochloride.

Examination of the phenomena mentioned above is now under way. No final conclusions can be drawn yet. In principle the examination of heteroazeotropes formed by coal tar oils with pyridine hydrochlorides is complicated by the increase of the number of components in the respective azeotropes. This may lead to some unpredictable generalizations. Secondary phenomena taking place owing to the chemical reaction of some coal tar constituents with hydrogen chloride at relatively high temperature require further investigation. Recently SOSNKOWSKA found that 2-picoline hydrochloride formed negative homoazeotropes with phenol and its derivatives.

Chapter XVIII

METHODS OF AZEOTROPIC RANGE DETERMINATION

§ 120. Ebulliometric Method. If pure substances are available throughout the whole limit of the azeotropic range, the most precise determination of the whole series of the boiling temperature isobars results from the use of the ebulliometric method [31]. If the azeotropic agent A or the representatives of the homologous series (H) are hygroscopic, a three stage ebulliometer is the most suitable device. In § 41, the determinations of azeotropic ranges made by KURTYKA [90] and by ZIĘBORAK and GALSKA are presented. In some cases only the lower tangent boiling temperature isobars can been examined by the ebulliometric method [1, 56].

In certain experiments it is more important to determine the lower limit of the azeotropic range. For instance, naphthalene forms a binary almost tangent azeotrope with m-cresol and an almost tangent zeotrope with m- and p-cresols [91]. The mixture of these cresols found in high temperature coal tar has a composition such that it forms a tangent boiling temperature isobar with naphthalene [91] and only small changes have been found at lower pressures, ranging form 300 to 700 mm Hg. [175]. In this way, the upper limit of the azeotropic range of cresols in relation to naphthalene has been determined [89]. LISICKI [170] succeeded in finding a naphthalene oil fraction composed of neutral constituents, boiling at 210.5°C, which formed an almost tangent isobar with naphthalene. The azeotropic depression did not exceed 0.01°C. In connection with these investigations, it should be emphasized that according to LISICKI's observations there are neutral compounds in carbolic and naphthalene oils which form azeotropes with naphthalene with a small azeotropic depression as well as some lower boiling fractions forming *almost tangent zeotropic* boiling temperature isobars.

Thus far, no extensive investigations have been carried out on other polyazeotropic mixtures.

§ 121. Distillation Method. The azeotropic range determinations carried out by distilling a mixture containing the azeotropic agent and a series of homologues their isomers and closely related substances belonging to another, homologous series are less precise. This method is often employed for collecting experimental data in the course of examination of polyazeotropic mixtures. It may be used also if three successive distillations are carried out, the first with one azeotropic agent (A), the second with two agents $(A+B)$ and the third with three agents $(A+B+C)$.

The main problem to be solved before starting any azeotropic range determination consists in choosing or preparing a mixture containing a large number of homologues and their isomers belonging to one series of compounds. Usually, petroleum fractions are used because we are mostly interested in obtaining the azeotropic range values for different hydrocarbons, or their binary or ternary azeotropes, in relation to the series of saturated hydrocarbons. If azeotropic ranges are to be determined in relation to other homologues, the liquid should be prepared by mixing these homologues. Such experiments might be avoided, by using the easier ebulliometric method described in the previous paragraph (§ 23).

In some particular cases mixtures containing homologous series other than hydrocarbons may be used because they are obtained or employed in carrying out some process on an industrial scale. These mixtures are used directly without any change in their composition. The benzene-gasoline dehydration mixture may be regarded as a typical example.

If, however, a hydrocarbon mixture like gasoline or a higher petroleum fraction is used for azeotropic range determinations, it should be submitted to fractional distillation and the distillation curves thus obtained should be carefully examined. If the curve has a similar shape to that shown in Figure XVIII. 1, the mixture may be used for azeotropic range determination, because of a relatively uniform distribution of paraffinic and naphthenic hydrocarbons in it.

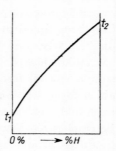

FIG. XVIII. 1. Gasoline distillation curve suitable for azeotropic range determination.

We used the following equation for determining the azeotropic range:

$$Z_A(H) = t_{H_k} - t_{H_e}.$$ (1)

If it happens that $t_{H_e} < t_1$ and $t_{H_k} < t_2$, neither the lower nor the upper limits of the azeotropic range can be determined. Such a case is shown in Figure XVIII. 2. We should point out that as a rule the condensation temperatures are plotted not against the amount of the whole condensate but against the amount of gasoline alone found in the receiver. Small samples should be collected and analysed, and the concentration of agent A subtracted.

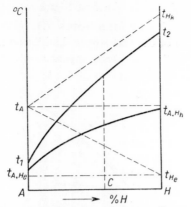

FIG. XVIII. 2. Distillation curves: t_1, t_2 of gasoline and t_{A,H_e}, t_{A,H_h} for which the lower t_{A,H_e} and the upper t_{A,H_k} limits of the azeotropic range $Z_A(H)$ lie below t_1 and above t_2.

In the case presented in Figure XVIII. 2, the gasoline fraction should be replaced by another having a larger condensation temperature range. Consider the case where the lower limit of the gasoline condensation temperature lies below the point t_{A,H_e}, whilst the upper limit of the gasoline boiling temperature t_2 is still too low.

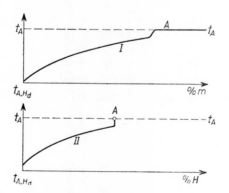

FIG. XVIII. 3. Curve *I* represents the condensation temperature plotted against weight per cent of the total distillate ($^0/_0$ *m*). Curve *II* is obtained by plotting the condensation temperatures against the weight percentage of collected gasoline ($^0/_0$ *H*). After gasoline exhaustion curve *I* transforms into straight line *A*, because the distillation continues and the further increase of the $^0/_0$ *m* value is due to the condensation of pure agent *A*. In curve *II*, after point *A* is reached no more gasoline is collected and the further condensation of agent *A* is represented by the point t_A.

Let us suppose now that the gasoline fraction starts to boil at $t_1 < t_{H_e}$ and that at $t_2 > t_{H_k}$ the distillation comes to an end. In these circumstances two different curves may be observed and these are shown separately in Figures XVIII. 4 and 5. It is easy to see that the section $t_{H_e}O$ shown in the first figure represents temperature changes observed when exclusively binary azeotropes (A, H_i) undergo distillation. At point O the ceiling line $t_A t_A$ of the azeotropic distillation is reached. The distillation curve becomes tangential to this line, and tangent or almost tangent azeotropes with

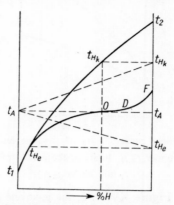

FIG. XVIII. 4. Distillation of pure gasoline curve $t_1 t_2$, and that obtained after mixing it with azeotropic agent A, boiling at t_A. Section $t_{H_e}O$ represents the distillation of the series of azeotropes (A, H_i). Section OD corresponds to the distillation of almost tangent binary zeotropes $(A, H_i)_z$. At the end of the distillation, sharp condensation temperature increases are noticed, indicating that normal zeotropic distillation takes place. The condensation temperatures are plotted against $\%$ H of gasoline.

a small amount of almost tangent zeotropes $(A, H_i)_z$ are collected in the receiver. Drawing a vertical line through O we find the point t_{H_k} on the pure gasoline distillation curve $t_1 t_2$, which is the upper temperature limit of the azeotropic range expressed by equation (1).

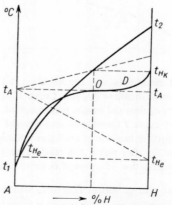

FIG. XVIII. 5. Curve $t_{H_e}OD$ intersects the gasoline distillation curve $t_1 t_2$ twice (see Fig. XVIII. 4).

In some cases the curve $t_{H_e}OD$ intersects the t_1t_2 curve twice as shown in Figure XVIII. 5. Such a phenomenon is associated with the fact that the condensation temperatures are plotted against $\% H$, expressing the percentage of gasoline alone, and not against the total amount of the condensate containing both the azeotropes (A, H_i) and the zeotropes $(A, H_i)_z$. Thus the abscissa values are shortened by the section corresponding to the total percentage of azeotropic agent A collected in the receiver.

§ **122. Critical Remarks.** Experiments have shown that the method described in the previous paragraph depends to a large extent on the effectiveness of the distillation column and on the nature of agent A or of mixtures of agents $(A+B)$ or $(A+B+C)$ for which the azeotropic ranges:

$$Z_{A,B}(B, H) = t_{B,H_{k+m}} - t_{B,H_{e+n}}, \tag{1}$$

$$Z_{A,B,C}(B, C, H) = t_{B,C,H_{k+m}} - t_{B,C,H_{e+n}} \tag{2}$$

are measured. If the two azeotropic ranges expressed by equations (1) and (2) are determined, instead of the gasoline fraction (H), the mixture of azeotropes (B, H) or (B, C, H), respectively, should be prepared and then azeotropes (A, B) and (A, B, C) should be added, and finally, the respective distillations should be carried out. On the abscissa axis $\% (B, H)$ or $\% (B, C, H)$ should be plotted against the condensation temperature measured directly.

We must also take into consideration that when using a very effective column and large reflux ratios we may often encounter some small amount of agent A (or agents $(A+B)$ or $(A+B+C)$), before the respective tangent azeotropes are formed. In such a case, the method may lead to an error usually depending on the $Z_A(H)$, $Z_{A,B}(B, H)$ or $Z_{A,B,C}(B, C, H)$ values which will be higher than the true ones. The point O shown in the two figures XVIII. 4 and XVIII. 5 will be shifted towards D. If this occurs, the upper azeotropic range limit found is larger than it really should be. The ebulliometric method leads to better results than the distillation method.

If the azeotropic range determination is carried out for large scale industrial purposes, the errors committed are not important, because the chemical engineer wants to know at what stage of the distillation a certain component or components appear in the receiver and not what exact values characterize the lower and the upper limits of the azeotropic range.

It should also be pointed out that the section of the distillation curve $t_{H_e}O$, close to the point t_{H_e} in all the diagrams starting with Figure XVIII. 2 and ending with Figure XVIII. 5, changes considerably in shape. Point t_e is shown without any emphasis on the characteristic changes observed in various experiments. The regularity is much improved (a) if the azeotropic range $Z_A(H)$ is exceptionally large, (b) if, instead of one agent A, two or three are used for determining the azeotropic ranges of binary or ternary azeotropes. In all these cases the condensation temperature of the almost tangent azeotropes is usually considerably lower than the condensation temperatures t_{H_e} t_{B,H_e} or t_{B,C,H_e}.

Referring to ZIĘBORAK's investigations [193] on the benzene 93–99°C gasoline mixture, it should be stressed that in most of his experiments he added benzene-gasoline and other mixtures to an excess of dehydrated ethanol. In addition, he was dealing with 93–99°C gasoline containing hydrocarbons belonging to the upper portion of the azeotropic range. Because of this, a sharp transition from the azeotrope to the ethanol ceiling line was observed in a series of distillations (Fig. XVI. 2, 3, 5 and especially 6).

§ 123. **Step-Wise Dosing Method.** Another method has been applied for the determination of the azeotropic range of an agent A in relation to series H of hydrocarbons found in gasoline or higher boiling petroleum fractions. The gasoline (or petroleum) fraction is first brought to the boil in a flask provided with a twenty or thirty plate distillation column. When a particular condensation temperature has been reached, the stopcock of the head of the column is closed to establish an equilibrium at total reflux. Then a known amount of the agent A is poured into the column. If the quantity of the agent added is not less than one half of the column hold-up, a mixture of binary azeotropes (A, H_{i-2}), (A, H_{i-1}), (A, H_i), (A, H_{i+1}), (A, H_{i+2}) are formed, and the temperature decrease can be observed. If the experiment is correctly performed, no hydrocarbons will be found in the head of the column and its upper portion except in the form of azeotropes with the agent A. The condensation temperature measured on the thermometer located in the well of the column head is approximately equal to the boiling temperature of the azeotropes (A, H_i) due to the fact that the influence of the lower boiling azeotropes (A, H_{i-2}), (A, H_{i-1}) is compensated to a large extent by the influence of the higher boiling azeotropes (A, H_{i+1}) and (A, H_{i+2}). The results obtained depend on whether or not the concentrations of all the representatives of the series (H) present are equal to one another. If this condition is fulfilled, the condensation temperature will be equal to, or only slightly different from the condensation temperature of the azeotrope (A, H_i) because the presence of lower and higher boiling azeotropes, as mentioned above, present in the fraction collected, almost entirely compensate for one another.

In Figure XVIII. 6 the application of the method just described is graphically represented.

Let us suppose that the first portion of agent A is added and no azeotrope (A, H_e) is formed, so that the collection of the low boiling representatives of the series (H) continues. The moment when the agent A in the distillate samples appears to the extent of 1–3 per cent, should be regarded as the starting point of the distillation of almost tangent zeotropes (A, H_{e-2}), (A, H_{e-1}) and a tangent azeotrope (A, H_e). From now on, small amounts of the next samples are collected separately and their refractive indices measured. After the whole amount of the agent A has been distilled off, the temperature decrease and the refractive index change is noted (in the case examined a decrease of the latter took place) and a new dose of agent A may be introduced after the equilibrium at total reflux in the column has been re-established. The graph shown in Figure XVIII. 6 illustrates the effectiveness of this method.

SZCZEPANIK [92] has used a modification of this method for determining the azeotropic range of naphthalene in relation to a narrow petroleum fraction. The

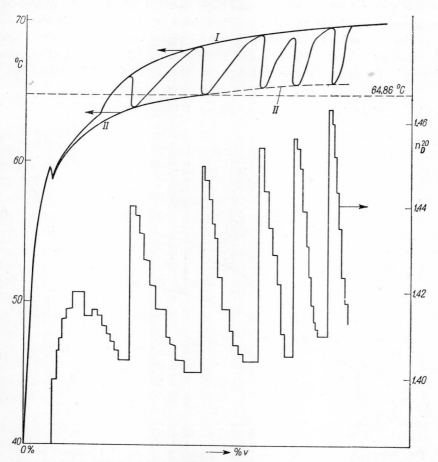

FIG. XVIII. 6. Graphical presentation of the application of the step-wise dosing method for determining the azeotropic range of agent A. Curve I represents the condensation temperatures of series (H). Curve II was obtained by joining the minimum condensation temperatures which occurred each time after 25–30 ml. of agent A was introduced. Below the refractive index changes of the samples collected after each dosing are shown. The dotted line is the ceiling line. Curve II has intersected the latter, due to the formation of almost tangent zeotropes.

graphical presentation of this method is given in Figure XVIII. 7. He submitted
petroleum to careful fractional distillation and obtained distillation curve *I*. In
the course of this distillation eight fractions were collected, each within a very narrow temperature range. The flask of the distilling column was filled with 1500 ml. of
pure naphthalene, which was brought to boiling point and total reflux maintained until
thermal equilibrium had been established in the column. Then, the first (1) petroleum
fraction was added and the lowest condensation temperature was measured. Apparently, this fraction boiled too low for any azeotropes with naphthalene to be formed.
After this first petroleum fraction had been distilled off, and the condensation
temperature of naphthalene (218.2°C) had been re-established and the column
was running at total refluxing again, a second petroleum fraction (2) was added.
In the same way, the remaining samples (3–8) were added, and curve *II* was drawn
as shown in the figure. The naphthalene azeotropic range was found to be:

$$Z_N(H) = Z_1 + Z_u = 21.2 + 12.8 = 34.0°C.$$

It is characterized by a distinctly pronounced lower asymmetry.

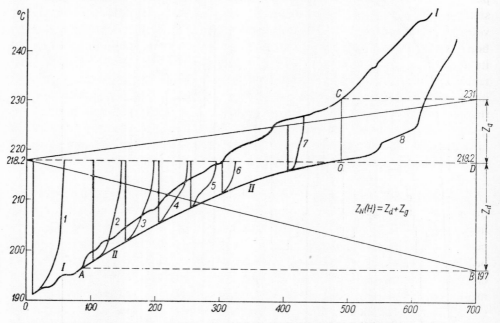

FIG. XVIII. 7. Azeotropic range determination by a modified method of successive step-wise dosing. The distillation column was filled with naphthalene. Eight
successive samples of eight narrow boiling petroleum fractions were introduced into
the distillation column. The petroleum distillation curve *I* is shown. Curve *II* was
obtained by joining the minimum condensation temperatures observed after each
addition of a new petroleum sample. Horizontal lines drawn through points *A* and
C indicate the lower (197°C) and the upper (231°C) limits of the azeotropic range
of naphthalene in relation to the petroleum fractions.

The experiments carried out by LISICKI and SOSNKOWSKA showed that in the course of fractional distillations of carbolic oil small quantities of naphthalene appeared within the range 196 to 203°C. It seems very probable that this high temperature coal tar constituent is often entrained by other substances even below the level of almost tangent zeotrope formation. This is due to the exceptionally high volatility of naphthalene.

§ 124. Azeotropic Ranges of Positive Binary and Ternary Azeotropes.
Besides the determination of the azeotropic range of single substances the question arises how to determine the azeotropic ranges of binary and ternary azeotropes:

$$Z_{A,B}(B, H) = t_{B,H_{k+m}} - t_{B,H_{e+n}}$$

$$Z_{A,B,C}(B, C, H) = t_{B,C,H_{k+m'}} - t_{B,C,H_{e+n'}}$$

m, n, m' and n' being positive or negative whole numbers. A large number of experiments have been carried out by SZCZEPANIK, ROSTAFIŃSKA, GRUBERSKI, LISICKI and KURTYKA [89]. For instance, SZCZEPANIK [92] examined the approximate value of the azeotropic range of 2-methylnaphthalene in relation to the hydrocarbons found in petroleum. ROSTAFIŃSKA [72] determined the ranges of pyridine and its derivatives, and GRUBERSKI [73] found a suitable method for naphthalene content determination in different coal tar oils. LISICKI [70] described methods of examining carbolic oil as a typical polyazeotropic mixture. In all these investigations the azeotropic range values played an important part [112, 113]. The problem requires still more basic research and more diversified methods [89]. ZIĘBORAK'S investigations on the ethanol dehydration process are an example of how to determine the azeotropic ranges of polycomponent azeotropes.

§ 125. Liquid-Vapour Equilibria in Polyazeotropic Mixtures.
ZIĘBORAK and his collaborators have undertaken long-range investigations of liquid-vapour equilibria [156]. Most of them deal with binary mixtures. Ternary mixtures have also been examined [89]. Polyazeotropic mixtures have not been investigated so far because of the many technical difficulties. In spite of the lack of precise physico-chemical investigations of these polycomponent mixtures some purely experimental work has been done with satisfactory results.

It has long been known that coal tar wash oil contains from 7 to 15 per cent of naphthalene which cannot be removed, because it is always accompanied by large quantities of coal tar constituents boiling considerably higher than naphthalene.

In another monograph [89] details are given how to remove a large amount of this naphthalene by mixing wash oil with the mother liquor obtained after removing naphthalene crystals. The presence of azeotropic agents in the mother liquor as well as of other lower boiling tar constituents makes it possible to remove at least 60 or 70 per cent of the naphthalene left in the wash oil.

It is quite probable that further investigations on polyazeotropic mixtures will be associated with a further increases in the yield of constituents of many other polyazeotropic mixtures. There are plenty of problems still remaining unsolved because the influence of a large number and variety of azeotropes formed in the course of fractional distillation was underestimated in the past. Consequently, there was a lack of the basic researches which always precede any valuable technical improvement.

§ 126. Azeotropic Ranges of a Series of Heteroazeotropes.

The methods of determination of the azeotropic ranges of heteroazeotropes are in principle similar to those used for homoazeotropes. However, a change in the structure of the ebulliometer and of the head of the distillation column is indispensable, as described in § 23. In most cases the formation of series of heteroazeotropes is associated with the presence of water which is a typical heteroazeotropic agent. If the mutual solubility of the members of the series (H) and water is very small, the composition of the respective series of heteroazeotropes (W, H_i) may be calculated with satisfactory accuracy. A restricted number of series of positive ternary azeotropes (A, W, H_i), where A is the main azeotropic agent, characterized by the lowest azeotropic range value, have been described. Recently, TRĄBCZYŃSKI [171] published the results of an investigation dealing with a series of heteroazeotropes composed of pyridine, water and normal paraffins. However, more experimental results are still required before any generalization can be made.

Recently, another powerful heteroazeotropic agent has come into use, namely 2-picoline hydrochloride (§ 119). This is one of the numerous pyridine base hydrochlorides which behave in a similar way. For convenience, 2-picoline hydrochloride is used because its melting temperature is low and no difficulties are caused by solidification of the base hydrochloride in the head of the column.

As mentioned above, the pyridine base hydrochlorides boil within the approximately determined range of 210 to 238°C. Difficulties arise in more accurate determination of the latter because of the partial dissociation of the hydrochlorides.

The use of the two liquid phase ebulliometer makes it possible to examine the normal boiling temperatures of a number of heteroazeotropes (§ 23). The very low mutual solubility of a large number of organic compounds with pyridine hydrochlorides is associated with large azeotropic ranges of different series of homologues and their isomers in relation to these "heteroazeotropic" agents.

Difficulties are encountered also due to secondary phenomena caused by the reaction of hydrochloric acid with different organic compounds. Recently, SOSNKOWSKA has started the examination of these heteroazeotropes. The observations made thus far are restricted and more experiments are required in order to prepare the way for generalization. The phenomena involved are interesting from a theoretical point of view (see Chapt. XVII. § 119).

Part IV

THERMOCHEMICAL EXAMINATION OF AZEOTROPES

Chapter XIX

EVAPORATION ENTHALPY DETERMINATIONS

§ 127. Thermochemical Azeotropic Constants. In spite of some progress in the theoretical and experimental development of azeotropy, there is a lack of basic research on the evaporation enthalpy of series of azeotropes, which are required for thermodynamic calculations. In 1957 TWOREK [181] described an apparatus for measuring the evaporation enthalpies of liquids. This device was based on the principle accepted in 1919 by DORABIALSKA and the author of this monograph. According to them [180] it is important to introduce into the condenser, located usually in the calorimeter, vapours which are superheated several degrees above the boiling temperature of the liquid examined.

The reason why the vapours should be superheated before they reach the condenser is to eliminate two sources of error. One is due to the presence of small droplets entrained by the vapour evolved from the boiling liquid; the other is caused by partial condensation of the vapours before they reach the condenser. Both these phenomena were observed by the author many years ago, when he tried to determine the condensation enthalpies of high boiling liquids and used the BERTHELOT device, improved by LOUGININ [184]. He then found that accurate results could not be obtained when employing devices which offered no possibility of eliminating the conditions causing the errors mentioned above.

In Figure XIX. 1 and 2 the apparatus described by TWOREK, and some detail of the superheaters *BNWC* are presented. Essential improvements have been introduced recently by A. ZIELENKIEWICZ [183], especially as regards the stopcock and all other parts involved in the prevention of heat losses from the surface of the leading tubes (*S* and *Z*, shown in Figure XIX. 2).

§ 128. Evaporation Enthalpies and Entropies of Series of Azeotropes. The following equation was used for calculating the gram evaporation enthalpy l_{Az}:

$$l_{Az} = \frac{K \cdot \Delta t}{a} - \bar{c}_b(t_b - t_n) - \bar{c}_v(t_{b+3} - t_b), \tag{1}$$

where K is the thermal capacity of the calorimetric system; a is the weight in grams of the liquid collected in the condenser; $\bar{c}_b$ and $\bar{c}_v$ are the respective average heat capacity values of the liquid cooled from the normal boiling temperature t_b to the final temperature of the main calorimetric period t_n, and the average capacity

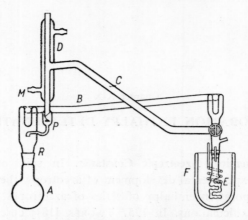

FIG. XIX. 1. Device for determining the evaporation enthalpy of liquids.
B and C are vapour superheaters, F is a Dewar vessel and E a condenser.

of the superheated vapour within the temperature limits $(t_{b+3}-t_b)$. If the data on the specific heats of the vapours of the azeotropes under examination were lacking, the value of $\bar{c}_v(t_{b+3}-t_b)$ was assumed to be 1.2 cal./g. The error due to this assumption was of the order of ± 0.15 per cent.

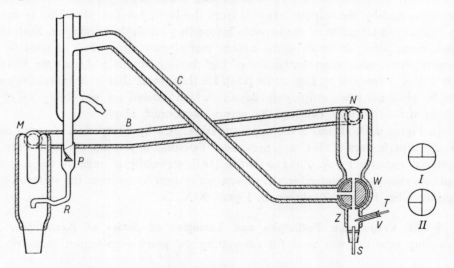

FIG. XIX. 2. MBNWZC—superheating system for vapours partly circulating, partly entering through stopcock WZS into the condenser E (Fig. XIX. 1) through leading tube S.

The $\bar{c}_v(t_{b+3}-t_b)$ values (Eq. (1)) were determined with a relative accuracy of ± 0.25 per cent. On the other hand, the error of $\bar{c}(t_b-t_n)$ determination was found to be approximately twice as great.

In Tables XIX. 1 and XIX. 2, the results are given for the evaporation enthalpies of binary azeotropes formed by the representatives of normal and isomeric alcohols with the respective aromatic hydrocarbons: benzene, toluene, and isomeric xylenes as well as of pyridine with normal paraffinic hydrocarbons [183].

FIG. XIX. 3. Condenser to be located in the calorimetric Dewar vessel.

The values of l_{Az} and T_{Az} for azeotropes 6,7,9,11–16 were determined by CIE-CIERSKA-TWOREK [182]. The results obtained are graphically presented in Figures XIX. 4,5,6.

These measurements were made by applying the same method and with the same calorimeter, but before some improvements in the heating of part S-Z (Fig. XIX. 1) and its control had been introduced by A. ZIELENKIEWICZ. In spite of this, the application of the method of comparative measurements, consisting in the determination of the calorimetric constant by using the evaporation enthalpy of water as a standard value, has eliminated the small errors which might have occurred owing to less precise heating control of the S-Z joining tube and the stopcock (Fig. XIX. 2).

In Figure XIX. 6 the respective curves expressing the relation between the molar evaporation enthalpy and the number of CH_2 groups in the alcohols are shown.

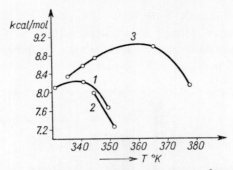

FIG. XIX. 4. Molar evaporation enthalpy plotted against absolute boiling temperature of azeotropes: *1*—benzene-series of normal alcohols; *2*—benzene-isoalcohols; *3*—toluene-series of normal alcohols.

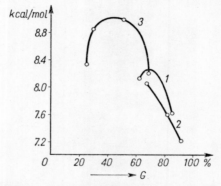

FIG. XIX. 5. Molar evaporation enthalpy of binary azeotropes against weihgt per cent of aromatic hydrocarbons: *1* — benzene-series of normal alcohols: *2*—benzene-series of isoalcohols; *3* — toluene-normal alcohols (Table XIX 2).

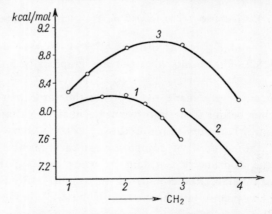

FIG. XIX. 6. Molar evaporation enthalpy plotted against the number of CH_2-groups: *1*—benzene-series of normal alcohols; *2*—benzene-isoalcohols; *3*—toluene-normal alcohols (Table XIX. 2).

TABLE XIX. 1

Evaporation Enthalpies and Entropies of Binary Azeotropes

1	2	3	4	5	6	7
I	1	p-Xylene n-Propyl alcohol	368.98	170.27	10.589	28.7
	2	p-Xylene Isobutyl alcohol	380.18	142.12	11.101	29.2
	3	p-Xylene n-Butyl alcohol	389.20	141.28	11.598	29.8
	4	p-Xylene Isoamyl alcohol	400.45	116.72	11.212	28.0
	5	p-Xylene n-Hexyl alcohol	411.49	94.96	10.040	24.4
II	6	Toluene Methyl alcohol	335.92	216.49	8.263	24.6
	7	Toluene Ethyl alcohol	349.60	161.77	8.879	25.4
	8	Toluene Isopropyl alcohol	354.60	148.13	10.673	30.1
	9	Toluene n-Propyl alcohol	365.08	123.32	8.944	24.5
	10	Toluene Isobutyl alcohol	372.64	114.75	9.539	25.6
	11	Toluene n-Butyl alcohol	378.20	95.55	8.169	21.6
III	12	Benzene Methyl alcohol	330.62	161.45	8.034	24.3
	13	Benzene Ethyl alcohol	340.30	128.66	8.201	24.1
	14	Benzene Isopropyl alcohol	344.42	112.50	7.990	23.2
	15	Benzene n-Propyl alcohol	349.40	102.20	7.616	21.8
	16	Benzene Isobutyl alcohol	352.35	93.56	7.187	20.4
	17	m-Xylene Isobutyl alcohol	380.09	144.86	11.174	29.4
	18	m-Xylene Isoamyl alcohol	400.47	119.36	11.413	28.5
	19	o-Xylene Isoamyl alcohol	402.33	131.44	12.593	31.3
	20	Pyridine n-Heptane	368.34	100.27	9.392	25.5
IV	21	Pyridine n-Octane	383.32	109.41	9.966	26.0
	22	Pyridine n-Nonane	388.24	117.97	9.706	25.0

The columns indicate: 1—the number of the series of azeotropes formed with the respective hydrocarbons; 2—the number of the azeotrope; 3—the components forming the azeotrope; 4—the absolute boiling temperature of the azeotrope T_{Az}; 5—the gram evaporation enthalpy, l_{Az}; 6—the molar evaporation enthalpy L_{Az}; at T_{Az}; 7—the entropy change ΔS.

TABLE XIX. 2

1	2	3	4	5	6	7
1	Benzene-methanol	330.62	8.073	8.269	0.196	24.4
2	Benzene-ethanol	340.30	8.201	8.516	0.315	24.1
3	Benzene-propanol	349.40	7.597	8.140	0.543	21.7
4	Benzene-Isopropanol	344.39	8.001	8.664	0.663	23.2
5	Benzene-Isobutanol	352.32	7.182	7.678	0.496	20.4
6	Toluene-methanol	335.92	8.283	8.584	0.301	24.6
7	Toluene-ethanol	349.60	8.871	9.351	0.480	25.4
8	Toluene-propanol	365.08	8.952	9.707	0.755	24.5
9	Toluene-butanol	378.20	8.167	8.967	0.800	21.6

The columns represent the same indication as given on page 197.

§ 129. General Remarks on Evaporation Enthalpies of Positive Azeotropes.
The experimental material collected so far is not sufficient for any generalization. It is also limited to positive binary azeotropes. The statement can be made, however, that in the series of (Ar_j, Al_i), azeotropes, the evaporation enthalpy is lower than $nAr_j+(1-n)Al_i$, n and $(1-n)$ being the molar concentrations of Ar_j and Al_i. This indicates that the heat of mixing of any aromatic hydrocarbon (Ar) with any al-

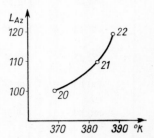

FIG. XIX. 7. L_{Az} values plotted against °K for the series of azeotropes formed by pyridine as the common azeotropic agent.

cohol $R \cdot OH$ is an endothermic process. As regards the three azeotropes formed by pyridine with three normal paraffinic hydrocarbons: heptane, octane and nonane, the heat of mixing seems to be a more complicated phenomenon than that of the (Ar_j, Al_i) series.

No evaporation enthalpies of positive ternary and quaternary homo- and heteroazeotropes have yet been examined. The investigations of bipositive-negative ternary azeotropes are under way.

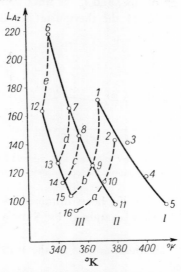

FIG. XIX. 8. L_{Az} values plotted against the absolute temperature °K for the series *I*, *II* and *III*, embracing 16 azeotropes. Each of the curves *a, b, c, d, e*, represents azeotropes containing the same alcohol.

It should be pointed out as regards heteroazeotropes, that special distillation flasks *A* (Fig. II. 8 *a, b*) are required to obtain the composition of the vapour entering the calorimetric condenser identical to that of the heteroazeotrope. These flasks resemble the devices used for ebulliometric measurements on liquids forming two phase systems (§ 23).

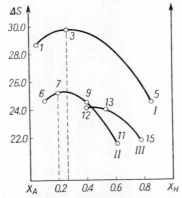

FIG. XIX. 9. Curves obtained by plotting ΔS against the composition of the three series of azeotropes.

§ **130. Mean Specific Heats of Azeotropes.** To calculate evaporation enthalpies, it is necessary to determine the mean specific heat C_v within the temperature range from t_{b+3} to t_n, t_{b+3} being the vapour temperature higher by $3°C$ than the boiling temperature of the azeotrope, and t_n the final temperature of the main calorimetric period. In Figure XIX. 11 the thermostat for heating the liquid samples is shown [185].

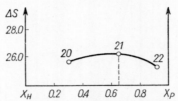

FIG. XIX. 10. Curves obtained by plotting ΔS against the azeotrope composition, pyridine (P) being the common azeotropic agent.

In Table XIX. 3 the mean specific heats obtained by our group are listed.

The systems 1, 2 and 3, were examined by SADOWSKA [186], the remaining six by ZIELENKIEWICZ [185].

No comments can be made thus far due to the restricted number and variety of the azeotropes examined.

No heteroazeotropes have been examined as yet. The necessary devices for the examination of two-liquid phase systems are being elaborated.

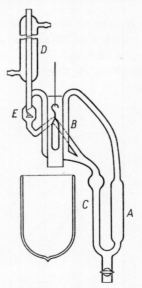

FIG. XIX. 11. Device for determination of the mean specific heat of liquids: B—constant temperature jacket; A, C—lower part of the one stage ebulliometer; E—drop-counter.

TABLE XIX. 3

Mean Specific Heats of Azeotropes

No.	Azeotrope	Temperature range °C	Mean specific heat cal. g^{-1} deg.$^{-1}$
1	Benzene-methanol	57.42–21.10	0.565
2	Benzene-isopropanol	71.37–21.48	0.562
3	Toluene-ethanol	76.41–21.54	0.608
4	Toluene-isopropanol	80.80–21.10	0.656
5	Toluene-isobutanol	99.10–21.42	0.587
6	p-Xylene-isobutanol	105.65–21.73	0.681
7	p-Xylene-isopentanol	125.11–21.90	0.601
8	m-Xylene-isobutanol	105.90–21.64	0.683
9	o-Xylene-isopentanol	126.67–22.18	0.630
10	Pyridine-acetic acid-n-heptane	93.3–21.8	0.589
11	Pyridine-acetic acid-n-nonane	129.0–22.1	0.562

Chapter XX

HEATS OF MIXING OF AZEOTROPE COMPONENTS

§ 131. General Remarks. The heat of mixing of azeotrope components plays an important role in many thermodynamic calculations, in particular the examination of any theory of azeotrope formation. In many cases, no numerical data are available for introducing of heat of mixing into thermodynamic equations.

If the liquids boil at a reasonably high temperature, the calorimetric measurements may easily be carried out without any danger that in the course of the measurements any evaporation of the liquid components will occur. Because of this risk, when dealing with volatile liquids, the experimenter should use more complicated calorimetric devices for avoiding the errors associated with partial heat losses.

Much more complicated are the direct measurements of the heat of mixing of components of ternary systems. Usually, a very large number of experiments are required to cover the Gibbs concentration triangle with a sufficient number of points, representing the composition of mixtures for which direct calorimetric measurements are required.

If exclusively positive azeotropes are investigated, the number of experiments may often be reduced owing to there being some regularity in the thermal processes under examination. More complicated still are systems composed of compounds forming bipositive-negative or binegative-positive ternary homoazeotropes. We are at present in need of numerous thermochemical data for all kinds of azeotropes, including quaternary systems. There is no reason, however, to think that the thermochemical examination of quaternary azeotropic system is too complicated, but it is obvious that it will require a very large number of calorimetric measurements for each system. As far as any kind of heteroazeotropes are concerned no experimental data have been found in the literature. Our group has not published any thermochemical investigation of this kind as yet.

§ 132. Heats of Mixing of Two Azeotrope Components. Recently, Wóycicka [187] has made a large number of calorimetric determinations of heats of mixing. In all these experiments two compounds, acetic acid and pyridine, played the role of azeotropic agents and members H_i of the homologous series (H) of normal paraffins served as second components in the (A, H_i) and (P, H_i) systems.

In addition, the curve of the heat of mixing for the binary systems composed of the series of pyridine bases (P) and acetic acid (A) has also been examined.

In Figures XX. 1, 2 and 3 the respective curves are presented. The heat of mixing of acetic acid with pyridine bases was always positive. On the other hand, for the (A, H_i) and (P, H_i) systems the mixing was endothermal.

The dotted curve II found by other authors [191] does not differ greatly from the curve I obtained by WÓYCICKA. Curve I, however, is more asymmetrical. The extremum point M is at about 60 mol. per cent of acetic acid. The maximum heat evolved is $+1.16$ kcal per mol.

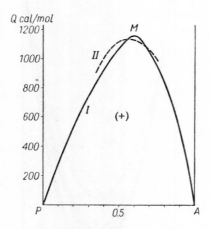

FIG. XX. 1. Heat of mixing curve I obtained for mixtures of acetic acid and pyridine. Molar concentrations are plotted versus heat evolved. Dotted curve II represents the results obtained by PUSHIN, FEDUSHKIN and KRGOVIC.

In the past several explanations have been given, by GARDNER [188], ZAWIDZ-KI [189] and NAUMOVA [190], as to why the maximum heat evolution did not occur with equimolar concentrations of the organic acid and organic weak base. It seems, however, that more experimental data are required for any further generalization. Series of weak organic acids and organic bases should be examined and a comparison of the data obtained should serve as the basis for an explanation of the phenomena taking place in this kind of mixture. At the present time, no difficulties are encountered in preparing the respective compounds needed for getting precise thermochemical data.

In Figure XX. 2, the negative thermal effects of mixing pyridine with the series of normal hydrocarbons starting with n-hexane and ending with n-undecane are presented. In this series the extremum points 1, 2, 3, 4, 5 and 6 are shifted toward the right, pyridine-rich side.

§ 133. Empirical Correlations. WÓYCICKA has used [187] empirical correlations of the heat effects with change in concentration:

$$H_{12} = x_1 x_2 [A_0 + A_1(x_1 - x_2) + A_2(x_1 - x_2)^2], \tag{1}$$

A_0, A_1 and A_2 being constant for each individual binary mixture. For n-heptane–pyridine and n-nonane–pyridine the constants A_2 are equal to zero. A_0 varies for

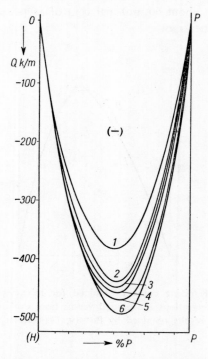

FIG. XX. 2. Heat of mixing curves *1, 2, 3, 4, 5* and *6* obtained for molar concentrations plotted against negative heat effects. *P* stands for pyridine; H_i—*1, 2, 3, 4, 5* and *6*—for n-hexane, n-heptane, n-octane, n-nonane, n-decane and n-undecane, respectively.

binary mixtures from 1520 to 1950. A_1 undergoes much larger changes than A_0; two of its values are even negative. For each of the binary systems the calculated H_{12} values agree well with the experimental data.

Heat is absorbed also if acetic acid is mixed with the four normal paraffins: n-hexane (*1*), n-heptane (*2*), n-octane (*3*) and n-nonane (*4*). The latter two hydrocarbons exhibit limited mutual solubility with acetic acid. On Figure XX. 3, the two-liquid phase regions are shown by dotted lines. Equations of the type (*1*) with three constants A_0, A_1 and A_2 for each binary system have been calculated and satisfactory agreement within the experimental errors has also been obtained.

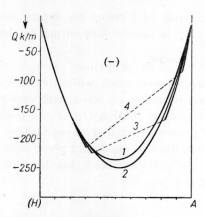

FIG. XX. 3. Heat of mixing curves *1, 2, 3* and *4* for acetic acid with n-paraffins. *A* stands for acetic acid, *H—1, 2, 3, 4*—for n-hexane, n-heptane, n-octane and n-nonane. Dotted lines *3* and *4* indicate the two liquid phase concentration ranges.

§ 134. Heat of Mixing of Components of Saddle Systems. Much more complicated and time-consuming are ternary bipositive-negative systems. WÓYCICKA [187] has examined in detail two such systems, both composed of compounds which, at appropriate concentrations, form ternary saddle azeotropes of the type $[(-)P, A(+)H_i]$, P being pyridine, A acetic acid and H_i n-hexane (H_6) and n-heptane (H_7),

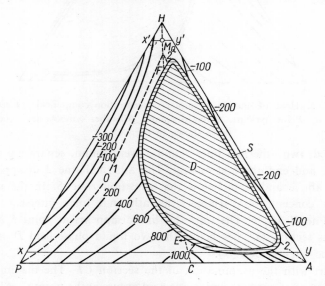

FIG. XX. 4. Heat of mixing of molar concentration components. *A* stands for acetic acid, *P* for pyridine, and *H* for n-hexane. Dotted lines and *2* represent the mixtures formed with zero heat evolution (athermal lines). Point M_Q lies on the thermal top-ridge line *HEC*, **D** is the two liquid phase field at room temperature.

respectively. The heat evolved on forming the binary systems $(P+A)$, $(A+H_6)$, $(A+H_7)$ $(P+H_6)$ and $(P+H_7)$ in various proportions has been examined previously (§ 133).

In Figures XX. 4 and XX. 5 the projections of equal mixing heat are presented. All calorimetric measurements were made within the temperature range 20–21°C. Owing to the low mutual solubility of acetic acid and paraffinic hydrocarbons, in both Figures a relatively large portion (D) of the triangle corresponds to the coexistence of two liquid phases. Space D is surrounded by a narrow zone S within the limits of which the transition of one liquid phase into two liquid phases takes place. The precise location of a distinct borderline between the homogeneous and heterogeneous regions is not possible.

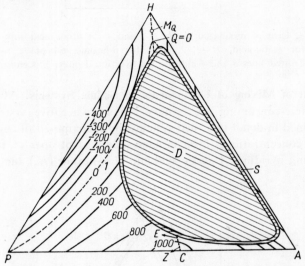

FIG. XX. 5. Heat of mixing of molar concentration component: A stands for acetic acid, P for pyridine, H for n-heptane. All other symbols are identical with those shown in Fig. XX. 4.

As expected, two athermal lines 1 and 2 were found, separating the two fields of exothermic and endothermic mixing. The athermal line 2 disappears when attaining from above and from below the transition zone S. In the upper portion of the Gibbs concentration triangle the athermal lines intersect at the point lying on the line $H M_Q F$. The top-ridge line disappears at point F and reappears at point E; its section EC, lies below the two liquid phase field D and below the transition zone S (Fig. XX. 4).

Let us start with the examination of the section CE. The maximum heat evolution by a mixture of pyridine and acetic acid occurs at the point C. Along the curve CE the heat of mixing of the respective mixtures decreases steadily, retaining, however, the same character as for C: for instance, if we mix together appropriate amounts of binary mixtures x and y so as to get the final composition Z, maximum heat will be developed as compared with other mixtures the compositions of which are represented by points lying to the left or the right of the point Z.

The section FM_QH has the same character as CE. Along curve FH the heat of mixing decreases, but each point on the curve represents the maximum heat evolution or absorption compared with mixtures the compositions of which lie on either side of the horizontal line drawn through the respective point lying on the curve EM_QH. Finally, point M_Q represents a mixture formed by mixing x' with y' so as to obtain a mixture having the composition M_Q. The endothermic effect corresponds to a minimum heat evolution compared with all others observed along the two sections HF and EC (Fig. XX. 4).

Figure XX. 5 is a similar diagram for the ternary system acetic acid, pyridine and n-heptane. Consequently, the two liquid phase field D is larger as compared with the previous system. It is to be emphasized that a very large number of mean specific heat determinations of ternary mixtures are required for obtaining a similar diagram of the results at boiling temperatures of the mixture examined under constant pressure.

Thus far no heats of mixing have been examined for the numerous systems described in §§ 86, which are characterized by a relatively short top-ridge line, merging either with the PH or AH sides of the triangle (See Figs. X. 25, X. 26).

§ 135. **General Remarks.** It is obvious that the thermochemical examination of azeotropic systems should be continued and more varieties of constant boiling mixtures should be investigated. In the case of a series of azeotropes the studies should be extended to zeotropic systems belonging to the same series. Attention should be paid to heteroazeotropes, especially series in which heteroazeotropes undergo transformation into homoazeotropes (§§ 88–91). The accumulation of thermochemical data should improve the thermodynamic treatment of homo- and heteroazeotropes, reducing considerably the number of assumptions which at present have to be accepted, owing to the lack of data found by direct experiments.

We should also bear in mind that besides a large variety of new kinds of individual azeotropes, mixtures obtained as fractions collected in the course of fractional distillation of most organic raw materials will require thermochemical investigation. The time will come when general or particular rules or generalizations, based on thermodynamic considerations, will correlate our observations, including the thermochemical data.

ADDENDUM

THE ESSENTIAL problem examined in the first part of this book differs considerably from those examined as yet by other authors. As regards individual azeotropes
great importance has been attached to the method of determining their composition of any kind of azeotropes with as high a precision as possible. More than
thirty years have been spent by the author and his numerous collaborators in developing the ebulliometric method and adapting different kinds of ebulliometers
to enable the examination of homo- and heteroazeotropic and zeotropic mixtures
to be carried out. To avoid any kind of accidental errors, the combined distillation
and ebulliometric methods have been recommended. As far as is known to the
author, no simpler method exists for deciding whether or not the main fraction
obtained by careful fractional distillation of the azeotrope components has in fact
the composition of the azeotrope under examination.

It is difficult to say definitely in which cases it might be possible to discover
the existence of quaternary positive hetero- or homoazeotropes or quaternary
positive-negative homoazeotropes without the use of two- and three-stage ebulliometers. It seems that these are still irreplaceable devices which enable any section
of the boiling temperature isobar to be examined by adding successively small
amounts of one mixture to another. By this simple technique, any portion of a complicated boiling temperature surface may be examined with high, or at least satisfactory, accuracy.

Numerous contributions published by our group during the last ten years contain
descriptions of various systems. Some of them deal with ebulliometric measurements on series in which direct transitions of heteroazeotropes into homoazeotropes, and then into homozeotropes take place. The homozeotropes coexisted
with the horizontal sections of the boiling temperature isobar, showing that a limited
mutual solubility of the two components, occurred. In the monograph *Ebulliometric
Measurements* published by the author in 1945, some chapters were devoted to
the application of ebulliometers to the study of azeotropes [31]. It could not have
been predicted that the same, or somewhat modified, apparatus would play an
important role in further experimental work dealing with new and much more
complicated types of azeotropes.

Ten years ago our knowledge of polyazeotropic mixtures was very limited. It
was necessary to suggest the new term "polyazeotropy" to emphasize that there
exists a large number of organic raw or synthetically obtained materials which

contain one, two or more series of homologues and their isomers. The presence of these series caused a very large number of azeotropes to be formed. The purpose of this book was to give a short survey of what has been done in examining these complex mixtures. We must still remember that our knowledge in this new field is very restricted. New methods and new means of examining the polyazeotropic mixtures should be found and their technique adequately developed.

The author would be satisfied if the appearance of this book stimulates further addition to our knowledge of "polyazeotropic mixtures".

REFERENCES*

REFERENCES GIVEN IN THE TEXT

[1] DALTON J., *Mem. Manchester Phil. Soc.* **5**, 585 (1802); *Ann. Phil.* **9**, 186 (1817); *J. für Phys. Chem.* (1) **28**, 363 (1820).

[2] ROSCOE H., *Ann.* **112**, 337 (1859); *Ann. Chem. Pharm.* (2), **40**, 203 (1860); *ibid.* (2), **45**, 346 (1869); *ibid.* (2), **49**, 318 (1863); *Ann.* **116**, 221 (1860); *Ann.* **125**, 321 (1863); with DITTMAR W., *Ann. Chem.* (3) **58**, 492 (1860).

[3] KONOVALOV D., *Ber.* **17**, 1531 (1884); *Wien, Ann.* **14**, 34, 219 (1881); dissertation (1884), *Ann. Chem. Pharm.* (3), **14**, 34 (1881); *Zhur. Fiz. Khim. Obshch.* **16**, 11 (1884).

[4] GIBBS J. W., *Collected Works,* Longmans & Green, New York, 1931.

[5] DUHEM P., *Ann. école norm, sup.* (3), **4**, 9 (1887); *ibid.* (3) **6**, 153 (1889); *Trav. mem. fac. Lille* **30**, 13 (1894).

[6] MARGULES M., *Sitz. Akad. Wiss. Wien* **104**, 1043 (1895).

[7] LEHFELD R., *Phil. Mag.* (5), **40**, 397 (1895).

[8] OSTWALD W., *Lehrbuch der allgemeinen Chemie,* Vol. 2, 1899, p. 611–648.

[9] ZAWIDZKI J., *Z. physik. Chem.* **35**, 129 (1900).

[10] YOUNG S., *J. Chem. Soc.* **81**, 707 (1902); YOUNG S., FORTEY E. C., *J. Chem. Soc.* **81**, 739, 752 (1902).

[11] WADE J. and MERRIMAN R. W., *J. Chem. Soc.* **99**, 997 (1911).

[12] ŚWIĘTOSŁAWSKI W., *Bull. Acad. Polonaise Sci.* **1933** A, 472.

[13] VREVSKII M. S., *Zuhr. Fiz. Khim. Obsh.* **42**, 1, 702, 1349 (1910); *ibid.* **43**, 1446 (1911); *ibid.* **44**, 1379 (1912); *Z. physik Chem.* **81**, 1 (1912) *ibid.* **83**, 537 (1913).

[14] LECAT M., *L'azéotropisme, données expérimentales, bibliographie,* Bruxelles, 1918.

[15] LECAT M., *Tables azéotropiques,* Vol. 1. Bruxelles, 1949.

[16] HORSLEY L. H., *Ind. Eng. Chem., Ed.* **19**, 508–600 (1947); *ibid.* **81**, 831–874 (1949).

[17] VAN DER WAALS J. D., *Z. physik. Chem.* **5**, 133 (1891); *Die Kontinuität des gasförmigen Zustands.* Vol. II, Leipzig 1900, 2nd ed.

[18] PAWLEWSKI B., *Kosmos* **6**, 498 (1881); *ibid.* **7**, (1882); *Ber.* **15**, 460, 2460 (1882); **23**, 3752 (1890); PAWLEWSKI B., STAUS J., *Zhur. Rus. Fiz. Khim. Obsh.* **12**, 207 (1880); *ibid.* **14**, 510 (1882).

---

* The references to the papers published in the period from 1946 until the present, by Polish scientists mostly, in English, require some explanation. Before 1953 the following references were used: *Bull. Acad. Polonaise Sci.* **1950** A without any volume number. In the period from 1953 to 1957 the chemical papers were published together with other sciences, and the references were of the form: *Bull. Acad. Polonaise Sci. III.* **I** etc. containing the volume number. From 1953 to 1957 the chemical papers were published together with geological, and geographical ones. Owing to the growing number of chemical papers, starting in 1960 separate volumes of the latter have been printed. The references now are: *Bull. Acad. Polonaise* Sci., *Séries des Sci. Chim.* Since 1953 the continuity of the volume numbers has been strictly observed.

[19] ŚWIĘTOSŁAWSKI W. and PIESZCZEK S., *Bull. Acad. Poloraise Sci.* **1937** A, 72; *Roczniki Chem.* **17**, 209 (1937).

[20] BANCROFT W. D., *The Phase Rule*, New York, 1897.

[21] ŚWIĘTOSŁAWSKI W., Methodes de mesures qui garantissent l'homogénéité des donnés physicochimiques, *Compte rendu de l'Union Internationale de Chimie* 1934; Ebuliometry, 1936.

[22] KAMIEŃSKI B., *Roczniki Chem.* **11**, 1 (1931).

[23] RABCEWICZ-ZUBKOWSKI J., *Roczniki Chem.* **13**, 193, 334 (1933).

[24] SOSNOWSKI S. and TRESZCZANOWICZ E., *Przemysł Chem.* **20**, 16 (1936).

[25] BĄKOWSKI S. and TRESZCZANOWICZ E., *Przemysł Chem.* **20**, 195 (1936).

[26] ŚWIĘTOSŁAWSKI W., *Ebulliometry*, Chemical Publishing Co., New York, 1937.

[27] ŚWIĘTOSŁAWSKI W. and ORSZAGH A., *Roczniki Chem.* **25**, 392 (1951).

[28] ŚWIĘTOSŁAWSKI W. *Roczniki Chem.* **25**, 96 (1951).

[29] ŚWIĘTOSŁAWSKI W., *Roczniki Chem.* **25**, 98 (1951); *ibid.* **25**, 109 (1951); *Bull. Acad. Polonaise Sci.* **19**, 29 (1950 AA).

[30] ŚWIĘTOSŁAWSKI W., *Physikalische Chemie des Steinkohlenteers*, N, J. Hoffmann-Verlag, Köln, 1959.

[31] ŚWIĘTOSŁAWSKI W., *Ebulliometric Measurements*, New York, 1945.

[32] WEISSBERGER A., *Physical Methods of Organic Chemistry*, chapter IV: Boiling and Condensation Temperature, W. ŚWIĘTOSŁAWSKI and J. R. ANDERSON, Vol. I, 107–140 (third ed.)

[33] ŚWIĘTOSŁAWSKI W., On the classification of Zeotropes and Azeotropes, *Bull. Acad. Polonaise Sci.* A 1932, 472.

[34] ŚWIĘTOSŁAWSKI W., BRZOSTOWSKI H. and KRAKOWSKI M., *Ann. Acad. Techn.* **1**, 115 (1935); *Fuel* **14**, 305 (1935); *Przemysł Chem.* **18**, 571 (1934); *Roczniki Chem.* **14**, 633 (1934).

[35] ORSZAGH A., *Roczniki Chem.* **29**, 623, 632, 636 (1955).

[36] ANDERSON J. R., *Ind. Eng. Chem.* **37**, 541 (1945); *ibid.* **37**, 1052 (1945).

[37] ŚWIĘTOSŁAWSKI W., *Roczniki Chem.* **26**, 632 (1952); *Bull. Acad. Polonaise Sci.* **1**, 632; *Bull. Acad. Polonaise Sci.* **7**, 63 (1953).

[38] ŚWIĘTOSŁAWSKI W., *Bull. Acad. Polonaise Sci.* **1**, 66, 70 (1953).

[39] MERRIMAN R. W., *J. Chem. Soc.* **103**, 628, 1790, 1801 (1913).

[40] ŚWIĘTOSŁAWSKI W., *Roczniki Chem.* **10**, 97 (1930).

[41] ŚWIĘTOSŁAWSKI W., *Separation and Purification Methods*, Warsaw, 1950 (in Polish).

[42] ŚWIĘTOSŁAWSKI W., *Bull. Acad.Polonaise Sci.* **1950** A, 19, 29.

[43] MARKOWSKA-MAJEWSKA H., *Roczniki Chem.* **29**, 67 (1955).

[44] CALLINGAERT G. and WOJCIECHOWSKI M., *J. Am. Chem. Soc.* **42**, 5310 (1950).

[45] BYLEWSKI T., *Roczniki Chem.* **12**, 311 (1932).

[46] ZMACZYŃSKI A., *Roczniki Chem.* **11**, 327 (1931); **11**, 449 (1931); **16**, 489 (1936); *ibid.* **18**, 910 (1938); *J. Chem. Phys.* **27**, 503 (1930).

[47] MOSER H. and ZMACZYŃSKI A., *Physik Zeit.* **40**, 221 (1939).

[48] ŚWIĘTOSŁAWSKI W., *Roczniki Chem.* **25**, 88 (1951); *ibid.* **25**, 107 (1951); *ibid.* **25**, 381 (1951); *Bull. Acad. Polonaise Sci.* **1950** A, *ibid.* **1951** A, 29; *ibid.* **1951** A., 87; *Bull. Soc. Chem. Belge* **62**. 10 (1953).

[49] ŚWIĘTOSŁAWSKI W., ZIĘBORAK K. and GALSKA A., *Bull. Acad. Polonaise Sci.*, Cl. III, *Série Chim.* **7**, 43 (1959).

[50] ZIĘBORAK K., *Bull. Acad. Polonaise Sci.* **1950** A, 15; *ibid.* **1951** A, 93; ZIĘBORAK K., ŚWIĘTOSŁAWSKI W., *ibid.* **1950** A, 9 and 13.

[51] GUINOT H., *Compt. rend.* **176**, 1623 (1923).

[52] ZIĘBORAK K. and ŚWIĘTOSŁAWSKI W., *Roczniki Chem.* **25**, 68 (1951); *ibid.* **25**, 388 (1951); *Roczniki Chem.* **25**, 92 (1951); *ibid.* **25**, 94 (1951).

[53] EWELL R. H. and WELCH L. M., *Ind. Eng. Chem.* **37**, 1244 (1945).

[54] LANG H., *Z. physik Chem.* **196**, 278 (1950).

[55] ŚWIĘTOSŁAWSKI W., *Bull. Acad. Polonaise Sci.* **1**, 66, 70 (1953).

[56] ZIĘBORAK K. and MAJEWSKA H., *Rocznik Chem.* **29**, 75 (1955); *Bull. Acad. Polonaise Sci. Cl. III* **2**, 341 (1954).

[57] ŚWIĘTOSŁAWSKI W., *Bull. Soc. chem. Belge* **62**, 10 (1953).

[58] ŚWIĘTOSŁAWSKI W., *Bull. Acad. Polonaise Sci.* **1**, 66, 70 (1953).

[59] ZMACZYŃSKI A., *Roczniki Chem.* **11**, 449 (1931).

[60] KEUSSLER O., Dissertation, Darmstadt, 1925; *Z. Ver. Deut. Ing.* **71**, 925 (1927).

[61] BYLEWSKI T., *Roczniki Chem.* **12**, 311 (1932).

[62] ZŁOTOWSKI I., *Roczniki Chem.* **10**, 288 (1930).

[63] MERRIMAN R. W., *J. Chem. Soc.* **103**, I, 628 (1913).

[64] KARPIŃSKI B. and ŚWIĘTOSŁAWSKI W., *Compt rend.* **198**, 2166 (1934).

[65] PIESZCZEK S. and ŚWIĘTOSŁAWSKI W., *Bull. Acad. Polonaise Sci.* **1937 A**, 72.

[66] KEUNEN J. P. and ROBSON W. G., *Phil. Mag.* **64**, 110 (1902).

[67] KRĘGLEWSKI A., *Bull. Acad. Polonaise Sci., Cl. III* **2**, 77 (1954).

[68] ZIĘBORAK K. and LEBECKA K., *Przemysł Chem.* **8**, 31, 422 (1952).

[69] ŚWIĘTOSŁAWSKI W., *Roczniki Chem.* **10**, 472 (1930); *ibid.* **11**, 543 (1931).

[70] LISICKI Z., *Przemysł Chem.* **9**, (32), 342 (1953).

[71] SZCZEPANIK R., *Przemysł Chem.* **9** (32), 263, 315, 375 (1953).

[72] ROSTAFIŃSKA D., *Przemysł Chem.* **9** (32), 357, 361 (1953).

[73] GRUBERSKI T., *Przemysł Chem.* **9** (32) 336 (1953).

[74] COULSON E. A. and JONES J., *J. Soc. Chem. Ind.* **65**, 169 (1946).

[75] MIERZECKI R., *Progress of Physics* **12**, 66 (1953).

[76] ŚWIĘTOSŁAWSKI W., *Przemysł Chem.* **7** (30), 363 (1951); *Bull. Soc. chim. Belge* **62**, 10 (1953).

[77] KRĘGLEWSKI A., *Roczniki Chem.* **27**, 125 (1953); *ibid.* **28**, 251 (1954); *ibid.* **29**, 95 (1955); *ibid.* **29**, 750 (1955); *Bull. Acad. Polonaise Sci., Cl. III* **2**, 191 (1954); *ibid.* **2**, 233 (1954).

[78] BOGUCKI T., Not yet published.

[79] ZMYSŁOWSKA H., Not yet published.

[80] ZIĘBORAK K. and GALSKA A., *Bull. Acad. Polonaise Sci., Cl. III* **3**, (1955) 383–387.

[81] ZIĘBORAK K. and M., *Bull. Acad. Polonaise Sci., Cl. III* **2**, 287 (1954); ZIĘBORAK K. and MARKOWSKA-MAJEWSKA H. *ibid.* **2**, 341 (1954).

[82] ŚWIĘTOSŁAWSKI W., *Przemysł Chem.* **30**, 363 (1951); *Bull. Soc. chim. Belge* **62**, 10 (1953).

[83] LONGUET-HIGGINS H. C., *Proc. Roy. Soc. A* **205**, 247 (1951); with COOK D., *ibid A* **209**, 28 (1951).

[84] BRIDGMAN P. H., *Rev. Modern. Phys.* **18**, 1–93 (1946)

[85] MALESIŃSKI W., *Bull. Acad. Polonaise Sci. Cl. III* **4**, 295, 303, 365, 371 (1956).

[86] HAASE R., *Z. physik Chem.* **195**, 362–385 (1950).

[87] ŚWIĘTOSŁAWSKI W. and KARPIŃSKI B., *Ebulliometry*, Warsaw, 1935, § 72; *Ebulliometric Measurements*, New York, 1945, § 109.

[88] ZIĘBORAK K. and LEBECKA K., *Przemysł Chem.* **31**, 422 (1952).

[89] ŚWIĘTOSŁAWSKI W., *Physical Chemistry of Coal Tar* (Polish Ed. 1956, Russian Ed. 1958, German Ed. 1959).

[90] KURTYKA Z., *Bull. Acad. Polonaise Sci. Cl. III* **3**, 47 (1955).

[91] MARKOWSKA-MAJEWSKA H., *Bull. Acad. Polonaise Sci., Cl. III* **2**, 291 (1954).

[92] SZCZEPANIK R., *Przemysł Chem.* **9** (32), 211, 265, 375, 478, 589 (1953).

[93] LECAT M., *L'azeotropisme,* Bruxelles 1918; *Ann. soc. chim. sci.* **61**, 63 (1947).

[94] LONGUET-HIGGINS H. C. and COOK D., *Proc. Roy. Soc. A,* **209**, 28 (1951).

[95] STEWART G. W. and BENZ C. A., *Phys. Rev.* **46**, 703 (1934).

[96] SKOLNIK H., *Ind. Eng. Chem.* **40**, 442 (1948); *ibid.* **43**, 172 (1951).

[97] MALESIŃSKI W., *Bull. Acad. Polonaise Sci.*, *Cl. III* **3**, 601 (1955).

[98] ŚWIĘTOSŁAWSKI W. and MALESIŃSKI W., *Bull. Acad. Polonaise Sci. Cl. III* **4**, 159 (1956).

[99] WAJCENBLIT R., *Compt. rend.* **193**, 664 (1931).

[100] ŚWIĘTOSŁAWSKI W., GALSKA-KRAJEWSKA W., *A. Bull. Acad. Polonaise Sci.*, *Cl. III* **2**, 475 (1954).

[101] KURTYKA Z., *Bull. Acad. Polonaise Sci.*, *Cl. III* **4**, 49 (1956).

[102] ZIĘBORAK K. and M., *Bull. Acad. Polonaise Sci.*, *Cl. III* **2**, 287 (1954).

[103] ŚWIĘTOSŁAWSKI W. and TRĄBCZYŃSKI W., *Bull. Acad. Polonaise Sci.*, *Cl. III* **3**, 607 (1955); *Roczniki Chem.* **31**, 1215 (1957).

[104] TRĄBCZYŃSKI W., *Bull. Acad. Polonaise Sci.*, *Cl. III* **3**, 333 (1955).

[105] ZIĘBORAK K., KACZORÓWNA-BADYOCZEK H. and MĄCZYŃSKA Z., *Roczniki Chem.* **29**, 783 (1955).

[106] ORSZAGH A. and LELAKOWSKA J., *Bull. Acad. Polonaise Sci.*, *Serie Sci. Chim. Géol. Géogr.* **6**, 513 (1958); and ŚWIĘTOSŁAWSKI W. *ibid.* **6**, 509 (1958); BEŁDOWICZ M., *ibid.* **6**, 419 (1958); and RADECKI J., *ibid.* **6**, 605 (1958).

[107] ZAWISZA A., *Bull. Acad. Polonaise Sci.*, *Cl III* **8**, 313, 319, 325 (1960); *ibid.* **9**, 141, 147 (1961).

[108] ŚWIĘTOSŁAWSKI W., *Bull. Acad. Polonaise Sci.*, *Cl. III* **1**, 3 (1953); *ibid.* **2**, 491 (1954).

[109] MALESIŃSKI W., *Bull. Acad. Polonaise Sci.*, *Cl. III* **3**, 601 (1955); *ibid.* **4**, 295 (1956).

[110] MARKOWSKA-MAJEWSKA H. and CIEPLAK T., Not published.

[111] ŚWIĘTOSŁAWSKI W., *Bull. Acad. Polonaise Sci.*, *Cl. III.* **2**, 491 (1954).

[112] LISICKI Z., *Bull. Acad. Polonaise Sci.*, *Série Sci. Chim. Géol. Géogr.* **6**, 523 (1958); Several papers in press.

[113] LISICKI Z., *Roczniki Chem.* **29**, 763 (1955).

[114] ZIĘBORAK K., ZMYSŁOWSKA H. and CHRÓŚCIELEWSKA A., Not published.

[115] LECAT M., *Ann. soc. sci.* Bruxelles, Belgium **47** B, 108 (1927).

[116] WÓYCICKI W. and WÓYCICKA M., In press.

[117] HAASE R. and LANG H., *Chem. Ing. Technik* **23**, 313 (1951).

[118] STORONKIN A. V., *Acta phys. chem.* **13**, 505 (1940) *Zhur. Fiz. Khim.* **15**, 68, 959 (1941); *ibid.* **21**, 617 (1953).

[119] STORONKIN A. V., *Vestnik Leningrad Univ.* (1953), No. 8, 187 (1954); *ibid.* 8, 170 (1954); *ibid.* No. 11, 153 (1954); Conditions of Thermodynamic Equilibria in Polycomponent Systems (Russian). 1948.

[120] Parvant A., *Chimie et Industrie* **63**, No. 3 bis, 434 (1953).

[121] ŚWIĘTOSŁAWSKI W., ZIĘBORAK K. and STECKI J., *Bull. Acad. Polonaise Sci.*, *Cl. III*, 4, 9 (1956).

[122] ZIĘBORAK K., MĄCZYŃSKA Z. and MĄCZYŃSKI A., *Bull. Acad. Polonaise Sci.*, *Cl. III* 4, 9 (1956).

[123] STECKI J., *Bull. Acad. Polonaise Sci. Cl. III* **4**, 283, 289 (1956).

[124] TIMMERMANS J., *Physico-chemical constants of pure organic compounds*, Brussels, Elsevier Publishing Co. 1950.

[125] WEISSBERGER A., *Physical Methods of Organic Chemistry*, Vol. 1, Part. I, New York 1949

[126] ŚWIĘTOSŁAWSKI W., *Ebulliometric Measurements*, New York 1945.

[127] MAJEWSKA H., *Bull. Acad. Polonaise Sci.*, *Cl. III* 2. 341−345 (1954).

[128] OTHMER D. F., *Ind. Eng. Chem.* **20**, 743 (1928); *Ind. Eng. Chem. Anal. Ed.* **4**, 232 (1932) *Anal. Chem.* **20**, 763 (1948). *Ind. Eng. Chem.* **44**, 1864 (1952).

[129] KARR A. E., SCHEIBEL E. G., BOWES W. M. and OTHMER D. F., *Ind. Eng. Chem.* **43**, 96 (1951).

[130] GILLESPIE D.T.C., *Ind. Eng. Chem. Anal. Ed.* **18**, 375 (1946).

[131] KATZ K. and NEWMAN M., *Ind. Eng. Chem.* **48**, 137 (1956).

[132] BUSHMAKIN I. N. and VOYEIKOVA E. D., *Zhur. Obsh. Khim.* **19**, 1615 (1949).

[133] BUSHMAKIN I. N., D. Sc. thesis, University of Leningrad, 1955.

[134] FOWLER R. T. and NORRIS G. S., *J. Appl. Chem.* **5**, 266 (1955).

[135] FOWLER R. T. and LIM S. C., *J. Appl. Chem.* **6**, 74 (1956).

[136] CORNELL L. W. and MONTONNA R. E., *Ind. Eng. Chem.* **25**, 1331 (1933).

[137] HALA E., PICK., FRIED V. and VILIM O., *Vapour-Liquid Equilibrium*, Pergamon Press, London, 1958.

[138] ŚWIĘTOSŁAWSKI W., ZIĘBORAK K. and BRZOSTOWSKI W., *Bull. Acad. Polonaise Sci., Cl. III, Série Chim.* **5**, 305 (1957).

[139] ŚWIĘTOSŁAWSKI W., *Bull. Acad. Polonaise Sci.* **1931 A**.

[140] ŚWIĘTOSŁAWSKI W. and STECKI J., *Bull. Acad. Polonaise Sci., Cl. III* **5**, 155 (1957).

[141] KRĘGLEWSKI A., *Bull. Acad. Polonaise Sci., Cl. III* **5**, 329 (1957).

[142] ZMACZYŃSKI A., Citations 80–85 in *Ebulliometric Measurements*.

[143] WOJCIECHOWSKI M., Citations 71–76 in *Ebulliometric Measurements*.

[144] ŚWIĘTOSŁAWSKI W., *Comp. rend. XII Conf. IUPAC*, Rome, 74 (1938); *Ebulliometric Measurements* §§ 73–79, New York, 1945; *Microcalorimetry* §§ 28–34, New York, 1946.

[145] ORSZAGH A., LELAKOWSKA J. and BEŁDOWICZ M., *Bull. Acad. Polonaise Sci., Série Sci. Chim. Géol. Géogr.* **6**, 419 (1958).

[146] STECKI J., *Bull. Acad. Polonaise Sci., Cl. III* **4**, 283, 289 (1956).

[147] ŚWIĘTOSŁAWSKI W., *Bull. Acad. Polonaise Sci., Série Sci. Chim. Géol. Géogr.* **7**, 1–16 (1959).

[148] ANDERSON J. R., *Ind. Eng. Chem.* **37**, 541 (1945); *ibid.* **37**, 1052 (1945).

[149] GALSKA A. and ZIĘBORAK K., *Bull. Acad. Polonaise Sci., Série Sci. Chim. Géol. Géogr.* **7**, 253 (1959).

[150] KOMINEK-SZCZEPANIKOWA M., *Roczniki Chem.* **32**, 283 (1958).

[151] BUSHMAKIN I. N. and KISS I. N., *Zhur. Priklad. Khim.* **30**, 200, 379, 561 (1957).

[152] MOLODENKO P. J. and BUSHMAKIN I. N., *Vestnik Leningrad Univ.* No. 10, 68 (1958).

[153] BUSHMAKIN I. N. and LUTUGINA N. W., *Vestnik Leningrad Univ.* **13**, No. 10, 75 (1957).

[154] ZIĘBORAK K., *Bull. Acad. Polonaise Sci., Cl. III* **3**, 531 (1955).

[155] ZIĘBORAK K. and GALSKA-KRAJEWSKA A., *Bull. Acad. Polonaise Sci., Série Sci. Chim. Géol. Géogr.* **7**, 253 (1959).

[156] ZIĘBORAK K. and BRZOSTOWSKI W., *Bull. Acad. Polonaise Sci., Cl. III* **5**, 309 (1957).

[157] KURTYKA Z. and TRĄBCZYŃSKI W., *Roczniki Chem.* **32**, 623 (1959).

[158] MALESIŃSKI W., *Bull. Acad. Polonaise Sci, Cl. III* **4**, 295 (1956); *ibid.* 709 (1956); *ibid.* **6**, 105, 433 (1958).

[159] ZIĘBORAK K. and WYRZYKOWSKA-STANKIEWICZ D., *Bull. Acad. Polonaise Sci., Sér. Sci. Chim. Géol. Géogr.* **6**, 377 (1958); *ibid.* **6**, 755 (1958).

[160] ZIĘBORAK K. and GALSKA-KRAJEWSKA A. *Bull. Acad. Polonaise Sci., Série Sci. Chim. Géol. Géogr.* **7**, 253 (1959).

[161] ORSZAGH A., LELAKOWSKA J. and BEŁDOWICZ M., *Bull. Acad. Polonaise Sci., Série Chim. Géol. Géogr.* **6**, 419 (1958); *ibid.* **7**, 51 (1959).

[162] STECKI J., *Bull. Acad. Polonaise Sci., Cl. III* **5**, 155, 161, 421 (1957), *ibid Ser. Sci. Chim. Géol. Géogr.* **6**, 47 (1958).

[163] SOSNKOWSKA K., In press.

[164] KRĘGLEWSKI A., *Bull. Acad. Polonaise Sci., Cl. III* **2**, 187, 191 (1954); *ibid.* **5**, 329 (1957); *ibid.* **5**, 431 (1957); Papers not associated with azeotropy: *Roczniki Chem.* **26**, 433 (1952); *ibid.* **27**, 125 (1953); *ibid.* **28**, 251 (1954); *ibid.* **29**, 95 (1955); *ibid.* **31**, 1001 (1957); *Bull. Acad. Polonaise Sci., Cl. III* **2**, 77, 191 (1954); *ibid.* **2**, 233 (1954); *ibid.* **4**, 233 (1956), *ibid.* **5**, 323, 667 (1957).

[165] MALESIŃSKI W., *Bull. Acad. Polonaise Sci., Cl. III* **4**, 303 (1956).

[166] MOSER H., *Ann. Phys.* (5) **14**, 790 (1932).

[167] SMITH E. R. and WOJCIECHOWSKI M., *J. Research Nat . Bur. Standards* **17**, 841 (1936); *ibid.* **18**, 461, 499 (1937).

[168] ŚWIĘTOSŁAWSKI W., *J. Chim. Phys.* **32**, 293 (1935).

[169] ŚWIĘTOSŁAWSKI W., ZIĘBORAK K. and GALSKA A., *Bull. Acad. Polonaise Sci.*, *Série Sci. Chim. Géol. Géogr.* **7**, 43 (1959).

[170] LISICKI Z., *Przemysł Chem.* **9**, 342 (1953).

[171] TRĄBCZYŃSKI W., *Bull. Acad. Polonaise Sci.*, *Cl. III* **4**, 629, (1956); *ibid.* **6**, 269 (1958).

[172] ŚWIĘTOSŁAWSKI W. and OLSZEWSKI K., In press.

[173] KURTYKA Z., In press.

[174] BRZOSTOWSKI W., MALANOWSKI S. and ZIĘBORAK K., *Bull. Acad Polonaise Sci.*, *Série Sci. Chim. Géol. Géogr.* **7**, 421 (1959).

[175] STADNICKI J. S., *Bull. Acad. Polonaise Sci.*, *Série Sci. Chim. Géol. Géogr.* **6**, 383 (1958).

[176] BARBAUDY J., *Contribution à l'étude des mélanges ternaires*, Hermann, Paris, 1925.

[177] ŚWIĘTOSŁAWSKI W., *Bull. Acad. Polonaise Sci.*, *Série Chim.* **7**, 1–16 (1959).

[178] LISICKI Z. and SOSNKOWSKA K., *Bull. Acad. Polonaise Sci.*, *Série Sci. Chim. Géol. Géogr.* **6**, 675 (1958).

[179] SOSNKOWSKA K., In press.

[180] ŚWIĘTOSŁAWSKI W. and DORABIALSKA A., *Compt. rend.* **185**, 763 (1927).

[181] TWOREK D., *Roczniki Chem.* **31**, 699 (1957).

[182] CIECIERSKA-TWOREK Z., *Roczniki Chem.* **32**, 929 (1958).

[183] ŚWIĘTOSŁAWSKI W. and ZIELENKIEWICZ A., *Bull. Acad. Polonaise Sci.*, *Série Sci. Chim. Géol. Géogr.* **6**, 111 (1958); *ibid.* **6**, 365 (1958); *ibid.* **6**, 367 (1958).

[184] BERTHELOT M., *Traité pratique de calorimétrie chimique*, Paris, 1905, p. 200; LOUGININ V., CHOUKAREV A., *Calorimétrie*, Moscou 1905, p. 97; ŚWIĘTOSŁAWSKI W., *Thermochimie*, Paris, 1933, p. 46, 47, 51; *Thermochemie, Handbuch der Allgemeinen Chemie*, V. 7. Leipzig, 1928, pp. 41, 42, 45.

[185] ŚWIĘTOSŁAWSKI W. and ZIELENKIEWICZ A., *Bull. Acad. Polonaise Sci.*, *Série Sci. Chim. Géol. Géogr.* **6**, 365, 367, (1958).

[186] SADOWSKA K., In press.

[187] WÓYCICKA K., *Pure and Applied Chem.* **2**, 147 (1961).

[188] GARDNER J. A., *Ber.* **23**, 1587 (1890).

[189] ZAWIDZKI J., *Z. Phys.* **35**, 129 (1900).

[190] NAUMOVA A. S., *J. General Chem.* **19**, 1216 (1949).

[191] PUSHIN N. A., FEDUSHKIN A. V. and KRGOWIC B., *Bull. Soc. Chim. Belgrade* **11**, 12 (1947).

[192] WILLE H., *Brennstoff Chem.* **23**, 271 (1942); *ibid.* **32**, 238 (1951).

[193] ZIĘBORAK K., *Sci. Contribution of the Institute of Ind. Chem.*, I, Warsaw (1951).

[194] ZIĘBORAK K. and MĄCZYŃSKA Z., *Roczniki Chem.* **32**, 295 (1958); and MĄCZYŃSKI A., *Bull. Acad. Sci., Cl. III* **4**, 153 (1956).

BIBLIOGRAPHY

Thermodynamics and Thermochemistry

1. BERG L. and HARRISON J. M., General Characteristics of Azeotropic Agents, *Chem. Eng. Progress* **43**, No. 9; *Trans. Amer. Inst. Chem. Engrs.* 487 (1947).

2. BRITTON E. C., NUTTING H. G., HORSLEY L. H., Changes of Equilibria of Liquid-Vapour Systems Composed of Alcohols and Ketones with Pressure Change, *Anal. Chem.* **19**, 601 (1947).

3. ENÜSTÜN B. V., Statistical Thermodynamics of Binary Azeotropes, *Comm. Fac., Sci. Univer. Ankara* **5 B**, I (1954).

4. HAASE R., Liquid-Vapour Equilibria in Polycomponent Systems. VII. Composition of Ternary Azeotropes, *Z. Physik. Chem.* **195**, 362 (1950).

5. HORSLEY L. H., Graphical Method for Azeotrope Formation and Examination of the Influence of its Composition, *Anal. Chem.* **19**, 603 (1947).

6. KUHN W. and MASSINI P., Enthalpy of Mixing and Azeotropy Phenomena Observed in the Case of Non-Polar Components, *Helv. Chim. Acta* **33**, 737 (1950).

7. LICHT W., Jr., DEUZLER C. G., Azeotrope Boiling Temperature and Evaporation Enthalpy Changes Produced by Change of Pressure, *Chem. Eng. Progress* **44**, 627 (1948).

8. MEISSNER H. P. and GREENFIELD S. H., The Composition and Boiling Temperature of Binary Azeotropes, *Ind. Eng. Chem.* **40**, 438 (1948).

9. MUSIL A. and BRETENHUBER L., Concentrated Liquid Mixtures, Margules Rule and its Consequences (Dissertation) *Z. Elektrochem.* **57**, 423 (1953).

10. NUTTING H. S. and HORSLEY L. H., Graphical Method of Composition Change Determination Produced by Pressure Changes, *Anal. Chem.* **19**, 602 (1947).

11. OTHMER D. F. and TEN EYCK E. H. Jr., Correlation of Azeotropic Data, *Ind. Eng. Chem.* **41**, 2897 (1949).

12. PRIGOGINE J. and DEFAY R., Transformation Phenomena in Azeotropic Systems, *Bull. Classe Sci. Acad. Roy. Belg.* **32**, 694 (1946): *ibid.* **33**, 48 (1947).

13. ROWLINSON J. S. and SUTTON J. R., Statistical Thermodynamics of Systems Composed of Asymmetric Molecules, *Proc. Roy. Soc. A* **229**, 271 (1955); *ibid.*, 396 (1955).

14. SIMMONS L. M., Mechanism of the Formation of Negative Binary Azeotropes Containing Water, *J. Proc. Roy. Soc. N. S. Wales* **80**, 196 (1947).

15. STUKE B., Theory of Azeotrope Formation., *Chem. Ign. Tech.* **25**, 133 (1953).

Azeotropy and Its Application

16. BERG L., HARRISON J. M., MONTGOMERY C. W., Purification of Styrene by the Azeotropic Method, *Ind. Eng. Chem.* **38**, 1144 (1946).

17. BERTI V. and BOTTIGLIO T., Extractive and Azeotropic Method of Aromatic Hydrocarbon Separation, *Riv. Combustibili* **5**, 329 (1951).

18. D'ARCANGELO T., Pure Hydrogen Isolation by Azeotropic and Extractive Distillation, *Bol. Inform. Petrol (Buenos Aires)* **24**, 387 (1947)

19. DUMMET G. A., Azeotropic and Extractive Distillation, *Petroleum (London)* **17**, 283 (1954).

20. FOWLER R. T., Binary Azeotropes under Lower Pressure, *J. Soc. Chem. Ind. (London)* **69**, 865 (1952).

21. FRANCK H. G., Azeotropic Distillation Applied to Separation of Coal Tar Components, *Brennstoff Chem.* **32**, 199 (1951).

22. GALPERIN N. I. and NOVIKOVA K. E., Separation of Binary Mixtures by the Two Stage Rectification Method under Two Different Pressures, *Zhur. Priklad. Khim.* **26**, 912 (1953).

23. HANOL S., Azeotropic Distillation *Tek. Tid.* **7b**, 1307 (1946).

24. JONES H. H. M., Azeotropic Extractive Distillation; Theory, Calculations and Apparatus *Chem. Process Eng.* **33**, 494 (1952).

25. JONES H. H. M., Fractional Distillation, *Chem. Process Eng.* **34**, 381 (1953).

26. LITVINOV N. D., Azeotropy, *Zhur. Fiz. Khim.* **27**, 476 (1953).

27. MARSHNER R. F. and COPPER W. P., *Ind. Eng. Chem.* **41**, 1357 (1949).

28. PARIS A., Three Separation Methods: Extraction, Extractive and Azeotropic Distillation, *Industrie Chimique* **40**, 97 (1953).

Separation of Azeotropic Components by Diffusion

29. HAGERBAUMER D. H., and KAMMERMEYER K., *Chem. Eng. Progr. Symposium, Ser.* **50**, No. 10, 25—44 (1954).
30. JONES A. L. and MILBERGER E. C., Separation of Organic Liquids by Diffusion, *Ind. Eng. Chem.* **45**, 2689 (1953).

Azeotropic Refrigeration Mixtures

31. PENNINGTON W. A. and REED W. H., Development of the Refrigeration Industry, *Modern Refrig* **53**, 123, 184 (1950).
32. PENNINGTON W. A., Binary Azeotropes as Refrigerator Mixtures, *Modern Refrig.* **16**, 59 (1953).

SUPPLEMENTARY REFERENCES TO THIS EDITION

Thermodynamics and Thermochemistry

1. HIDEBRAND J. H., *J. Am. Soc.* **51**, 69 (1929).
2. GUGGENHEIM E. A., *Proc. Roy. Soc A* **148**, 304 (1935).
3. FOWLER R. T. and GUGGENHEIM E. A., *Statistical Thermodynamics*, Cambridge, 1939.
4. KIREEV V. A., *Acta Phys. Chim. U.S.S.R.* **13**, 552 (1940); *ibid.* **14**, 271 (1941).
5. PRIGOGINE I., *Bull. Soc. Chim. Belg.* **52**, 115 (1943).
6. REDLICH O. and SCHULTZ P. W., *J. Am. Chem. Soc.* **66**, 1007 (1944).
7. PRIGOGINE I. and DEFAY R., *Thermodynamique Chimique*, Dunod, Paris, 1946.
8. COULSON E. A. and HERINGTON E. F. G., *J. Chem. Soc.* **597** (1947).
9. COULSON E. A. and HERINGTON E. F. G., *Nature* **158**, 198 (1946).
10. REDLICH O. and KISTER A. T., *J. Chem. Phys.* **15**, 854 (1947).
11. LICHT W. and DENZLER C. G., *Chem. Eng. Progress* **44**, 627 (1948).
12. OTHMER D. F. and TEN EYCK E. H., *Ind. Eng. Chem.* **41**, 2897 (1949).
13. PRIGOGINE I., MATHOT V. and DESMYTER A., *Bull. Soc. Chim. Belg.* **58**, 574 (1949).
14. HILDENBRAND J. H. and SCOT R. L., *Solubility of Nonelectrolytes*, Reinhold Publ. Corp. New York, 1950.
15. PRIGOGINE I. and GARIKIAN G., *Physica* **16**, 239 (1950).
16. KUHN W. and MASINI P., *Helv. Chim. Acta* **35**, 737 (1950).
17. HAASE R., *Z. Physik Chem.* **195**, 362 (1950).
18. LONGUET-HIGGINS H. C., *Proc. Roy. Soc. A* **205**, 247 (1951).
19. KIRKWOOD J. G. and PUFF F. P., *J. Chem. Phys.* **19**, 774 (1951).
20. PRIGOGINE I. and DESMYTER A., *Trans. Faraday. Soc.* **47**, 1137 (1951).
21. HAASE R., *Z. Elektrochem.* **35**, 29 (1951).
22. BAXENDALE J. H. and ENÜSTÜN B. V., *Phil. Trans. Roy. Soc., A* **243**, 185 (1951).
23. KORTÜM G. and BUCHHOLZ-MEISNHEIMER H., *Distillation and Extraction Theory of Liquids*, 1952, Springer-Verlag.
24. GUGGENHEIM H. A., *Mixtures*, Oxford Univ. Press., 1952.
25. STORONKIN A. V. and SUSAREV M. D., *Zhur. Fiz. Khim.* **27**, 1650 (1953).
26. SAROLEA L., *Trans. Faraday. Soc.* **49**, 8 (1953).
27. ENÜSTÜN B. V., *Commun. Facult. Sci. Univ. Ankara., Ser. B* **5**, 1 (1954).
28. CLEGG H. P. and ROWLINSON J. S., *Trans. Faraday Soc.* **51**, 1333 (1955).
29. HALA E., PICK J. FRIED V. and VILIM O., *Vapour-Liquid Equilibrium*, Prague, 1955.
30. BARKER J. A., BROWN J. and SMITH F., *Discussions Farad. Soc.* **42** (1953).

31. STORONKIN A. and MORACZEWSKI A. G., *Zhur. Fiz. Khim.* **30**, 1297 (1956).
32. PRIGOGINE I., BELLEMANS A. and ENGLERT-CHOWLES A. *J. Chem. Phys.* **24**, 518, (1956).
33. SCOTT R. L., *J. Chem. Phys.* **25**, 193 (1956).
34. FOWLER R. T. and LIM. J. G., *J. Appl. Chem.* **6**, 74 (1956).
35. MASHIKO Y. and YOSHIMOTO T., *Togyo Kogyo Shikensho Hokoku* **52**, 158 (1957); *ibid.* **52**, 165 (1957); *Bull. Chem. Soc. Japan* **29**, 990 (1956); *ibid.* **30**, 56 (1957).
36. YOSHIMOTO T., *Bull. Chem. Soc. Japan* **30**, 505 (1957).
37. PRIGOGINE I., BELLEMANS A. and MATHOT V., *The Molecular Theory of Solutions*, Amsterdam, 1957.
38. REED T. M., *J. Phys. Chem.* **61**, 1213 (1957).
39. KUHN W. and KUHN H. J., *Helv. Chim. Acta* **40**, 2433 (1947).
40. STORONKIN A., MORACZEWSKI A. G. and BIDOUSOV V. P., *Vestnik Leningrad Univ.* **94** (1958).
41. GURIKOV J. V., *Zhur. Fiz. Khim.* **32**, 1980 (1958).
42. GUMIŃSKI K., *Roczniki Chem.* **32**, 569 (1958).

Azeotropy and Its Applications

43. MAIR B. J., GLASGOW A. R. and ROSSINI F. D., *J. Research, Nat. Bur. Standards* **29**, 39 (1941).
44. DONYER R. L., FIDLER F. and LOWRY R. A., *Ind. Eng. Chem.* **41**, 2725 (1949).
45. HORSLEY L. H., *Azeotropic Data*. American Chem. Soc. Washington 1952.
46. BINEAU A., *Ann. Chim. Phys.* **7**, 257 (1843); *ibid.* **68**, 417 (1858).
47. DUFT S., Vapour Pressures of Propyl and Isopropyl Nitrates, *J. Appl. Chem. (London)* **5**, Pt. 12, 642 (1955).
48. FOWLER R. T. and LIM S. C., Azeotropism in Binary Solutions; Carbon Tetrachloride-Benzene System, *J. Appl. Chem. (London)* **6**, Pt. 2, 74 (1956).
49. HINC J. and EHRESON, S. J., Empirical Method for Prediction of the Boiling Point of Halomethanes, *J. Org. Chem.* **21**, 819 (1956).
50. EISEMAN B. J., Azeotrope of Monochlorodifluoromethane and Dichlorodifluoromethane, *J. Am. Soc.* **79**, 6087 (1957).
51. HOLLÓ J., EMBER Gy., LENGYEL T. and WIEG A., The Vapour-Liquid Equilibrium of the Quaternary System: Ethanol-heptane-toluene-aniline, *Acta. Chim. Acad. Sci.* **13**, 307 (1957).
52. IKARI A., Prediction of Composition and Boiling Point of an Azeotropic Mixture in a Binary Azeotrope, *Kogyo Kagaku Zassi* **60**, 7 (1957).
53. KOGAN V. B., FRIDMAN V. M. and DEIZENROT, Azeotropic Mixtures of Aliphatic Alcohols. Normal Paraffin Hydrocarbons and Water, *Zhur. Priklad. Khim.* **30**, 1339 (1957).
54. LEIBNITZ E., KÖNNECK and NIESE S., Ternary Liquid Systems III, *J. Pract. Chem.* **4**, 278 (1957).
55. PRENGLE H. Wm., Thermodynamics of Solution, *Ind. Eng. Chem.* **49**, 1769 (1957).
56. SIMKHOVICH Z. J., Relation between the Temperature and Pressure of the Vapour of Constant-Boiling Hydrochloric Acid, *Zhur. Priklad. Khim.* **30**, 1243 (1957).
57. SIMKHOVICH Z. J., Relation between the Temperature and Pressure of the Constant Boiling Hydrochloric Acid, *Zhur. Priklad. Khim. U.S.S.R.* **30**, 1312 (1957).
58. THODOS G., Critical Constants of the Aromatic Hydrocarbons *A.I.Ch.E. Journal* **3**, 428 (1957).
59. TOSHIO YOSHIMOTO, Azeotropic Mixtures, IV. Physical Basis of Azeotropic Correlation Rules, *Bull. Chem. Soc. Japan* **30**, 505 (1957).
60. YOSICHIRO MASHINO and TOSHIO YOSHIMOTO, Molecular Interpretation of Azeotropic Phenomena, *Tokyo Kogyo Shikanso Hokoku* **52**, 158 (1957).
61. BIELDISCOMBE D. P. and MARTIN J. F., Vapour Pressures of Phenol and the Cresols, *Trans. Faraday Soc.* **54**, 1316 (1958).

62. GUMIŃSKI K., The Azeotropic Point, *Roczniki Chem.* **32**, 569 (1958).

63. HÁLA E., Mutual Dependence of Equilibrium Compositions of the Liquid and Gaseous Phase in Real Systems, *Roczniki Chem.* **32**, 365 (1958).

64. HOLLÓ J. and LENGYEL T., Vapour-Liquid Equilibrium of Binary Homo-azeotropes, *Periodica Polytech.* **2**, 173 (1958).

65. KENNETH J. M., Boiling Point-Composition Diagrams for the Systems 2-Ethoxyethanol-Ethyl Acetate and 2-Ethoxyethanol-Propyl Acetate, *Chem. Eng. Data Ser.* **3**, 239 (1958).

66. MALTESE P. and VALENTINI G., Liquid-Vapour Equilibrium Curve of Dimethyl formamido-formic Acid., *Chim. Ind.* **40**, 548 (1958).

67. NOVIKOVA K. E. and NATRADZE A. G., A Graphical Method of Calculating Binary Azeotropic Mixtures, *Khim. Prom.* **1958**, 102.

68. PUCHALIK M., Relation between Parachor and Concentration in Binary Mixtures and Binary Activity, *Bull. Soc. Amis Sci. Lettres, Poznań, Ser. B*, **14**, 209 (1958).

69. STORONKIN A. V., MORACZOWSKI A. G., BELOUSOW V. P., The Effect of Temperature on the Composition of Binary Heteroazeotropes, *Vestnik Leningrad Univ.* **13**, No. 10 *Ser. Fiz. and Khim.* No. 2, 34 (1958).

70. TIERNEY J. W., Correlation of Vapour-Liquid Equilibrium Data, *Ind. Eng. Chem.* **50**, 707 (1958).

71. ROLLET J. B., Ebulliometry of Volatile Solutes, I. *Publ. Sci. Univ. Alger. Ser. B., Sci. Phys.* **2**, 391—402

Series of A. Orszagh's Papers on Azeotropy and Azeotropic Ranges

72. ŚWIĘTOSŁAWSKI A. and ORSZAGH A., The Determination of Azeotropic Concentrations of Binary and Ternary Mixtures, *Roczniki Chem.* **26**, 608 (1951).

73. ŚWIĘTOSŁAWSKI W. and ORSZAGH A., The Azeotropic Composition of a Series of Homologues and Two Azeotropic Agents, *Roczniki Chem.* **26**, 625 (1952).

74. ORSZAGH A., On Investigations of Liquid Mixtures I., *Przem. Chem.* **32**, 333 (1953).

75. ORSZAGH A., On the Methods of Separation of Organic Substances, Chapter I, Preparation of Organic Substances, PWT, Warsaw, 1954.

76. ORSZAGH A., On Investigations of Liquid Mixtures, II. *Przem. Chem.* **34**, 133 (1955).

77. ORSZAGH A. On Homoazeotropes Formed by Benzene, Aliphatic Alcohols and Hydrocarbons Contained in the Benzene Fraction 56–97° C, *Roczniki Chem.* **29**, 623 (1955).

Series of W. Malesiński's Theoretical Papers on Azeotropy

78. MALESIŃSKI W., Series of Binary Positive Azeotropes, *Roczniki Chem.* **30**, 1231 (1956).

79. MALESIŃSKI W., Composition of Ternary Positive Azeotropes, II, *Bull. Acad. Polonaise Sci., Cl. III* **4**, 523 (1956).

80. MALESIŃSKI W., Boiling Temperature of Positive Ternary Azeotropes, II, *Bull. Acad. Polonaise Sci., Cl. III* **4**, 609 (1956).

81. ŚWIĘTOSŁAWSKI W. and MALESIŃSKI W., Composition or Positive, Saddle and Negative Ternary Homoazeotropes, *Bull. Acad. Polonaise Sci., Cl. III* **4**, 701 (1956).

82. MALESIŃSKI W., Azeotropic Depression as a Function of the Composition of Series of Ternary Positive Azeotropes, *Bull. Acad. Polonaise Sci., Cl. III* **4**, 693 (1956).

83. MALESIŃSKI W., On the Relation between the Composition of Binary and Ternary Azeotropes, *Bull. Acad. Polonaise Sci., Cl. III* **5**, 177 (1957).

84. MALESIŃSKI W., Composition of the Series of Ternary Homoazeotropes, *Bull. Acad. Sci., Cl. III* **5**, 183 (1957).

85. MALESIŃSKI W., Compositions, Boiling Temperatures and Vapour Pressures of Multicomponent Homoazeotropes, *Bull. Acad. Polonaise Sci., Serie Chim. Géol. et Géogr.* **6**, 61 (1958).

86. MALESIŃSKI W., Boiling Temperatures of Positive and Positive-Negative Ternary Homoazeotropes, *Bull. Acad. Polonaise Sci., Cl. III* **4**, 711 (1956).

AUTHOR INDEX

The first figures refer to references, the second to the
section numbers